PATTERNS
OF SURVIVAL

PATTERNS

Illustrations by STANLEY WYATT

OF SURVIVAL

by LORUS J. MILNE and
MARGERY MILNE

All photographs by Lorus and Margery Milne
unless otherwise credited

PRENTICE-HALL, Inc., Englewood Cliffs, N.J.

Third printing .... September, 1970

Patterns of Survival
by Lorus J. Milne and Margery Milne

To Ralph and Mildred Buchsbaum
Whom we met
in Anemone Cave,
searching for survivors
from the swirl of the sea.

Other books by Lorus J. Milne and Margery Milne

Living Plants of the World
Gift from the Sky
The Crab That Crawled Out of the Past
The Biotic World and Man
Water and Life
Because of a Tree
The Valley: Meadow, Grove and Stream
The Senses of Animals and Men
The Mountains
The Balance of Nature
The Lower Animals: Living Invertebrates of the World
Plant Life
Animal Life
Paths Across the Earth
The World of Night
The Mating Instinct
Famous Naturalists
A Multitude of Living Things

Introduction

EVER since Herbert Spencer invented the phrase "survival of the fittest"—and Darwin made "survival" the key to evolution—the concept has haunted the mind of modern man.

It soon ceased to be thought relevant to biology alone and gave birth to "social Darwinism" or the theory that all human institutions should imitate nature by encouraging the elimination of those "least fit to survive." This theory has been discredited by many—perhaps by most—contemporary psychologists on the ground that the fittest to survive may not be fittest for anything else. But there are still psychologists who maintain that the only criterion for judging the validity of any moral or prudential code is simply the question: Are those who follow it more or less likely to, as one recently put it, "be here tomorrow?"

A virtue of this fascinating book is its treatment of the biological aspects of survival in so wide-ranging a fashion that it is sure to interest and inform even those who know a good deal about, and have pondered a good deal upon, the subject.

The title suggests, first of all, the most familiar aspect of survival, namely the almost infinite number and variety of the devices which enable present-day animals and plants to survive the fierce competition for food and territory—offensive and defensive weapons, concealment, prodigious reproductive capacity or effective parental care, the exploitation of otherwise empty ecological niches and so forth. Being widely traveled as well as widely read, the authors present an unusually rich and varied panorama of the contemporary patterns for survival. But they also do more. They go back to the earliest beginnings when survival meant the survival of the most elementary forms of life itself which might conceivably have been extinguished completely right then. They proceed to the biological aspects of the problem for man himself.

Particularly striking is their emphasis on the crises which arise from time to time and present organisms with some crucial problem. One of the earliest probably was, surprisingly enough, the increase in oxygen produced by the flourishing of green plants, which threatened the existence of other early organisms to which oxygen was, as it still is to some bacteria, a poison. The latest crisis is the population explosion which may possibly be more difficult to control than that of the atom bomb.

During the billions of years which lay between the present and that time when oxygen threatened most existing forms of life (and when many of them doubtless succumbed) there have been many other crises. Their exact nature is still the subject of speculation and debate, but they certainly led to the rapid extinction of some types and the rapid development of others. Why, for example, did the trilobites, which had flourished for a time incomparably longer than man has been here, suddenly disappear at the end of the Permian? Why did the dinosaurs fade away, the mammals and the flowering plants begin to emerge toward the end of Cretaceous? Change of climate? Changes in the chemical constitution of the air? Development of forms of competition the earlier forms could not meet? Some mysterious old age of a species?

These are all large and teasing questions. In this book they supply a background which gives added interest and importance to the dramatic account of the infinite and ingenious variety of nature's patterns for survival.

—Joseph Wood Krutch

Contents

Foreword

"THE secret of success," declared Benjamin Disraeli, the eminent British statesman of a century ago, "is constancy to purpose." Surely no purpose outranks survival. All other purposes are secondary.

Today falls not only in the Age of Man, but also in the time of success of more kinds of living things than the world has ever known before. Paleontologists assure us that fully a thousandth of all the species that have ever lived are still alive today. Some species show their success in ancient lineage, others in superior size, a few in great age of individuals. Mankind is among those that prove their gains by immense numbers and wide distribution. Yet none of these measures points to the human species as atop a pinnacle, uniquely able to survey the rest of life.

No single pattern ensures survival. Bats find success by staying out of sight, winging dexterously through darkness to capture insects that reflect echoes of their high-pitched cries, hibernating in a cool cave or migrating thousands of miles to match the weather. They can afford to have a single baby a year and to give it the kind of parental care we admire. Rats thrive by being opportunists, eating whatever they can find, reproducing three to five times a year with litters of four to twelve. In a normal lifetime of three years, a pair of rats can have 610,302 descendants. In the same period, a pair of bats would produce only three, each with a life expectancy of a dozen years.

The domestic cat links its lot to that of people. It maintains an air of independence, but has kittens to spare only when given a soft bed and regular meals. By contrast, the little fruit flies, which pop through the mesh of a window screen, search for the smell of fermenting fruit indoors or out. Their tiny maggots feed on the fungi that cause the fermentation, and can fit all of their growth into a single week, letting a pair of parents produce two hundred offspring in eleven days at summer temperatures. Timing their lives by the sun to emerge just before dawn, the flies expand their delicate wings in the most humid hour of the day, and are off to seek their fortunes by midmorning. In the most lightweight of portable armor, the fruit flies have true independence and are in no danger of extinction.

As we search for the hidden meaning in each of the fascinating techniques by which living things survive, we realize that no single feature provides the answer. The giraffe gains equally from its long legs and neck, which let it reach up to feed from the flat top of an acacia tree; from its incredible ability to munch down spiny stems as well as the leaves they bear; and from its skill at kicking out with sharp hoofs in all directions at a lion when its camouflage is not enough. Only on the African savannas, where the trees are spiny acacias and the predators are lions, do these special abilities confer an advantage over other animals.

We honor the horseshoe crab for its ancient lineage—virtually unchanged from ancestors fossilized 300 million years ago—and recognize how well its versatility of diet and armored back match its habits in feeding along the margins of the sea. For at least 600 million years the seas have offered nourishment of acceptable kinds in the same situations. The crab's armor has deflected the jaws of fishes and dinosaurs, and now serves equally well against the teeth of seals or the beaks of birds.

We respect the redwoods which grow so straight, so tall, so old, in one narrow band of territory close to the Pacific Ocean. But we should feel more kinship in success to the poplars that spring up all around the Northern Hemisphere, filling vacant land left by a forest fire, a glacier or a man. The poplars and dandelions, like people and house sparrows, survive best on disturbed land. Their constancy to purpose is served by a readiness to disperse their offspring to distant places, there to adapt to whatever new situations arise.

Through the complexities of life shine the patterns that have meant survival. Hidden in the rocks, in the bodies and ways of life of plants and animals is the mindless wisdom of at least 2 billion years. With his superb brain, man is ready to learn from nonhuman inhabitants of his solar system and perhaps more distant worlds. He can seek to discover how his own kind and other creatures have survived so far, while so many have disappeared without issue. By finding and applying the patterns of survival, man is most likely to extend his own future.

—L. J. M. and M. M.
Durham, New Hampshire

PATTERNS
OF SURVIVAL

chapter one

Successful Patterns

S PRING is a season that tests our tolerances. Critically we watch the grass begin to grow and the birds patrol the lawn in search of worms. Should we guide the lawnmower around the scattered white violets, Johnny-jump-ups, Siberian squill (*Scilla*), and grape hyacinths that have escaped from the flower borders—at least until they are through blooming? We glare at the golden dandelions and the rosettes of hawkweed, wondering if it is worthwhile to spud and poison them again this year. We keep an eye on the birdhouses to be sure that the doorways are the right size: big enough for a house wren or tree swallow, but too small for an English sparrow or European starling.

Deliberately we play favorites, and hope that our neighbors will do the same. One man's neglected lot of ragweed is a dozen others' hayfever. We look to the woodlands near our home: are trailing arbutus and lady's slippers still escaping the despoilers—the plant diggers and the bulldozers? We watch the newspapers to learn if hunters have held their fire while large white birds passed on a long flight from Texas to northern Canada: the few remaining whooping cranes in the world.

No one need fear that dandelions or European starlings will become extinct. These immigrants to America show more vigor and adaptability than we appreciate. They crowd out plants and animals that we prefer. Despite private and community-wide campaigns to exterminate them, the

3

weed species move right back in. Usually they annoy us so much by their persistence that we overlook our own hand in their success. Neither dandelions nor starlings thrive in America where land is left undisturbed. If we let our own lawn return to its native condition—an unbroken forest of oak and beech, hemlock and pine, wintergreen and partridgeberry, lady's slippers and woodland ferns—not a dandelion or starling would invade it. Deep shade and dense shrubbery are their enemies. We and our ancestors have kept the landscape biased in just those ways that match the needs of weeds.

Each kind of living thing has its own requirements. Each relies, for the success of individuals and the continuation of the species, upon an intricate pattern of special features—adaptations that improve chances for survival. Few patterns promote success in more than a narrow context. The physical and the living environment press upon living things too differently from place to place to permit real versatility. Progressively, too, these pressures change, quickly or slowly with storms and volcanic action, droughts and prolonged rain, rise and fall in average temperature. Shorelines shift and mountains crumble. Living neighbors move in or out. Some become extinct.

The plants and animals that survive in their progeny are the lucky ones. They hold the winning combination: a successful pattern fitting one place and time, and the ability to modify the pattern in the correct direction as fast as the environment changes. The luckiest of all have an adaptation ready, still unused, as though prepared for alteration that has not yet come. They gain a head start in the altered world. Less fortunate are those whose pattern limits them to a single situation. They vanish forever when their offspring can no longer find this living space. Koala "bears" in Australia, which eat foliage only from a few kinds of eucalyptus trees, and Monterey pines along the California coast, unable to get their seeds to suitable unoccupied territory inland, are highly vulnerable. Fossils provide records of the many living things that failed to hold a place on earth, and of the changes whereby other lines of descent kept pace with changing times.

The distinguished paleontologist Dr. George G. Simpson has extracted from his broad knowledge of fossils an educated guess about the number of different plants and animals the world has known, and the total kinds alive today. He regards as conservative an estimate of 4.5 million species now living—only a third of them yet given distinctive names by scientists. Going back to the very beginnings of life, about 3 billion years ago, adds enough extinct species to raise the total only a thousandfold, to about 4 billion. According to this calculation, a thousandth of all kinds of creature ever on earth are alive today, and the average lifetime of a species—from its appearance to extinction—lies somewhere between 500,000 and 5,000,000 years.

We can still find some plants and animals that have become extinct under wild conditions and many that appear on the brink of disaster. Why have they reached the end of the line? Perhaps the talisman that allows survival might be recognized in living things now losing it.

Recently, while traveling in Europe, we became aware of a household insect we had almost forgotten. In homes and hotels where woolen cloth is the usual fabric, small cream-yellow moths flew about, mating and laying eggs where their caterpillars would have hair to eat. In America today these insects are growing scarce—except in old houses—for they face fabrics impregnated with insecticides, closets reeking of fumigants far more potent than the naphthalene "moth balls" our parents used, deadly solvents in the dry-cleaning establishments, and a major replacement of edible wool by synthetic fibers for which the caterpillars have no suitable digestive agents.

Ever since man invented spinning and weaving and began using wool for garments and rugs, generation after generation of these caterpillars have eaten holes in man's handiwork. Prior to that, presumably, clothes-moth caterpillars fed on the hairy skins of animals with which people clothed themselves. Today, the whole future of the two kinds of clothes moths depends upon those that live with man. Both species have been extinct outdoors for thousands of years. But as long as any of them exist, they still have a chance to change their ways and gain a new lease on life—as their ancestors did in following man indoors. Today is again a time of test for them. They might even begin laying eggs on the non-living hair of our household pets—live dogs and cats, which their caterpillars could digest. After all, they have relatives in the American Tropics that live in the fur of the sloths. Unless clothes moths can break the pattern that has been successful into the twentieth century, they may follow malaria into oblivion, first in Anglo-America and then throughout the world.

Equally orphaned in man's care are the maidenhair trees (*Ginkgo*) that provide shade along so many of New York's streets. Had not monks in the Far East fancied this tree thousands of years ago and grown it in temple courtyards, it would be known today only from fossils. Its tri-

The "lost camellia" tree—a living fossil—is known only in cultivation. Known now as *Gordonia alatamaha*, it is a member of the tea family native to Georgia, apparently extinct in the wild.

The St. Lucia parrot is known from no other place than this one small volcanic island in the West Indies. If the forests in which it lives are cut down, it is likely to vanish.

angular, fan-shaped leaves, which drop to the ground in autumn, give little hint that the maidenhair is a close relative of pines and other evergreens with needle leaves. Since plant explorers have been unable to find maidenhairs competing with other trees under natural conditions, we have no way of knowing why they dwindled into extinction. Almost certainly the adaptations man finds to his liking in this tree gave it little advantage in the wild. Unlike conventional conifers, it grows quickly from cuttings and can be propagated without waiting for seeds to form and sprout. Unlike most other trees, the maidenhair readily collects its water and nourishment from soil sealed in by pavements. Sturdy in its solitude, it rises from squares of city soil which are no more than two feet in each direction, unpoisoned by soot or the fumes from trucks and automobiles. By shading man under these harsh conditions, maidenhair trees have become partners in human culture. Without man's help, the *Ginkgo* seems no longer fitted for the present or the future.

Once they catch man's interest, plants that can be propagated easily have a much better chance than animals of being rescued while making their last stand. Sheer coincidence may then save a species from extinction. Who could have known, for example, the plight of a little grove of trees discovered in 1765 by the pioneering botanists John Bartram of Philadelphia and his son William? The unfamiliar trees grew along the swampy border of the Altamaha River, which flows into the Atlantic Ocean just north of Brunswick, Georgia. The men collected flowers and leaves of the tree and later, when the plant proved unknown to science, gave it the name *Franklinia* in honor of Benjamin Franklin. Riding again through Georgia in 1790, William Bartram revisited the grove and gathered seeds and cuttings. These he introduced into his father's botanic garden, where they became graceful trees whose narrow leaves and large white flowers delighted many horticulturalists. But despite several expeditions to the same and similar localities in the American Southeast, no one since that time has found Franklinia growing wild. The grove the Bartrams found must have been the final outpost of a vanishing species. Had the botanists not cultivated their seeds and cuttings, it would be easy to accuse them of imagining the tree they described—a strange member of the tea family, the "lost-camellia tree."

Similarly the famous bird artist, John James Audubon, had no idea that he shot the two last "carbonated warblers" the world has ever known. He collected them near the village of Henderson, Kentucky, in May 1811 and drew them immediately in Plate 60 of his great *Birds of America*.

Both are males, and Audubon believed them to be not yet in full plumage. Their markings are distinctively unlike any related birds, leading the committee members who compile the American Ornithologists' Union checklist to place "carbonated warblers" in the hypothetical or doubtful category. Unless Audubon's specimens were rare hybrids of other species, such as blackpoll and Cape May warblers, it now seems unlikely that anyone will ever see the living birds again. No one has a clue to why they disappeared.

Plants and animals that vanished in the wild during recent years were known too superficially for anyone to suspect their coming end. Today, scientists seek to solve the riddle of extinction by studying in special detail those species whose numbers or territories are shrinking. To provide a central clearinghouse for information, the International Union for the Conservation of Nature established a Survival Service, centered in the Union's headquarters at Morges, Switzerland. Soon this committee drew up a list of 69 species of mammals most threatened by extinction. In 1963 the World Wildlife Fund added 21 more, bringing the total endangered to 90. The Survival Service compiled and published in 1965 a list of 334 rare birds, including "those thought to be so, but of which detailed information is still lacking." One of the six warblers on the list was painted by Audubon: Bachman's warbler, depicted against a branch of Franklinia flowers and leaves. Kirtland's warbler is listed too. Both may well become extinct before the rare tree does.

Bachman's warbler is probably the rarest small bird now in America, with only a few pairs left. Formerly, at least, it spent the winter in Cuba and came to river-bottom swamps of the South to breed. But following 1900, when deforestation and drainage of these nesting areas changed them into fields of corn, cotton, and potatoes, the birds were doomed— unable to find acceptable substitutes. Comparable intolerance of human modifications in the landscape may also doom Kirtland's warbler. Probably less than a thousand individuals remain in existence, all of them spending the winter in the Bahama Islands, where they are admired, counted, and left unmolested. All of the Kirtland's migrate to an area of central Michigan about 85 miles north to south and 100 miles east to west. There they hunt for open stands of young jack pines between three and eighteen feet high. Younger trees offer too little cover. Older forests contain too few insects for young warblers. As soon as the trees mature, the warblers move elsewhere or spend the whole breeding season searching—without raising a family. What the birds need is a good fire every few years to open up the forest and make a place for new jack pines to rise. Since May 1964, the Michigan Department of Conservation, which likes to boast about this warbler, has been trying "controlled burning to provide suitable habitats for Kirtland's warblers and other wildlife that thrives only where trees are starting.

Each year for the past 140 centuries, man and his favored plants and animals have occupied progressively greater areas of the earth. Yet during this time, the planet's land has grown drier. Its deserts have spread, and its capacity for sustaining life has diminished. For every extra human mouth and cultivated crop and domesticated beast, the world has seen a compensating decrease in the untamed life that was once conspicuous on every continent. Faster and faster the wilderness and "waste lands" shrink, reducing the space and food available to wild things and endangering their future.

Among earlier ages of the earth we look in vain for evidence of a change that was comparably swift. But never before, it seems, has an alteration of such magnitude come in so few decades. None of the earlier tests faced by living things have demanded such quick new adjustments as the price for their survival. We see no sign, either, that human populations are about to attain some ideal level, a maximum number of people the world should support. Instead, the rate of increase rises—and with it the rate of extinction of plants and animals that cannot tolerate the ubiquity of man. An extreme of versatility, perhaps greater than at any time in the past, has become essential for living things. This too is a requisite feature of a successful pattern of survival.

chapter two

The Earthly Stage

M OST major changes that tested living things in the past came slowly, over centuries or millennia or even millions of years. And although history may seem to repeat itself in the rising of the tide or the sun or the seedling, over the longer time true repetition is never faced by living things. For just as plants and animals become modified in their progeny by the molding forces of their environment, so too the environment changes because life is present.

Geologists now believe that until green plants released oxygen into the earth's atmosphere a billion years ago, this gas was too rare to support the activity of animals anywhere on the planet. Prior to that time, only microbes inhabited the seas. Nothing at all lived on land. The microbes gained modest amounts of energy for life by fermenting organic compounds that had formed spontaneously in shallow lagoons under the influence of sunlight, lightning, and cosmic rays. The fermentation released carbon dioxide into the water and increased its concentration in the atmosphere as well.

Green plants differed in a new adaptation: the possession of the green pigment chlorophyll. It allowed them to capture energy from sunlight. By the complex chemistry of photosynthesis, they split off the hydrogen from water molecules and combined it with the carbon and oxygen in carbon dioxide to form their own organic compounds. No nongreen mi-

11

crobe could match them for efficiency. Gradually the green plants became dominant in the seas at all depths penetrated by sunlight. They became the producers of organic matter upon which all other life soon came to depend. They serve this role today.

The oxygen freed by the splitting of water molecules in photosynthesis remained a useless byproduct to green plants. For most microbes it was poison. Dr. William D. McElroy of the Johns Hopkins University suspects that to escape from being poisoned by the oxygen, a majority of the nongreen microbes rapidly became adapted to getting rid of the active gas. Their principal adaptation may well have been production of two new compounds: luciferin and a protein called luciferase. In the presence of luciferase, oxygen combines with luciferin, producing a little flash of useless light. Microbes that could twinkle in this way passed along the successful pattern to their myriad offspring. Quite a number of different bacteria and dinoflagellates still show this ability, displaying it only when oxygen reaches them in generous amounts.

Probably the oxygen released by photosynthesis created the first real crisis for life on earth. To use it profitably, rather than merely to get rid of it through luminescence, required cells to evolve one of the most wonderful series of reactions yet discovered. Into this series goes a steady stream of organic food, which is simplified progressively, freeing useful energy and also hydrogen. The hydrogen is combined with oxygen to form harmless water. So extraordinary a sequence of steps could come about only through a major overhaul in the internal chemistry of cells. Yeasts are still fitted to operate in either way if they fall into solutions rich in organic compounds—particularly sugars. Without oxygen they ferment the sugar, releasing about 2½ percent of the energy it contains, and leaving alcohol as a dangerous byproduct. With oxygen they release all of the energy, gaining for their own processes almost twenty times as much as is possible by fermentation.

In the seas, however, free oxygen degraded organic compounds so rapidly and uselessly that many kinds of fermentative microbes starved to death. So rare did these energy-containing compounds of carbon and hydrogen become that the chance combination of various kinds to produce life ceased altogether. Thereafter, all life arose only from preexisting life. The living things of that day were the ancestors of all things living now, as well as the ancestors of all species that have become extinct during the passing eons.

In the seawater, oxygen attacked the various soluble compounds of phosphorus and of iron, oxidizing them to substances of far less solubility. To survive, cells had to develop new chemical means for capturing and concentrating the meager amounts available to them, spending energy to make the materials usefully soluble again for incorporation into important molecules.

Even the spectrum of sunlight at the earth's surface was changed by the addition of oxygen to the atmosphere. Reaching stratospheric heights, some of the oxygen (O_2) underwent molecular reorganization and became ozone (O_3), forming a thin blanket-like layer that filtered out much of the short-wave light rays and converted them to heat. Far less ultraviolet reached the earth than previously, and green plants that depended upon this energy-rich part of the solar spectrum either became adapted to the new kind of daylight or became extinct. Probably the original type of photosynthesis required drastic changes to let the algae continue to operate on light of longer wavelengths. Many plants today retain their ability to use ultraviolet if it is given to them, although too little penetrates the ozone blanket to be significant as a natural source of energy.

Among the minute creatures that evolved almost a billion years ago, many gained the ability to absorb from the surrounding seawater the raw materials needed for production of a supporting skeleton. Golden-green algae (diatoms) began withdrawing from their environment some trivial amounts of dissolved silica (quartz), and laying it down around their protoplasm in the form of boxes. A second adaptation saved the diatom from being weighed down by its glassy box and perhaps dragged deeper than sunlight penetrates. Each of these cells began producing a droplet of oily fat which buoyed up the diatom and helped it drift in sunny waters. Microscopic animals called radiolarians also absorbed silica from the sea. They secreted it in radiating slivers of glassy material upon which their protoplasm extended, capturing other microbes to eat. Still other animals (the foraminiferans) drew upon the surrounding sea for lime, and used it to cover themselves with limy enclosures scarcely thicker than a bubble. Through a multitude of tiny windows in the shell, the animal could reach for food.

Supported by their nonliving secretions, the living cells stayed where they could sense the sunlight and capture energy, could grow and reproduce. To numerous descendants they passed on the ability to absorb the necessary raw materials and to secrete new hard parts with adaptive

values. Only the capacity to draw upon the environment and to mold its
ingredients was inherited. The nonliving skeletons were left over. As
individual diatoms and minute animals died, their hard parts settled
slowly through the oceans. On the bottom the debris built into layers of
incredible thickness. The layers accumulated and changed the world for
future generations.

Recently we stood on some of this material which prevented history
from endlessly repeating itself. We were as close to the Baltic Sea as we
could go dryshod on the Danish island of Møn. Above us towered great
gray-white cliffs of chalk, kept almost vertical by eroding storms. Across
the cliff face, undulating dotted lines of dark stones showed how folded
and modified this soft mass of chalk had become since it accumulated as
sediments in an ancient sea. So easily did the chalk crumble that tiny
particles of it remained suspended, changing the blue-green Baltic waters
to an imitation milk as far as fifty feet from shore. Waves took away the
chalk so rapidly that the beach was mostly flinty stones. In head-sized
boulders and larger, they lay about. Fragments clanged like bits of metal
when kicked against one another. At the water's edge the smaller flint
pebbles rattled with each wavelet, like glass marbles shaken in a bag.

We marveled, as we have done before where the waves of the English
Channel beat against the famous chalk cliffs of Dover, that these ram-
parts of the land consist almost entirely of microscopic shells of microbes
long dead. The great Thomas Huxley told their story in his classic essay
"On a Piece of Chalk." But suppose the minute foraminiferans had not
lived in the ancient seas, contributing a steady rain of tiny limy shells in
astronomical abundance to accumulate as chalk. Suppose the equally
small radiolarian animals and diatomaceous plants had been absent and
no silicious remains had sunk to the bottom, there to be consolidated into
rounded flinty masses. What would we be standing on, hearing the waves
wash together? Sound alone was enough to identify our location where
the products of life were once more being stirred by the sea.

The ocean bottoms continue to accumulate these remains of living
things in surface water. But the open seas contribute most of the skeletons
that become preserved in the deep sediments. Only along the continental
shelves near shore and in shallow lagoons or estuaries is it likely that a
sampling of plants and animals familiar to man will be fossilized. For
records of past life on land we are similarly limited to sedimentary rocks
formed in the areas of the present continents, then raised by earth movements to elevations far above sea level.

Chalk cliffs at Møn, Denmark, formed of shells of microscopic organisms settling on sea bottom.

Looking about on the continents today, it is easy to assume that the great land masses have always had their modern outline and their characteristic living things. But for the first 500 million years or more after marine life became well established, no plant or animal had the adaptive pattern that would allow it to tolerate the fresh waters of a river or a lake. Less than 500 million years ago these adaptations appeared and broadened the stage for life into the interior of the continents, into wetlands, and onto earth that was dry between showers. The smallest of the new terrestrial creatures began producing soil, and thus made still other adaptations (such as roots) worthwhile. Down through the thousands of millennia, the scene has continually changed and continuously been populated by living things in wondrous succession. Most living things lived only a few millennia among the then-current kinds of plants and animals, and were replaced by the descendants of some—descendants that possessed still more suitable patterns, matching the changed environment.

All kinds of plants and all kinds of animals save one are limited strictly by features of chemistry and physical build. The one exception is the human species, which has been spreading over the terrestrial areas of the world's stage for less than 150 centuries. Man's inherited adaptations no longer limit him seriously because he has learned to use his brain and hands to overcome life's challenging obstacles. He has developed a unique heritage of cultural features that can be handed on, freeing his offspring from the need to learn everything freshly. New human generations can be both versatile and successful because the most important part of their heritage is now cultural. And culture gains momentum because people benefit from experiences described in folk song or written word, or built into the tools and treasures of civilization.

Once a man grasps a situation and identifies a new challenge imposed by his environment, he begins consciously to seek out ways to overcome or circuit the barrier. He has already learned to survive for long periods in parts of the world for which his chemical and physical adaptations alone do not suffice. He has scaled the highest mountains, but not made himself at home on their summits. He has plunged to the ocean's greatest depths, but not yet colonized the underwater world. Neither the tropical rain forests nor the world's great deserts afford enough of the amenities he needs for progress. The moon and distant planets are likely to be even less productive. But cultural adaptations will probably let him also explore them before long. Like the drifting life in the sea, he is slowly changing every part of his environment within reach, sometimes deliberately; sometimes wisely, sometimes not.

At first, man's changes were simple: burning a log in the mouth of a cave when the sun no longer warmed his home directly; wearing a furry mammal's skin outside his own when the weather's chill robbed him too quickly of body heat; extending his arm with a spear or arrows to get food he could not catch bare-handed; saving his legs by planting near home the seeds of plants whose fruits were good. His nonhuman companions came to be the living things he found useful, adaptable, beautiful, or somehow like himself. From a few kinds of grass he bred a rich variety of grains and corn. One kind of pig and of dog were enough. Only a few ancestral lines provided all the cattle or the roses he saw need to cultivate. Many of his chosen partners can no longer survive without his continual care. With their support for his culture, he has moved apart from the rest of the natural world, as though pretending that his sprawling domain is an island. By simplifying his world, man has made his decisions easier.

Only in the nonliving world of crystals and machines does simplicity go with stability. Among living things the converse is true. And while man would like to engineer his croplands, his fisheries, his forests and even his outdoor recreational areas into machinelike, efficient, simple systems, he is alone against time. No simple context provided the stability of working adaptations in plants and animals, allowing them to add refinement on refinement to match a changing world. No simple context led to man. And to earn an indefinite future, man has need to use his brain to the fullest toward understanding the complexity of living systems and fitting himself into the one grand pattern that continuously unfolds.

Man's chosen partners are not enough. It is still the myriad non-domesticated kinds of life that renew the air he breathes, produce and anchor the soil upon which he raises food, keep the rivers flowing and support the crops of fishes he harvests. He cannot long ignore and injure his complex outer environment without ruining the island world he has built and mastered.

chapter three

Individuality

"M AY the best man win" is more than good sportsmanship. It
matches a scientific idea, called natural selection, that leaped into
fame in 1859, relating only to living things as they compete for energy
and space. Today natural selection takes on fresh meaning as the molding
force on earth. It seems inevitable that before life appeared, more than
2 billion years ago, the best molecule or community of molecules won
a place in the future.

Evolution through natural selection, as proposed first by Charles Darwin and Alfred Russel Wallace, has become the most far-reaching idea
contributed from the biological sciences. In modern guise, it extends to
the limits of the cosmos, beyond our universe and galaxy to any planet
of any star where the conditions are suitable for life. There, biologists
predict, living things will almost certainly arise and diversify. In the near
future, confirmation seems likely from data obtained by a space probe
or an exploring team of astronauts.

Meanwhile, biologists are learning all they can from the astronomers
and geochemists, trying to imagine in detail how our own world may have
differed at a time long ago when life was just starting its long journey.
Leapfrogging backward in time, biologists search for a plausible sequence
whereby life can have emerged from the nonliving, on earth or anywhere
else under similar conditions.

What information can astronomers and geochemists offer? These scientists are now in good agreement that our universe came into existence between 7 and 13 billion years ago. New surveys of the sky may soon allow them to considerably narrow this range. In any case, it seems likely that our solar system evolved about 5 billion years ago from a cloud of primitive dust containing most of the chemical elements. Within about half a billion years, the whirling masses of dust condensed further, separating into a central giant sun and a whole series of planets.

Information available on the composition of the sun today, of interstellar dust, of meteorites, and of the earth, all supports the conclusion that the original atmosphere of the earth was rich in hydrogen, as is that of the sun today. All chemical elements that combine readily with hydrogen would then be linked to it: carbon into methane, nitrogen into ammonia, oxygen into water, and some carbon along with some nitrogen into hydrogen cyanide. Supposedly these were the chief ingredients of the earth's atmosphere. No oxygen as a free gas, carbon monoxide or carbon dioxide seem to have existed on our planet at that time.

Many people have wondered whether the gases in the early atmosphere surrounding the earth might have reacted with one another. They would have been subjected to intense sunlight, particularly ultraviolet waves which contain the most energy. Decay of radioactive materials, especially potassium-40, in the crust of the earth would have bombarded the gases with electrons. Electrical storms and volcanic heat might have induced changes. Even the gravitational energy released by the cosmic dust as it condensed to form a solid earth must have been available for a while, before it radiated off into space.

At the University of Chicago, Dr. Harold C. Urey decided to find out what was possible in the imagined atmosphere of the early earth. He had already won a Nobel prize in chemistry for discovering that 156 out of every million hydrogen atoms in water differ from the "ordinary" by being "heavy hydrogen." He led one of his students, Dr. Stanley L. Miller, to build a special hoop-shaped apparatus of glass tubing to hold water and selected gases (water vapor, hydrogen, methane and ammonia) where they could be kept cycling past an electric spark imitative of natural lightning. At one point the water received gentle heat, causing it to boil and give off water vapor. At another, the vapor was chilled to condense it and return water to the boiler.

For a week the gases kept swirling slowly past the spark while the water continued its cycle. Then the liquid in the boiler was analyzed to see if anything had changed. It contained new ingredients: half a dozen different amino acids in astonishing amounts, traces of formaldehyde and of hydrogen cyanide. These particular compounds have special significance. Amino acids serve as the building blocks for proteins, the most characteristic compounds in all kinds of life. Formaldehyde absorbs ultraviolet light and can then react spontaneously with itself to form sugars, including ribose and deoxyribose which are now known to be parts of the molecules that carry heredity. For the first time in history, the formation of organic compounds had been shown to be possible with no living things present to guide the synthetic reactions.

More of the essential building blocks for life turned up when other scientists tried similar experiments with different combinations of gases that might have been present in the earth's atmosphere 2 billion years ago. At the Exobiology Laboratory of the National Aeronautics and Space Administration at Moffett Field, California, Drs. R. S. Young and Cyril Ponnamperuma replaced the electric spark with a beam of high-energy electrons to imitate the effect of radioactive materials in the crust of the primitive earth. The mixture of water, water vapor, hydrogen, methane and ammonia combined in somewhat different ways. Under these conditions it yielded remarkable organic compounds called guanine and adenine. These are two of the five key components now recognized as joining with ribose and deoxyribose and to phosphate to spell out the genetic code. They are essential for hereditary features to be stored away safely in a cell.

The scientists at the Exobiology Laboratory persisted, for they were eager to know what may be expected when man sets foot on distant planets. They shone ultraviolet light on a solution of adenine and ribose in the presence of a compound containing phosphorus. From this imitation of a lifeless world came the chief carriers of energy in living cells. Known as ATP (for adenosine triphosphate) and ADP (for adenosine diphosphate), they are compounds classed as nucleotides. Every kind of life uses them to get things done.

In 1965 the Exobiology group had new success to report. At temperatures no greater than those in a thermal spring, such as in Yellowstone National Park, they had induced all five of the key components of the genetic code to link up with either ribose or deoxyribose and phosphate. The processes were faster at higher temperatures and were best when the amount of water was small. With no living cell to guide the chemical reactions, the researchers had produced everything needed as building blocks in the special molecules of inheritance—DNA (deoxyribose nucleic acid) and RNA (ribose nucleic acid).

Perhaps it was only natural that the scientists who were so intent on discovering the processes by which life may have arisen should have ignored the hydrogen cyanide in the imagined atmosphere of the early earth. Cyanide is among the most deadly poisons known for virtually everything that breathes. But in the beginning, and until free oxygen was available, nothing breathed! A research team headed by Dr. Clifford N. Matthews of the Monsanto Chemical Company reported in 1966 on new experiments designed to remedy the oversight. To their surprise these men found that hydrogen cyanide gas, when subjected to a source of energy such as ultraviolet light, would combine readily with water to form at least fifteen of the twenty different amino acids important to any kind of life. They expressed hope that the process they discovered might be used toward synthesizing food for mankind, since proteins composed of amino acids are everywhere the most expensive part of any diet. (In the meals eaten by the undernourished people of the world, proteins are particularly inadequate.)

But no mixture of water, sugars, amino acids, nucleotides and other key components placed in sterile glassware under an artificial atmosphere will snap together and come alive. The marvelous qualities of life arise from its ultramicroscopic organization, which allows life to absorb from a complex solution surrounding it what is needed for maintenance, growth and reproduction. So far biologists and chemists have succeeded spectacularly well in learning exactly which molecules are needed for life and where each fits into the organization. This is the vocabulary and the grammar of living things. Yet none of the real complications have been solved, the ones that would account for the origin of this organization. We can hope still to discover how the cell uses its chemical words for conversations among its parts, how its accumulated experience is stored away in DNA like sentences in an enormous encyclopedia, how the living cell chooses which page of what volume to refer to for the detailed instructions needed minute by minute to survive. But we have yet to account for the steps by which it all began.

We cannot deny the importance of an environment suitable as a starting place for life. Over millions of years each organic compound dissolved in seawater must have slowly accumulated. The solution would be richest in the coastal lagoons and tide pools, where energy from the sun and outer space was most plentiful. So long as no oxygen could reach any of the compounds and release their energy through oxidation, they would remain inert. Yet they would be ready to combine into still more complex organic substances when influenced by heat, or electrons, or lightning, or ultraviolet radiations, or even by cosmic rays. Accumulations of this kind may well be in progress on many other planets in the universe, as though getting ready for the appearance of life.

Like Shakespeare's "tide . . . Which, taken at the flood, leads on to fortune," the most ideal conditions for life to arise and continue would not persist indefinitely. Astronomers and geochemists point out that our earth, being a middle-sized planet, produces a gravitational attraction that holds most of the gases from its primitive atmosphere, but not the lightest ones. They believe that the earth lost the hydrogen and helium from its atmosphere within the first few billion years. The change altered the suitability of the shallow seas both as a place in which organic compounds might form spontaneously and as a home for the earliest living things.

As the concentration of hydrogen decreased, compounds of this gas with other elements in the atmosphere would tend to decompose when affected by light and other forms of energy. Ammonia, particularly, separates into nitrogen, which remained to become the most abundant gas, and hydrogen, which escaped. Dr. Harold C. Urey believes that some water also decomposed, freeing oxygen as well as hydrogen. Yet water is such a stable compound that the amount split would be small, even by high-energy radiations. Presumably, any free oxygen combined promptly with carbon to form carbon monoxide.

Gradually the nature of the earth's atmosphere transformed, with less hydrogen and ammonia and more nitrogen and carbon monoxide. Conditions for chemical evolution changed correspondingly. Fewer amino acids and nucleotides arose. The chance diminished that new living things could develop from nonliving substances. Those that were present found less suitable materials around them from which to make more of their distinctive kinds.

What sort of creature might the first living thing have been? No longer does any scientist consider an ameba or an euglena as a candidate. Although single cells, both are much too complex. They fit only a world with free oxygen and carbon dioxide. Amebas flow about in search of other cells to eat, with the habits of animals. They could not exist without their prey, and thus could not have been the first life on earth. At least the bacteria and microscopic algae on which they feed must have been in existence earlier. Euglenas are independent, able to manufacture all of the food they need from water, carbon dioxide, sunlight and inorganic substances. Without carbon dioxide they starve. And carbon dioxide is not among the gases the astronomers and geochemists list for the atmosphere of the primitive earth.

Even the simplest bacterial cell alive today is more complex than the first living things needed to be. Bacteria have to be able to make their own ATP. Doing so requires each bacterial cell to carry on many chemical activities that were unnecessary in ancient lagoons and tide pools, where ATP itself and many other organic compounds were available, ready-formed through the action of the lightning, heat, ultraviolet light and electrons from radioactive elements.

Although biologists know of no living system simpler than the smallest bacterial cell, they can imagine one to match a primitive world where organic substances in shallow seas resembled a nutritious soup. This first microbe would absorb all of the building blocks it needed for growth from the ready-made supply, taking in ATP to provide energy for assembling the building blocks into its own larger molecules, and would be able to reproduce. Probably it reached some definite size and then divided into two equal daughter cells, just as most microbes do today.

This earliest life would still have individuality. It would resemble all living things today in being enclosed by its own thin membrane, isolating its internal chemistry from the general environment and from any other cells. Formation of a boundary membrane of exactly the right kind may have been a rare event in the lifeless world. Perhaps only one type was suitable—the type that surrounds all modern cells. Composed of a firm protein and a fatty substance in the form of a sandwich, with protein on both sides and fat in the middle, it would have been 1/254,000-inch thick. This kind of boundary around living protoplasm allows water to pass through freely in either direction. To larger molecules it is selective, admitting some substances and shutting out others. It prevents the loss from the cell of important compounds such as DNA and RNA.

Inside each of these earliest living cells, some of the same chemical activities would be necessary that are found today in bacteria and other microbes. As the first live cell grew, it would have to make more cell membrane—more of the correct protein and fat—and then fit them together in place.

Each chemical reaction within a living cell proceeds so inconspicuously that it is easy to forget that detailed guidance, as well as energy exchange, is necessary. Guidance comes from molecules of protein which somehow hold temporarily in matching positions the raw materials that can interact spontaneously. The spontaneity which is then so essential depends upon a simple principle: The action will take place if, through it, some energy is released as heat.

Only the directions for making these special proteins—the special enzyme for each different reaction—are inherited. Each living cell must be able to decode the instructions it inherits in its spiral, ladderlike molecules of DNA, as well as to replicate them exactly for posterity. The replicas must be parceled out into the daughter cells when the parent cell divides. Only in this way can the heritage be continued, spelling out the molecular patterns of the essential proteins.

At least one enzyme is needed to transfer the coded message from its storage center in the cell into a messenger molecule of RNA. Elsewhere in the cell, messenger RNA serves like an expendable paper pattern to specify the details of a particular protein that is to be made. No one yet knows all the steps required to bring the units of amino acids in proper sequence into line along the messenger. But certainly another enzyme is necessary to link them together to form the protein. Still a different enzyme brings components together to replicate the master molecules of DNA.

Even though we credit the earliest living things with being able to obtain from their environment all they needed of amino acids and other building blocks for maintenance and growth, one more critical enzyme must be included. Without it no cell can transfer from the nucleotide ATP the necessary amounts of energy to other organic compounds, making them useful in the chemistry of life. This enzyme is seldom mentioned by its full name, adenosine triphosphatase, because ATPase is so much shorter and easier to say. It alone holds a molecule of ATP in the way that allows the nucleotide to split into inorganic phosphate and ADP. For virtually every reaction that takes place inside a cell, this splitting must occur beforehand.

Surrounded in its sea of nourishment, the first living cell of all may have needed only half as many enzymes as the simplest life today. But how many enzymes are required in the smallest modern reproductive unit known? It is a spore of the minuscule bacterium known only as PPLO ("pleuropneumonia-like organisms"), at the very bottom of the scale for self-sustaining life. These spores contain about forty molecules of DNA, ready to spell out the sequence of amino acids in forty different proteins of average size, as enzymes for no more than forty different reactions. No other form of life is known to be so vulnerable for, with no duplicates among its instructions, the spore loses its ability to survive if an accident strikes any one of its forty molecules of DNA. Every one of is reactions is essential. We can scarcely think of a primitive cell with less than half of this repertoire, no matter how favorable its environment might have been.

Somehow the excitement in these recent discoveries at the molecular and electron-microscope level passed us by until we heard Dr. Ernest C. Pollard of Pennsylvania State University talk like an engineer about what would be required to construct the simplest bacterial cell from nonliving materials in the laboratory. Suddenly we realized the fantastic pace at which events follow one another to let a bacterial cell grow and reproduce —doubling itself in every detail in less than thirty minutes.

Here is a loop of DNA, nine hundred times as long as the cell itself, folded back and forth to fit in so confined a space. Along that loop an enzyme molecule rushes, transcribing the code into messengers of RNA at the rate of thirty thousand messages per second. The RNA speeds off to the cell surface where incoming raw materials can be combined to make proteins, fats and carbohydrates. Right behind the transcribing enzyme another molecule speeds along to replicate the DNA, spinning off a second loop, getting it ready for a daughter cell before the old cell splits in two. At many places around the cell membrane, enzymes seize passing molecules of appropriate kinds, stopping their aimless jittering for just long enough to produce reactions, making more cell membrane and secreting new cell wall outside it. All through the cell, similar activity provides the new distinctive parts that soon will be needed.

Time is up! The last messages are read off the original DNA. The cell begins division. The twin loop of DNA moves off in one direction, the old DNA in the opposite. Enzymes called for by those last messages finish off the ends of the constricted daughter cells. At once the whole sequence begins again, as though in a desperate hurry. While conditions are right for life, the cell makes the most of them.

How many of these events differ from those in the very first life? They seem close to the irreducible minimum, and probably equally close to the truth.

Under the strange conditions of the primitive earth and its oxygen-free environment, the spontaneous formation of these large and more complicated molecules may have been a rare event. Perhaps the successful combination came into existence only a few times in all the millions of years while conditions were favorable for the appearance of life. But once a cell had its enclosing membrane, its nucleic acids (DNA and RNA) and the appropriate enzymes they specified, it held a magic pattern. It could nourish itself from the organic materials in the surrounding sea. It could grow and duplicate itself exactly. In DNA it concealed the basis for inheritable variations, for evolution, for improvement by increasing complexity in adaptations to match a changing world. Individually, each cell held the promise of a limitless future.

chapter four

The Light of Day

FOOD shortages are nothing new. They surely developed within a few million years after life appeared on our planet. Any microbes—even the most primitive ones—can reproduce faster than spontaneous chemical actions can replace their nourishment. Some microbes differed enough from others in their nutritional requirements to be better suited for survival. Others became extinct. New kinds evolved.

Sooner or later, a situation of this kind was inevitable. Changes in the atmosphere, as hydrogen escaped and the supply of new organic nutrients spontaneously fell off, merely hastened the day of challenge. Probably ATP, the universal energy compound, was the first to become scarce. At a time when (as Rudyard Kipling wrote) "The world was so new-and-all," any microbe that could make its own ATP must have had the equivalent of a gold mine. While lesser microbes competed to absorb this compound from the shallow seas, the better-adapted cells relied upon their own special chemical process. They took in some organic compound that was still plentiful, oxidized it a step at a time, and captured some of the energy released. They linked a phosphate group to ADP, making ATP. Elsewhere in the cell the microbe could reconvert the ATP to ADP and phosphate to spend the energy in combining nutrients that were important for growth and reproduction.

In imagining our way into the ancient past on earth, we have many

29

guideposts. All of them point toward life of familiar kinds in a modern world. Every sign repeats one theme: an underlying similarity between the earliest living things and the most recent. We can be sure that some microbes added new patterns of internal chemistry, allowing them to release useful energy from organic nutrients. Other microbes remained conservative, weakening, starving and dying. For thousands of years their tiny bodies drifted with the seawater or settled to the bottom.

When we go to the seacoast today we notice bits of seaweed washing up and down the beach, being pounded by the waves and broken into progressively smaller fragments. Other pieces are tossed ashore to be dried in the sun, crack and crumble, and be leached of soluble substances by every rain. We realize that these processes contribute to the fertility of the coastal waters. Every river and shore-edge spring adds inorganic materials in solution. From the distant past to the present, the fringe of the seas and the water at the bottom have offered more nutrients to living things than are to be found remote from land. But the violent breakers along the shore and the constant hazard of being stranded place a high price on making use of the resource.

We see seaweeds and barnacles cemented to rocks; limpets and abalones clinging with a single foot spread like a suction cup; mussels tethered in place by fine threads of their own making; sea stars and sea urchins holding fast with multiple tubefeet. How do the microbes manage in this tumultuous environment, or have they any means for staying close to the rich supply of food and raw materials?

Recent studies of modern bacteria, using the ultra-high magnification of the new electron microscopes, have revealed short peglike extensions from the cell wall which are believed to serve in temporarily holding the cell to a support wherever food is abundant. Surely some early microbes added to their successful patterns the chemical processes needed to produce similar features, letting them adhere wherever the sea bottom was firm.

We can only speculate about what happened when early microbes stuck themselves to dead cells instead of firm supports. Only a membrane would separate them from a rich supply of food. A live microbe with the right proteins added to its sticky secretion could digest its way through the membrane and reach the nourishment, which otherwise would remain unavailable. The cell might have to expend the energy from a few molecules of ATP to drive the chemical reactions for which the new proteins gave aid as enzymes. But in return for its investment it would gain food, some of which might be used in producing still more ATP.

As soon as a microbe has a way to get food and energy from dead cells, it is a decomposer—an agent of decay. If it fastens itself to cells that are still alive and hastens their death, it is a parasite. Bacteria and fungi serve both roles today. Decomposers help prevent the chemical constituents of life from accumulating uselessly in dead bodies, occupying space and rendering scarce elements still scarcer. Decomposers keep these materials in circulation by absorbing complex organic compounds and simplifying them. They discard residues from which they can extract no more that is useful. Each decomposer may accomplish only a step or two in the chemical degradation of a compound. But the wastes of one decomposer may be the food for another, and a whole series can act in chain-style before the organic compound gives up every bit of chemical energy it contains.

Our world now harbors thousands of different kinds of decomposers. They simplify organic substances in the seas and bottom sediments, in fresh waters and the soil on land, either with or without oxygen. Still the members of the National Aeronautics and Space Administration fear that other kinds will be brought back by astronauts from Mars, or even in a live but dormant state from dust on the moon. Any living things that are able to survive on celestial bodies less hospitable than the earth might possess superior adaptations, giving them a dangerous advantage on our planet. They could contaminate the clothing and bodies of the astronauts, as well as the space ships in which the men return. Spreading into the sea or the soil, these exotic stowaways conceivably could bring chaos.

We know from experiences that were costly in the 19th century how quickly a newcomer can devastate a resource for man. The "late blight" fungus caused disastrous famine in Ireland, just as a few American cactus plants and European rabbits upset the economy of Australia. Unearthly microbes might replace the cultivated crops on which human civilization depends, as well as most of the wild things in our natural environment. At an uncontrollable rate, they could disrupt the cyclic regeneration of nutrient materials upon which all earthly life relies for co-existence. In just a few years or decades, the newcomers might upset a state of equilibrium that took eons to evolve.

Our world has already been changed profoundly by the activities of

Sea star *Asterias* clinging to a rock at low tide along Maine coast.

microbes, ruining it for some kinds of life and making it more suitable for others. Primitive cells built into their own organic compounds the carbon that the primitive atmosphere offered in the form of methane. This one gas must have been abundant, accounting for at least a fourth of the total that remained around the earth after the original hydrogen and helium escaped into outer space. Living things transferred its components into their own structure. So far as we know, methane provided virtually all of the carbon incorporated into protoplasm from the day of the very first life until the present. Yet today methane is a curiosity, liberated by several kinds of bacteria that promote decomposition in the mud of swamps and marshes where oxygen is lacking. Methane is "marsh gas," which escapes unpredictably in bubbles. Sometimes it ignites— combining with the oxygen in our modern atmosphere to yield carbon dioxide, water, and eerie lights at night. Once they were known as jack- o'-lanterns or will-o'-the-wisps. Now they may be reported as flying saucers or UFOs.

For eons after the first life appeared and the decomposers began simplifying the organic compounds in dead cells, the carbon that once had been in methane moved from one microbe to another along a multitude of chemical pathways. Among the assorted products of decomposition were many that other microbes could use for food. One exceptional compound—carbon dioxide from fermentation—remained useless. It contained no available energy and, without oxygen free in gaseous form or solution, offered nothing valuable to cells. Slowly it accumulated. Dissolved in sea water, it combined to produce some molecules of carbonic acid. They made the seas faintly sour, like stale soda water with a little salt added. In the atmosphere its concentration rose to one percent, to two percent, to three percent.

In air with carbon dioxide accounting for three percent, a person inhales and exhales about twice as much as usual, but suffers no ill effects. Other modern animals and plants are similarly immune. Yet the whole world was profoundly influenced as a living place for microbes by this modest increase in the concentration of carbon dioxide in the atmosphere a billion years ago. The useless gas interfered with the passage of infrared waves in sunlight, absorbing them strongly and converting their energy into heat. It captured this energy as the sun's rays penetrated the atmosphere toward the earth. It caught still more as infrared waves reradiated toward space from surfaces warmed by the visible part of sunlight, to which carbon dioxide is transparent. The temperature of the entire planet increased in much the same way as the contents of a green-house or a closed automobile do when the sun shines through the glass.

Slowly the oceans grew warmer. More water vapor rose from the sea when the sun shone on the waves. The cloud cover thickened, reducing the amount of sunlight reaching the earth. For life, these were perilous times.

The challenge provided by carbon dioxide and a higher temperature almost demanded something new and far-reaching among inheritable adaptations. Among microbes, it was a remarkable molecule, chlorophyll. This substance, which appears green because it reflects and transmits green light (while absorbing blue and orange), became the badge of the green plants. They alone in the world use the energy in visible light to split molecules of water, and to transfer the hydrogen from the water into organic compounds. No other kind of living thing has ever become so nearly independent.

Using chlorophyll, the green plants closed a great cycle of nutrients that the decomposers had begun. Now carbon dioxide from fermentation could reenter the chain of chemical changes, instead of accumulating as a useless gas that changed the climate of the world. The carbon of carbon dioxide went into complex compounds of green plants, soon to be transferred through a series of decomposers and to reemerge in carbon dioxide gas, only to be recaptured.

In this new process of photosynthesis—incorporating solar energy into organic compounds—green plants proved so efficient that they threatened to use up the carbon dioxide upon which they depended. Faster than fermentation could renew the supply, they absorbed and used it. The concentration of the gas in the atmosphere decreased to two percent, to one percent, and to the modern $\frac{1}{30}$ of one percent. As less carbon dioxide remained in the atmosphere, the "greenhouse effect" decreased. Infrared parts of the sun's full spectrum again passed readily, both to and from the earth's surface. The planet and its oceans cooled down somewhat, changing once more the conditions for life.

From being a novelty somewhat over a billion years ago, photosynthesis in green plants has become the keystone of modern life. Green plants regularly produce far more organic compounds than they use in their own activities. The surplus feeds all of the nongreen plants and all of the animals, either directly or indirectly. Mankind competes for a large share and seeks ways to increase it. Rarely, however, is it easy or worthwhile to enrich the air around crop plants to the four or five percent of carbon dioxide that seems ideal for them. More can be accomplished by supplying inorganic nutrients such as nitrates and phosphates, potash and lime. These substances are often scarcer near plants than carbon dioxide, despite the low concentration of this gas in the atmosphere today.

Under earthly conditions the full versatility of modern green plants is never explored. But now that plans are being made to land an unmanned space craft on Mars before 1971, experiments are under way to learn what effects the atmosphere of Mars could be expected to have on plants. At the Union Carbide Research Institute near Tarrytown, New York, Dr. Sanford M. Siegel has built an airtight greenhouse to enclose an imitation of the Martian atmosphere: mostly nitrogen, with about ten percent inert argon, three percent carbon dioxide, two percent oxygen, and only traces of water vapor—all at a low pressure corresponding to that at 82,000 feet above the earth. Among nearly 250 kinds of seeds tested, more than 50 germinate with no oxygen at all. With only a tenth as much oxygen as is in our air, cucumber seedlings seem unharmed by being frozen every night and thawed each morning. On Mars, hardiness of this kind could be extremely important, since the thin atmosphere does so little to retain heat at night. After a summer day when the surface of Mars reaches the 60's Fahrenheit, the temperature falls to the freezing point about sundown, and well below zero before dawn. No earthly vegetation has yet been found to do more than germinate and survive a few months under these condition. But Mars may have its own highly adapted plants, waiting for a space explorer to collect them.

The colors and markings seen on Mars by the Dutch astronomer Christian Huyghens in 1695 started the first speculations about life on the reddish planet. The English science writer Arthur C. Clarke once had a Martian character predict that the planet Earth must be lifeless because of the high concentration of the poisonous gas oxygen. Virtually all of the oxygen in our atmosphere was liberated by green plants as a by-product of photosynthesis. The presence of this gas, in concentrations that increased slowly to nearly 21 percent, has had consequences for life even more far-reaching than those of carbon dioxide.

Oxygen combines readily with a great variety of substances, oxidizing them. If any hydrogen remained in the earth's atmosphere when the first free oxygen came from photosynthesis, the two gases combined explosively to form water every time lightning triggered the reaction. With oxygen, methane burns to form water and carbon dioxide. One molecule of oxygen can turn two molecules of carbon monoxide into carbon dioxide. Oxygen transforms the more soluble salts of iron and of phosphorus into meagerly soluble ones, forcing all modern living things to use roundabout routes to concentrate and absorb the amounts of iron and phosphorus they need. Oxygen degrades organic compounds in water so rapidly that any type of life needing these materials for food is sure to starve into extinction.

High above the earth, oxygen (O_2) recombines to maintain a layer of ozone (O_3), which is remarkably opaque to ultraviolet wavelengths of light. As the oxygen concentration increased in the earth's atmosphere during the long period of geological time beginning about 750 million years ago, green plants that depended upon the energy in ultraviolet gradually disappeared. Some of their descendants possessed new adaptations that let them continue by using the lesser amounts of energy in visible light.

On Mars, oxygen is too scarce to cause the formation of an ozone blanket, filtering out the ultraviolet. Any living things there probably wear a heavy armor protecting them from the damaging effects of this harsh light. Nothing delicate and akin to life on earth could survive, even at the greater distance from the sun and lesser intensity of sunshine that are features of Mars' orbit. For this reason the designers of the vehicle scheduled to explore Mars automatically after the unmanned landing may have to install a "cookie-cutter" as the sampling instrument to remove specimens from the Martian landscape. A gentler tool, such as a strip of adhesive tape rolled out and then back into the field of view of a television microscope, might fail to dislodge any plant or animal capable of withstanding the living conditions on Mars.

On earth, the altered light of day and the presence of oxygen made active animals possible. By detecting the light and staying where it was intense enough for photosynthesis, microbes that lived at the expense of green plants could remain close to a good supply of food. Those that developed a mouth and pushed plant cells inside their bodies to be digested became plant-eaters—herbivores. Those that fed on animal cells in a similar way were animal-eaters—carnivores. All of these new animals showed one feature in common: they used oxygen in a new type of respiration consisting of a novel series of chemical steps. The food they ate, then digested and absorbed, was simplified in a way that transferred nearly half of its energy into useful ATP. The rest turned into heat, at a rate that raised the animal's temperature no more than was safe. Carbon in the food was released in carbon dioxide, and the hydrogen of the organic compounds combined with free oxygen to form waste water.

The new pattern of respiration in animals produced ATP with an efficiency nineteen times as great as in the fermentation processes of the decomposers. Animals had plenty of ATP to spend on moving themselves around, hunting for food and mates. Devouring the green plants directly or indirectly, they had energy to spare for new adaptations. Each change in their patterns that aided in survival brought them closer to becoming animals of the present day.

chapter five

A Company of Peers

MODERN scientists would like to know how far back in time the
first cooperation appeared on earth. How soon did living cells
stick together in clusters, in colonies, in multicellular individuals? What
was gained and what was lost by the change? The answers are hidden
in Precambrian rocks dating from 1.2 to 0.6 billion years ago, when
many-celled plants and animals appear for the first time in the fossil
record. With new techniques of chemical and optical analysis, these ancient rocks now reveal details that eluded discovery until the present
decade.

The catalogue of antique seaweeds and sponges grows slowly. From
the fragmentary remains and irregular shapes of these masses of cells,
the features that distinguish various kinds emerge at unpredictable intervals. But in all of them the same change can be seen in patterns that
improved the chances of survival. A single cell divided to become two
daughters, and the two became four, then eight, then more, all clinging
together instead of going their separate ways.

This process repeats itself today every time a fertilized egg begins to
develop into an embryo. It happens without sex too, when the minute
spore of an alga or a fungus divides repeatedly to form a new plant.
And no one is sure how soon sex appeared on earth. It may have an-
tedated the clustering of cells into individual masses with some division

of labor. Or it might have come later, as a new difference that opened fresh doors to the future.

When two daughter cells cling together, the area of contact provides for exchange of substances between them. It increases the likelihood that each cell will influence the other, the shared substances acting like messengers. Only the most minute amounts of messenger material are needed to link two cells or more into a team against the world. These chemical conversations coordinate their actions and provide the basis for new adaptations toward mutual benefit.

Often one cell or group of cells becomes specialized for getting energy while others attend to reproduction for the team. Through progressive division of labor, the colony or the multicellular individual grows more efficient. Yet the cells that contribute toward the increased complexity of the social group gain this efficiency by specializing. They relinquish many capabilities that are necessary for any solitary cell to feed, to grow and reproduce its kind. The more complex the whole multicellular organization becomes, the simpler are its component cells.

The most tremendous step came about inconspicuously. The new partnerships evolved until, in achieving greater efficiency, many cells relinquished their ability to reproduce. Other members of the colony, or other cells in the complex individual, then had to ensure the propagation of the species. This change may have seemed slight. But any cell that can no longer reproduce has lost its own potential immortality. It cannot live forever. At least in a statistical sense, its end becomes predictable. With no awareness of what they were doing, cells in the more complex kinds of living things during Precambrian times began to make the ultimate sacrifice. For the good of the multicellular individual, in which only a few parts specialized in reproduction, all other cells progressed through the process of aging that ends in natural death. Today it seems incredible that so great a change could have entered the world so silently.

Even the simplest partnership among cells combines the possibilities of gain with the certainties of loss. The individual cells in each group have a partner in at least one direction, where it serves as a shield from danger and a possible source of nourishment by sharing in times of special need. Yet wherever it is in contact with adjacent cells, each cell has lost its direct connection to the sea—the original environment. Cells at the surface of the group have one side exposed through which to pass food materials, energy and wastes. But through the reduced area, these essentials must pass at higher rates, with greater efficiency than is required of a solitary individual which has surface exposed on all sides. The necessity for increased efficiency is part of the price of partnership.

Surely some change in the Precambrian environment fostered the first clustering of cells into colonies and multicellular individuals by allowing a sudden increase in efficiency beyond anything known before that time. It must have come about all over the world at about the same time, for fossil remains of multicellular plants and animals appear almost simultaneously in the ancient rocks of Asia, Australia and the Americas. As scientists began recently to assemble all their facts into a logical picture, they realized suddenly that one key part of the jigsaw puzzle had been in their hands for more than a century. Scarcely appreciated, it lay waiting in the *Bulletin* of the Chemical Society of Paris for June 28, 1861. They needed only to reexamine and polish this piece of information to see it as the key to the Precambrian change.

In 1861 the wine makers of France were supporting the research work of Louis Pasteur. To everyone's surprise, he had proved that the production of alcohol from sugar solutions depended upon the activities of microscopic yeast plants, which performed this reaction only in the absence of oxygen. Pasteur tried to increase their efficiency by bubbling air through the vats of sugar solution. On June 28 he reported the results of these experiments. With oxygen the yeasts grew at a tremendous pace, not at the pitiful rate he had seen while air was excluded. They required far less sugar for this growth and produced more carbon dioxide. But they ceased abruptly to make alcohol. For the time being, at least, the wine makers would have to get along with the slow growth of yeasts while fermentation progressed in the absence of air. Other scientists found more to interest them in the new discovery, for yeasts could change reversibly from inefficient use of sugar in fermentation to efficient reactions using oxygen in respiration like that of animals. These men confirmed Pasteur's results and called the change from fermentative to respiratory use of sugar the "Pasteur effect."

Until a few years ago, no one really cared how much oxygen a yeast needed to change from fermentation to aerobic respiration. Pasteur's dream of finding other plants that would make alcohol more efficiently than yeasts remained unfulfilled. But if a little oxygen made so much difference to a yeast plant, perhaps it was equally important to other kinds of life during Precambrian times. How little oxygen does a yeast need to use sugar efficiently? To unravel this clue to the remote past, Pasteur's experiments were repeated and refined in several research laboratories. All showed the same concentration of oxygen as the critical point at which the yeasts change their chemical operations: 1/100 of the modern amount of oxygen in our atmosphere. Known now as the "Pasteur point," this low concentration could have been reached easily in the ancient environment after green plants carried on photosynthesis for a few million years.

Even if the ancestors of yeasts did not develop a multicellular way of life, other nongreen organisms in the ancient seas did change. They gave up fermentative chemistry to use the free oxygen, although doing so required them to add new adaptations in every cell. How much efficiency could they gain by using this gas released by green plants in sunlight? Again the yeast cells gave the answer: they are nineteen times as efficient with oxygen as without it. Other fermentative organisms gained similarly. Their greater efficiency allowed clustering of cells, each losing some of the surface it previously had exposed to the sea. Active movement became possible because energy could be released from foods more plentifully. Some of the decomposers began to search for food, as the first animals devouring plants and one another. Even the green plants of the Precambrian began using oxygen at night. By replacing the inefficient fermentative chemistry that earlier had alternated with daily photosynthesis, they too could be multicellular.

Some of the first patterns in many-celled life have survived to the present day, both in the sea and in fresh water. These living things seem simple and conservative by comparison with conspicuous plants and animals. Many of them are long threadlike filaments, consisting of cylindrical cells cemented end to end. Every cell retains its contact with the environment and its capacity to reproduce. Sometimes the end cell shows a special feature, becoming a "holdfast" that anchors the filament to some solid support. Filamentous plants are common among the algae and the fungi. Mushrooms and puffballs contain nothing but filaments twisting around one another to form the firm fungi we all recognize.

Algae along the world's seacoasts include the flimsy fronds of sea lettuce which grow in shallow water to a length of two feet and a width of six inches. Each single sheet consists of bright green cells in just two thin layers. An inconspicuous holdfast tethers the sea lettuce to a rock or other firm object on the bottom. But every cell has a face to the sea and can reproduce by freeing into the water from four to eight minute swimming spores, each capable of settling to the bottom and growing to become a separate plant.

The coarser brown algae, such as kelps, thrive in the same places, with a thicker, ribbonlike blade and often a ropelike stalk from a large holdfast. Many of their cells, surrounded by others, are shut off completely from the sea. They depend upon their partners for nourishment and are destined to die without participating directly in reproduction.

To people who poke into tide pools and find living things that cling to rocks along the seashore, the boundary between the plant kingdom and the animal has long been inconspicuous. Indeed, the same Greek word *sphongos* gave us the two terms fungus and sponge. The great Greek naturalist Aristotle knew one from the other, and remarked that sponges "are in every way like a vegetable" while including them among the animals. He had been told that a sponge clings to its rocky support more firmly when disturbed, which no plant can do. Some sponges are bright green, due to microscopic green plants embedded in them. Others are golden yellow, pink, brown or black. None of them react in obvious ways when jostled. Yet recent discoveries show that sponges solved problems of life and death by different means than is to be found elsewhere among either animals or plants.

Many sponges have no obvious shape of their own, but conform to the surface of the rock upon which they grow. Others are in many-fingered masses or irregular balls or spreading cups with a flaring rim. All of them, while alive, bear one or more large openings from which water flows gently, and a multitude of tiny pores by which the water enters. Further details can be discovered by use of a microscope, but even these give no hint of the transformations possible in a sponge.

At any moment each cell in a sponge occupies a definite site and serves a particular role. It may be a pore cell, shaped like a doughnut, located in the outer surface of the sponge. Water passes through the hole at its center (the pore), carrying oxygen and particles of food into one or more large central cavities. The water moves under the lashing action of long whiplike flagella on other cells, located in the walls of the central cavities. These cells also take from the water the bacteria and other particles passing by. They capture this food on the sticky, flexible rims of living material called "collars" because of their shape. Collar cells share the food they catch with still different cells, the wandering ones which move about within the thickness of the sponge wall, feeding the pore cells. Wandering cells also cooperate in little clusters of two or three to secrete the nonliving skeleton of the sponge. It may be needles of lime or of glassy silica, or a protein (spongin) forming a network as flexible as soft plastic. A bath sponge is just the protein skeleton, which arose through the combined efforts of the wandering cells and then supported millions of pore cells and collar cells.

Until recently the strangest feature of sponges seemed to be their ability to capture and digest minute pieces of food from the surrounding water without having any special digestive cavity. This set them apart from all other multicellular animals. Then, in the early 1950's, Maurice Burton of the British Museum of Natural History began experimenting with live sponges he found along his favorite coast at Tor Bay, Devonshire. From one day to the next, he discovered, each sponge colony kept reorganizing itself, changing details of its shape. Its component cells exchanged roles. And in season many of the collar cells became wanderers, moving into the thickness of the sponge wall to transform into eggs or sperms. (Each sponge produces both types of reproductive cells.) Apparently every cell in a live sponge retains its ability to serve in reproduction and is potentially immortal.

Sponges seem unique among living things in their ways to flout death. Not only do they offer a mouthful of inert skeletal material to any larger animal that bites them, but fragments can break away, drift off, become attached, and grow into whole sponges on their own. Anyone can test their outstanding ability to repair damage and renew themselves from mere fragments. In an experiment that became a classic, H. V. Wilson provided an extreme challenge to small live sponges in 1907. He crushed them through a fine cloth screen, and washed the surviving cells into a shallow dish of seawater. By the following day, the cells had settled to the bottom of the dish. They wandered about, found one another, and began to cooperate in constructing a diminutive sponge.

More recently, biologists tried to combine two sponges of different kinds, one identified with a harmless red dye, the other with a blue. When both sponges were crushed through the same cloth and their surviving cells began wandering about in the same container, the red cells sorted themselves out from the blue cells. Each cluster built a new small sponge of its own particular kind. Biologists assume that the subtle materials that allow chemical conversations between cells differ from one species to another and serve as badges for identification. Two sponges of the same species use the same messenger substances, and although dyed different colors, form a single sponge if crushed into the same dish.

Most multicellular plants and animals do more than take death in stride. They benefit from it. They can keep their reproductive cells simple, conservative, scarcely changing because of a host of new adaptations in their other cells, the ones that will surely die. The body, now clearly mortal, becomes specialized in countless ways that contribute to the chance that the reproductive cells will be immortal. The patterns we see among familiar plants and animals are chiefly in cells that usually bring success to their species before life ends for the individual.

The adapted cells that die in helping the less-adapted reproductive cells survive are no worse cells than the ones given potential immortality. All of them in a single species of plant or animal bear the same inheritance. The mortal cells meet their fate merely because of their position in the multicellular body. Even when scientists learn to listen in on the chemical conversations between the body's cells, we need never expect to hear a hero's farewell. Only we can imagine a body cell telling a reproductive cell in parting what Sydney Carton said in Charles Dickens' *Tale of Two Cities:* "It is a far, far better thing that I do, than I have ever done; it is a far, far better rest that I go to, than I have ever known."

chapter six

A Difference in Pace

CLAIMING that "Not every one is always able, To recognize a vegetable," one of America's foremost physicists, Professor Robert Williams Wood of Johns Hopkins University, produced a short book of verses and illustrations showing people *How to Tell the Birds from the Flowers*. It quickly became a minor classic, and for three generations has delighted millions with humorous distinctions between animals and plants whose names make them sound alike.

For every reader, the resemblance that Professor Wood points out borders on the absurd: to tell a crow from a crocus, a parrot from a carrot, an antelope from a cantaloupe. After chuckling over these supposed similarities, we never expected to find ourselves unable "To recognize a vegetable." Yet in the open savanna country of equatorial Africa, we discovered that to untrained eyes, full-grown live elephants can stand in plain view only a few hundred yards away and be indistinguishable from the clumps of tree euphorbias and other unfamiliar vegetation. Patiently our Uganda guide and driver pointed out the gigantic animals he saw along the road leading into Murchison Falls National Park. He stopped the car while we searched with field glasses, trying to locate the largest animals on land. Suddenly we would focus on something that had been only a dark silhouette to us before. In the hazy distance an elephant would flap its huge ears, switch its short ropelike tail, and with deliberate

47

slowness move its trunk or a sturdy leg. We needed two days of intensive training before we could spot an elephant at a distance and know it to be animal—distinct from any elephantine plant.

In the last analysis our identification is based upon patterns we can recognize in silhouette. They correspond on the one hand to living things that move from place to place and eat vegetation or smaller animals, and on the other to plants that remain rooted to one spot and capture energy from the sun. This distinction is ages old and fits a maxim that biologist-philosopher Ludwig von Bertalanffy recognized a few years ago as a feature of all life: "It can be done this way, but it can also be done the other way." Clearly, there is no one *best* mode of life. Each way has its advantages and disadvantages. Some combinations of good features and bad allow survival, while other combinations fail. As naturalist Paul L. Errington liked to say, after observing plants and animals living together outdoors, "Nature's way is any way that works."

The features that allow us to distinguish between familiar plants and animals all evolved in the mortal bodies, not in the potentially immortal reproductive cells. Throughout the vegetable and animal kingdoms the spores and eggs and sperms remain single cells, conservatively simple and usually microscopic. But hidden within each reproductive cell are the special molecules that specify how a single spore or a fertilized egg will develop by orderly processes to the final shape we recognize. Every year new details come to light on the processes of development, giving us a fuller understanding of just what happens and how the molecules control the changes produced in growth.

Increasingly, scientists marvel at the subtle timing of the chemical actions in the growth process. The inherited specifications provide a recipe of incredible complexity. Not only do they determine which reactions will take place in what sequence and for how long, but they also cause the living protoplasm to have ready the raw materials for each reaction at exactly the right time if conditions in the environment allow. To have these materials waiting at the correct moment is a far, far more improbable event than that they will react in the proper way. Yet this marshaling of materials goes on inconspicuously. Only the products of the many reactions fit together to provide the body we see. The reactions are completed before we become aware of what they have produced.

Miracles in progress today outside our study windows show the regular results of this inner timing. A flower stalk of yucca rises four inches higher than it was yesterday, and its side branches diverge enough to remind us of the way the buds will face when each has swollen and opened, contributing its share to the plumelike display which Indians of the Southwest call a "candle of God" when they see it glistening white against the blue summer sky. Near one study window hangs a gourd in which a pair of house wrens have tended a family; each wrenlet is now eager to peer outside the inch-wide doorway, and tomorrow or the next day the youngsters will be airborne—too impatient to wait longer inside the nest for the insects their parents have been bringing them from dawn till dusk at a rate averaging more than one a minute! This is the second brood of youngsters the parent wrens have tended in a month, when they returned from Mexico or the southern states and set up housekeeping with us. Soon the youngsters will be on their own, and the parents may start a new round of producing for posterity.

In their chatter and hurry the wrens are far easier to understand than the yucca. When one of the parents hesitates, with a big insect in its beak, to scold from the branch supporting the gourd nest, we recognize the reason. A pair of blue jays are less than fifteen feet away, one pulling at a strip of wild honeysuckle bark and the other perched as though watching with approval. The jays are courting again and building their second nest for the season in one of the tall spruce trees. The scolding wren watches them a while, perhaps deciding whether to drive the jays away by dashing at them headlong, or to feed the babies. In routing the blue jays the wren might lose the cutworm and have to hunt for another insect. In ignoring the jays the parent might reveal where the wrenlets wait—silent now that they hear the alarm note. "It can be done this way," we tell ourselves. "But it can also be done the other way." Meanwhile, the jays ignore the wren and the wren flips quickly to the doorway in the gourd, stuffs a waiting mouth, and flits off again without a pause in the chattered complaint.

Looking again at the yucca, we need imagination as well as facts if we expect to trace the silent activities with which the plant readies its waxy blooms, from which can come plump capsules full of ripe, black seeds. Each of the narrow leaves which radiate from the bottom of the flower stalk begins work before sunrise and continues until dusk. For all the hours with light enough for a wren to search for insects, the yucca absorbs the radiant energy of day and stores it in complex organic compounds. Many of these are carbohydrates which can be converted to sucrose and simpler sugars for transport throughout the plant by long, slender living cells. Some of the sugars yield their energy to drive the chemical reactions of maintenance and growth. Others are linked together to form the cellulose and lignins of cell walls, particularly in the flower stalk where so much is now happening.

The same long, slender cells carry from the leaves a few dozen different amino acids and fatty acids, as building blocks with which all cells of the plant can fashion proteins and fats as needed. Along with these soluble materials go hormones of many kinds, only a few of which have been identified. Among them are auxins that induce the young cells in the rising stalk to elongate fully before each gets ready to divide again; unknown hormones adjust the rates of cell division. Florigen is the mysterious substance that redirects the activities in a yucca from producing more leaves and induces the plant to come into bloom. Somehow the leaves begin to yield florigen as the summer nights approach their shortest, whether in Sante Fe and Baghdad, Boston and Bucharest, or Sitka and Stockholm. Of these, only Santa Fe is a native home for a yucca, and there the night is never shorter than about six hours. At summer solstice in New England twilight encroaches upon the darkness, cramping true night to less than five hours. And in southern parts of Alaska and Sweden, the sky stays bright from sundown until sunup, hiding the fainter stars completely at this time of year. Yet in every one of these places, introduced yucca plants respond to the season by producing florigen and flowers.

The pointed green leaves of the yucca, from which these hormones and other organic compounds spread into the growing flower stalk, show none of the complex inner organization to be found in a wren's body. Long slender cells take the place of a circulatory system with heart, arteries, capillaries and veins containing blood. Other elongated cells with thickened walls give the leaf its stiffness. Overlapping with one another, they parallel the conducting tubes and in no way resemble the jointed skeleton of the bird. Through the waxy upper and lower surface of the leaf, minute openings provide for the entry of carbon dioxide gas and the release of oxygen; a pair of special guard cells flanks each opening like a valve, adjusting the size of the hole according to the rate at which photosynthesis proceeds. All the rest of the leaf consists of the green cells in which photosynthesis takes place, using water from the roots as the chief raw material supplied by other parts of the plant. Somewhere in these green cells hides the secret mechanism that can compare the lengths of night and day and trigger the reproductive steps toward seeds.

A counterpart of the plant's night timer governs the general behavior of the wren. A special center in an unconscious part of the bird's brain is equally affected by the proportions of night and day. By the time the parent wrens have raised their third brood to independence, the nights will be too long for the brain center to call forth another round of mating and nest construction. Instead, the adult birds will eat every bit of food they find, building fat for a migration flight to winter territories a thousand miles or more south of the nesting site. And there, next year, the timing center will again induce the wrens to feed at a frantic pace before setting out on their long return journey, paralleling the poleward sweep of springtime.

Both the wrens and the yucca seem to possess a reliable calendar, if not a stopwatch, to measure the night hours. In the bird a few cells near the nervous pathways between eye and visual centers in the brain regulate the seasonal changes in feeding behavior, migration and nesting. Probably these cells are fewer than the pollen grains produced by a single yucca stamen and weigh scarcely more. A pair of adult wrens weigh less than a medium-sized yucca leaf. But in the plant the cells that produce florigen yield so little that at least a dozen leaves on the same branch from the root must contribute this hormone before a flower stalk begins to grow. The same leaves provide the carbohydrates, amino acids and fats that are stored in the ripening seeds—if seeds form. Then the whole whorl of them dies, and any new growth of the same yucca plant depends upon fresh branches arising from the hidden roots.

Wherever the wrens nest, they are likely to find plenty of insects upon which to raise their young. At first the parents bring small insects to match the size of their hatchlings. Without seeing the babies we can trace their growth by the dimensions of the flies, moths, caterpillars and spiders the adults carry to the nest. Yet even when a pair of wrens manages to rear three broods, perhaps totaling two dozen wrenlets, all of the active youngsters may succumb to natural hazards before a year goes by. Over the centuries the number of wrens changes very little. On the average just two of the offspring will survive to take the place of each pair of parents. We wonder which of those hungry mouths in the gourd outside our window belongs to a bird that will be alive and a parent a year from now. What will the other fledglings do wrong that could have been avoided if their inherited specifications had been a little different? What would save them from a predator, a disease, an accident or a fatal change in the weather?

At the modern stage in their evolution, it is little things that make the difference between a successful and an unsuccessful house wren. It is abilities like the one that lets a successful wren find its way back, year after year, to the gourd nests we hang outside our window. Storms may sweep the flier off its path. Cold weather that keeps insects in hiding can slow the arrival of a wren. But for eight successive years, similar gourds in the same site have caught the fancy of nest-hunting house wrens on May 13, May 7, May 3, May 5, May 7, May 5, May 7 and May 4. Perhaps May 6 is actually the target date, even in Leap Year.

Our yucca plants open their first flowers in mid-July. But unless we transfer some of their golden pollen from a stamen to a pistil, they blossom fruitlessly. Reacting to an environment far north of their normal range, they fulfill their inherited specifications at the wrong time, in the wrong place, and attract none of the one type of small white moth that can successfully transfer their pollen and insure a generous set of seeds. Insects in other parts of the world where yucca plants have been introduced may visit the attractive flowers. Rarely do they dislodge the sticky pollen the plant produces. We wonder if some yucca in a foreign land will yet change its inheritance slightly and begin producing a nonsticky pollen, in separate grains that would become entangled in the hairs or feathers of a flower visitor.

Yucca is a Haitian word and a genus of about thirty different kinds of plants all from warm parts of North America. All of them rely completely for pollination upon moths of the genus *Tegeticula,* whose geographic distribution coincides.

The various kinds of wrens probably originated in the same general area, but they have spread all the way to Tierra del Fuego, southern Canada and Alaska, and across the Old World from easternmost Siberia to Scandinavia, the British Isles, Iceland and North Africa. The sixty different kinds of wrens in the New World and one (the winter wren) in the Old seem willing to nest in almost any modest cavity that can be entered through a small doorway; they are the original troglodytes. But this adaptability of wrens seems matched by the ease with which yucca plants take root in most dry or well-drained soils, tolerating extremes of heat and cold, unharmed by the blazing rays of the desert sun or the cool open shade of a northern garden. Perhaps the greater success of wrens, as measured by their wider geographic range and number of separate species, depends largely upon the readiness of these birds to take as food almost any soft-bodied insect or spider they find. If yucca plants could be equally versatile in use of insects as pollinators, the natural barriers

The pair of house wrens that nest in an empty gourd outside our study window raise a dozen youngsters to the flying age every summer, sometimes two broods yearly.

Photo by courtesy of Esther Heacock

they now inherit might fade away. This extra versatility would become the price of survival if anything were to wipe out the *Tegeticula* moths upon which each yucca still depends.

The rapid growth of the wrenlets, the coming and going of the parent birds, catch our attention more frequently than the slow rise of the floral spike or its swaying in the breeze. The difference in pace distinguishes the animal from the plant even more fundamentally than that one has warm red blood and overlapping brown feathers while the other stays as cool as the morning from its green buds and leaves to its anchoring roots. The wren can live at the slow rate of a plant, at a temperature within a degree of its surroundings, only in the egg for the few days while the mother bird is laying the rest of her clutch, before she begins to incubate the tiny embryos inside. Even then, the wren requires its carbohydrates ready-made, its fats and proteins and vitamins in complex form.

The yucca stays dormant all winter, with no circulation of materials, no division of cells, no growth or repair. Given warmth, light, soil, water, air and space, the plant produces all of the organic substances it needs. Without stirring, it grows and gains weight faster than any free-flying wren. Given a few minutes of assistance by pollinating moths, the yucca produces dozens of flat black seeds in a shaker capsule. Each seed contains a dormant embryo with its own supply of food, but one that is able to wait for months or years to begin to grow when moisture seeps through its hard outer coat.

In some ways the seedling that develops from a water-soaked seed reminds us of a little bird that has just left the nest. Food provided by the parent plant helps the seedling to grow, following its own inherited specifications, even after its little root has pushed into the soil and a leaf or two are raised into the air. The plantlet may need a day or two exposed to the daylight before its pattern of chemical reactions fills in, and photosynthesis can proceed at a useful pace. A fledgling wren takes just as long or longer, while its stubby wings carry it fluttering from bush to bush, and its big feet hold unsteadily to the shrubbery. Gradually its broad, yellow-rimmed baby beak narrows and darkens. Its nervous system matures the extra amount needed to coordinate the wrenlet as it begins to peck at and capture its own insects.

For seedling and fledgling, the greatest challenge surely comes when the new individual reaches precarious independence—no longer nourished by the parents. Can it manage on its own? Instead of competing only with its peers in the pod or in the nest, it now faces unaided the full struggle for survival. Whether at the pace of a plant or with the agitation of an animal, it must pass each hazard, testing the abilities specified by its inheritance against the realities of the day.

The number of tests that have been passed since the larger plants and animals appeared on earth staggers our imagination. But recently Dr. Verne Grant of Rancho Santa Ana Botanic Garden in California tried to measure the results. "By making use of a few arbitrary but reasonable assumptions," he estimated that during Cambrian times 600 million years ago, the sea world in which everything lived contained about 25,000 different kinds of plants and animals. A corresponding estimate for modern life from pole to pole and marine abyss to mountain peak gives a total of at least 4,530,000 different species. Comparatively few of these are simple, conservative, and confined to the open seas. The others, which provided the 180-fold increase in variety, came about as the ancestral types added, little by little, to their inherited specifications. They became complex, and able to live where simple plants and animals cannot.

At their more leisurely pace, the plants of the world require far fewer forms than the animals to succeed in the places they colonize. Of the estimated 4,530,000 kinds of life today, only about 1,537,000 are plants. Yet they provide the food upon which all living things depend, refresh the atmosphere with oxygen and absorb its carbon dioxide, anchor the soil against erosion and shield the shorelines from wave action.

In our garden plants supply the gourds in which the house wrens raise families year after year, and the nesting material the parents install so carefully, as well as the tree branch from which the gourd hangs. We share a little in these miracles by cutting a doorway in a dry gourd and wiring the nest in place before the wrens arrive in spring, by taking the place of the missing moths when the yucca comes into flower—making it fruitful, so that its pods bulge with seeds in due season.

By helping new generations toward success, we hope some day to learn what underlies the maxim, "It can be done this way, but it can also be done the other way." So far, we cannot tell which is cause and which effect. A plant may live at a leisurely pace just because it is a plant, and therefore needs no intricate adaptations such as muscles, nervous system, blood vessels and blood, ventilating gills or lungs, excretory and endocrine systems. Or, lacking all of these interacting complexities, it may be restricted to low rates of activity. Perhaps these great alternatives rest on something deeper, older, and more fundamental. With the development of photosynthesis may have come an adjustment in the hereditary mechanism to the fact that every dawn starts another day. Animals often hurry as though suddenly aware that today might be their last.

chapter seven

Defense against Gravity

EVERY space traveler counts on beginning and ending his trip in a supporting contour couch. People over much of the modern world understand why this precaution is necessary. Every schoolboy has imagined himself belted into such a seat, the powerful thrust of the rocket motors pressing his body into the supporting pads at liftoff. His eyes would sag deep into their sockets against a natural layer of fat as the acceleration increased. Yet he would try to focus them on an instrument comparing his acceleration with the effect of ordinary gravity on earth— a dial calibrated in G's (gravitational units) from 1 to 2 to 3 and so on up to more than 5.

In the early 1940's no one knew how much acceleration a person could endure. Aviation medicine and flight physiology were still too young. Yet engineers sought desperately for ways to protect cargo ships from attack by enemy submarines. If a steam catapult were built to throw a small airplane into the air from a ship's deck, carrying depth charges to counter a submarine, could a human pilot survive the takeoff? Merely to become airborne the airplane would have to accelerate from a stationary position to a speed greater than 100 miles an hour in just the few seconds before going over the side of the ship, beyond reach of the assisting catapult.

We recall the experiment that gave the encouraging answer. An expendable stand-in—an amiable chimpanzee—took the place of the airman in the machine. But in order to watch with special care for possible damage to the brain, surgeons had prepared the chimp well in advance of the simulated launching. Under anesthesia, the whole top of the animal's skull was replaced by a transparent plastic dome through which the living brain could be seen and photographed. Fully recovered, the chimp was strapped in the padded seat of the imitation airplane with extra support behind and around its head, while a movie camera bolted to the cockpit focused on its face and brain. The camera also recorded the acceleration meter to show the force to which the animal was subjected.

The chimp survived the severest tests, and recovered its appetite by the time it was unstrapped from the machine. Yet the movies frightened the physiologists. As the powerful catapult accelerated the cockpit in which the animal rode, the skin at the sides of the chimp's face lagged behind the underlying skull. The animal's lips drew back and its mouth opened in a hideous grimace. Its eyelids closed tightly as the eyes themselves pressed deeper into their sockets. The brain rocked far backward and then forward again, quivering like a mound of jelly under the plastic dome. No one had dreamed that a brain could move so freely inside the skull without tearing loose every nerve and blood vessel. But nothing broke in the chimpanzee. The test machine reached a speed corresponding to that of an airplane in stable flight. The chimp's face relaxed, its mouth closed, its brain steadied, its eyes blinked. A great yawn developed in a normal way. The animal stretched slightly against the confining straps, as though to get more comfortable. Then the test was over. Soon the larger contour seat and the steam catapult went into operation. The era of fast takeoff began for man.

When we think about the ruggedness of the body in man and chimpanzee, we marvel that adaptations provide so broad a margin of safety. How often in the remote past, we wonder, did the survival of the human species depend upon tolerance for blows on head and trunk comparable to those exchanged by prizefighters in the sports ring? Nothing on earth could make a chimpanzee accelerate as fast as in the military test. Deceleration, however, applies comparable forces. When an animal strikes the ground after falling from a tree or cliff, it changes from go to stop in a very brief time. Was this such a necessary part of primate activity that the skull and rib cage became so strong, the brain and inner organs so protected?

If these hard bones around soft parts served only as armor, we would have more reason for surprise. The skull must be firm, too, for the attachment of the many muscles that support and turn the head and of those that work the jaws and structures in the throat. The bone must not warp out of shape when those muscles tighten, for turning the head and managing food until it is on its way to the stomach are extremely important in survival. In a mammal the ribs and breastbone do more than protect the heart and lungs. They are parts of the lever system with which the dimensions of the chest are changed, causing air to move in and out, ventilating the lungs and blood. Muscles from rib to rib can produce these breathing movements only if the ribs stiffly retain their shape and yield solely where they are attached at their ends to the breastbone and backbone. Ribs and skull bones are thicker and stronger than they would be otherwise because they also enclose some of the marrow tissue in which red blood cells are produced. Serving so many purposes at once, the bones must be heavier than if each played a single role. No longer does success in one direction suffice in promoting the animal's survival. Our generous margin of safety arises in large degree through diversification of tasks for each part.

Both in animals and plants, most parts that provide stiffness confer several advantages. Often the original role can be singled out only by comparing the final adult features with the earlier stages of embryonic development or with the fossil remains of ancestors and their near kin. The roof bones of a human skull originated as armorlike plates in the skin over the top of the head. Ribs seem primarily to have been parts of the breathing apparatus. Each arose through a beneficial modification in the inherited specifications of the animal, and each offered new possibilities for further advantageous change. Generally the products of evolution show this cumulative nature. Opportunities multiply at the same time that complexity increases.

Until men actually experienced several consecutive days orbiting the earth, the weightlessness awaiting them in the hurtling space capsule was expected to cause distressing dizziness, perhaps nausea, but nothing else. However, these proved to be no problem. Instead, the bony skeleton of each astronaut lost appreciable amounts of the calcium that gives it stiffness. Measurements made on men before and after their trips of four days and eight days in 1965 showed a rapid change. If this loss continued for the weeks or months that men might spend in an orbiting laboratory or on a prolonged flight to another planet, the whole skeleton might easily become too fragile to withstand the deceleration necessary to make a landing. Since the cells that make and destroy bone depend so clearly upon the stimulating stresses produced by gravity, we can conclude that the prime role of our bones is to support us.

Every living thing in air needs a comparable defense against this all-pervading force. A fish with a gas-filled swimbladder, however, may match so well the weight of the water its body displaces that it remains essentially weightless for its whole existence. Many microscopic single cells do as well by containing an oil droplet of just the right size and density to buoy up the few harder parts that are denser than water. Each of these creatures benefits from its adaptive defense against gravity so long as it remains within a narrow range of depths. Often they respond to changes in the pressure of the water, which increases 15 pounds to the square inch for every 32 feet of extra depth. By swimming or adjusting their flotation device, they regain the levels that are hospitable.

While swimming in its natural element, a fish with a swimbladder is like a human balloonist in air, except that its gas bag is inside its body. If the fish rises too far above its normal range of depths, the lower hydrostatic pressure on all sides forces its swimbladder to expand beyond control. If the fish goes too deep, the higher pressure compresses its gas bag, reducing the buoyant effect until gravity seizes hold and drags the helpless creature down.

The feeble jellyfishes encounter no such dangers, for the thick jelly that constitutes most of their bodies is the adaptive feature that makes them match so well the density of the water in which they move. A softer creature would be hard to find. Yet a few jellies that swam in the seas of Cambrian times more than 500 million years ago settled in death on fine silts so yielding that their bodies left a lasting impression.

Many kinds of small jellyfishes in modern seas are sexual individuals sent out as emissaries from sexless branching colonies of quite different animals. The fully-formed jellies escape and swim away to feed on plankton and to mingle among potential mates. Eventually they release from below their bell-shaped bodies large numbers of tiny embryos which settle to the bottom. The life history continues as each embryo becomes attached and begins secreting about itself a thin sheath that will support it against the slight pull of gravity. The covering is composed of transparent chitin—the same inert carbohydrate that gives strength to the body of most insects and spiders. At first, every branch bears at its open end a food-collecting "head" of the colony, each one a polyp with extended tentacles bearing batteries of nettling cells. Later, new branches are added in which small globular bodies separate and escape into the sea just as each transforms into a complete little jellyfish. Thereafter it relies upon its buoyant jelly to support it, and upon rhythmic contractions of the bell to move it from place to place.

Visitors to the seacoast often notice the branching, sheathed colonies from which the small jellyfishes emerge. Although brown or pale tan in color, they are known commonly as "whiteweed" or "sea firs" or "sea ferns," from their resemblance in fine branching or frondlike appearance to these land plants. Some novelty shops sell small bunches of these colonies that have been dried and dyed. The first ones sold in this way were always a realistic shade of green, and clerks sometimes promoted sales by telling housewives that here, at last, they could buy a plant guaranteed to stay green without water. Who cared that the "plant" would never grow? Later the same "plants" appeared in deep reds and golden yellows to match other ideas of decor. Intrigued, we bought samples and sent pieces to a specialist at Yale University, to learn the scientific name of the hydroid polyps that produced the delicate supporting skeletons. Back came the information: *Thuiaria cupressina* was the creature, one that produces distinctive sheaths as much as twelve inches long in dense colonies along both sides of the Atlantic Ocean.

No doubt the sheath that supports a sea fir against gravity also keeps the many feeding polyps in a colony facing in different directions. They are spread on the frondlike branches into more water, within reach of more food, than could be managed otherwise in such a simple way. But the jellyfish stage manages well without this support, moving in water currents and under its own power from place to place among the plankton. Its defense against gravity is so successful that it is always in danger of being washed ashore or stranded on a mud flat when the tide goes out.

Coral animals are near kin of the small jellyfishes and their matching colonial polyps. The corals carry to extreme the secretion of hard parts that cup their soft bodies against gravity and oceanic currents that might displace them from their sites on the sea bottom. A few of the colonial kinds known as soft corals probably show how simply this adaptation started out. The one called "dead men's fingers" feels almost gritty if crushed. It grows attached to the bottom in shallow water near shore along many temperate coasts, supported only by minute needles and granules of lime embedded within the thin jelly that separates its outer layer of living cells from the inner layer. As in all creatures of this type, the inner cells surround a digestive cavity. In a dead men's fingers colony the cavity opens through small pores in the granular jelly at hundreds of places where dainty, transparent columns rise from the surface, each tipped by a tiny mouth surrounded by eight branching tentacles. Suited for capturing only the microscopic particles of food among the drifting plankton, these delicate feeding parts shrink at the slightest commotion. Quickly they turn outside-in like the fingers of a glove, pushing themselves to safety through the pores in the granular jelly into the digestive cavity.

The branching colonies of precious coral, which grow on the bottom in western parts of the Mediterranean Sea and in the eastern North Atlantic Ocean around the Cape Verde Islands, seem to have changed their adaptation in a single step. Instead of producing a flexible skeleton of separate needles and granules of lime, they secrete a solid one which, for limy material, is intensely hard. The familiar reddish or pink material is produced within the jelly layers of the coral animals, leaving its feeding polyps permanently exposed, each atop a little eminence. In the daylight that penetrates to the depths where precious coral grows, the eight feathery tentacles of each polyp shine pure white. They radiate like the fancy petals of a tiny flower.

Each piece of precious coral has a tubular cavity running through the middle of it, as though already drilled to be strung on a necklace. The cavity is lined in life by the cells that carry on the digestive process. We wonder how long ago a beachcomber along a Mediterranean shore picked up a colorful fragment of this kind and noticed the convenient hole. In Roman times children were given necklets of coral to ward off danger. Caesar found the Gauls using precious coral to decorate their weapons and war helmets. In more recent times, these skeletons from 100 to 160 feet down in the Mediterranean Sea have provided trade goods of the highest value for markets in India and the Far East.

In shallow water around tropical seas it is much easier to find a related coral which often contributes to the formation of spectacular reefs. Known as organ-pipe coral, it begins as a small, matlike colony. From this many polyps grow upward simultaneously. Against the pull of gravity, each maintains its upright position by adding needles and granules of lime within its jelly layer, in the form of parallel tubes. Gradually the spaces between the skeletal pieces disappear, filled in with brick-red lime.

Higher and higher the slender "organ pipes" rise, each with an emerald-green polyp at its tip. As every polyp elongates, the distance between the tentacles and the intercommunicating digestive cavity in the matlike base increases more and more. Suddenly a new adaptation appears. All of the polyps begin extending themselves horizontally to form a common platform within which intercommunication is established on a higher level. Below the new platform the old tubes are abandoned. Time after time, growth of the colony raises the individual polyps higher from the bottom. Yet their few extra adaptations in an interconnecting skeleton stabilize the colony and give the coral reef a structural strength that withstands the pounding of waves. Innumerable small animals burrow into the abandoned tubes and claim them as hideaways. The presence of the successful organ-pipe corals alters the environment for a great many other kinds of life, adding to the nooks and crannies in which timid creatures can find shelter.

The differences in details of development to be found in the skeletons of soft coral, precious coral and organ-pipe coral remind us of the variations upon a single theme which delight musicians. Just as the melodic genius of a Paganini caprice can impel a Kreisler to varied heights of virtuosity, or as an Ellington can offer a jazz number in endless improvisations, so too the inherited pattern in these comparatively simple animals is modified in this direction and that—always retaining glimpses of the original ancestry and producing a combination of features harmonious enough for survival. Even the raw material of the skeleton allows variations. The closest kin to the organ-pipe coral are not the conspicuous producers of great coral reefs but more decorative colonies in which the limy skeletal material is associated with or replaced by a horny protein called gorgonin. These are the "horny corals," known as sea whips, sea plumes and sea fans—the vivid yellow or orange or red or purple underwater "shrubbery" that lures skin divers to shallow waters of the Caribbean, of southern Florida, the Mediterranean and the tropical Indo-Pacific Ocean.

On an island in the Great Barrier Reef that parallels for a thousand miles the eastern coast of Australia, we visited with scientists who braved sharks to dive at night among the corals. In the beams of their underwater flashlights they had seen a spectacular array of minute polyps colorfully studding every exposed surface of each live horny coral. These polyps expand their tentacles only in darkness. Their timing matches the arrival of plankton crustaceans that migrate upward from the depths at sunset and down again at dawn. They also expose themselves while the gaudy parrotfishes, which munch on corals by day, are sleeping.

Fascinating fishes of other kinds, which compete for the small crustaceans or feed on one another, dart through the darkness among the colonies of horny corals which hold firmly as though rooted. Actually each rises from a short, trunklike part, flaring where it is cemented to a rock or some buried piece of shell. Sea whips branch mostly near the trunk region, and rise in slender, blunt-ended wands as much as two feet in length. Sea plumes bear a series of branches on each side of the upright stalk, and resemble fern fronds or giant feathers three to four feet long. Sea fans have side branches all interconnected to form a network. In gardens of sea plumes and sea fans, every colony grows with its edges facing the two directions from which the prevailing currents bring planktonic food. In this position, the polyps on both faces of the plume or fan have equal chances to capture microscopic particles from the water going by, and the current is least likely to dislodge the colony from its hold on the bottom.

To disappear as much as possible every day, mostly by drawing in every tentacle and remaining motionless, is the habit too of most stony corals. While fishes and sea slugs that eat coral animals are active, they remain hidden. Scientists generally call these creatures "true corals" to remind themselves of a fundamental difference in the way the skeletons arise. Stony corals, really limestony corals, secrete their supports exclusively on the outside, below and around the sides of each individual polyp, revealing every crease in its surface. They show none of the flexible compliance of horny and soft corals which can be deformed temporarily by any reasonable pressure against the outstretched tips. Stony corals yield only to the blows of a sledgehammer, the sharp jaws of a parrotfish, or the acid secreted by some of the large snails and sea urchins that etch pockets into the lime.

Stony corals follow a way of life that matches the marine environment of almost any era. Yet change after change is recorded in rocks since the late Ordovician period some 450 million years ago, when the ancestral members of this group of animals began producing limy supports that have been found as fossils. Until the end of the Paleozoic about 240 million years ago, the tetracorals abounded, each polyp beginning life with four tentacles and continuing to show this four-part pattern as it grew and added lengthwise vanes of lime to its skeleton. Many tetracorals remained solitary, building conical supports ridged and ringed externally, so similar in general form to the drinking horns of olden days that paleontologists call them "cup corals." Other tetracorals showed an intensely gregarious habit, very similar to that found in the great human cities of the world. Immense thicknesses of limestone, like cities built upon cities, or huge domes and branching structures, like skyscrapers in the sea, record the activities of these animals over centuries as they extracted calcium from the surrounding sea and secreted it in skeletal form. When these masses are cut across, the vertical or radiating tubes reveal where the individual polyps lived, each with its body wall creased lengthwise in fours or some multiple of four. Between the tubular cavities the apartment walls are thin—a single sheet of lime—and lack pores that could have allowed sharing of food resources. Probably it is a mistake to call these tetracorals "colonial," for each individual could withdraw into its own compartment and ignore its neighbors, achieving the loneliness of the crowded cities of mankind today.

Far more cooperative were the tabular corals of the Paleozoic and Mesozoic. They were true colonists, blending respectable independence with provisions for sharing with one another. Every polyp secreted its own tube in relation to its neighbors, making every wall between polyps a double sheet of lime. But as the columnar or prismatic tubes increased in length, new floors (tabulae) were installed and fresh "mural pores" provided in the walls, connecting each polyp to every one of its immediate neighbors. Today these pores resemble the "push-through" openings modern architects sometimes provide in the partition between two adjacent rooms. The intercommunicating tubes of tabular corals are often so densely packed as to have earned the name "honeycomb coral." Accumulations of this limy material compose the limestone of Ordovician age over which Niagara Falls plunges. Honeymooners who hold tightly to one another beside the brink rarely know that the solid rock the great river undercuts and breaks away is mostly the product of a honeycomb coral, *Favosites*. The skeletal material the coral built so firmly now holds a new world against the pull of gravity.

The stony corals in modern seas are all hexacorals, which begin life with six tentacles on each polyp. Particularly in the South Pacific, they help to provide natural breakwaters around volcanic islands, protecting the shores from erosion by storm waves.

Carrying like a third leg a sturdy length of wood as a "reefing stick" in case gravity should drag us downward through a thin place in the coral platform, we sloshed through the ebb tide to see these corals just beyond the sandy beach on Fiji. Actually, the reefs in the South Pacific are as much the work of limy algae as of corals. But the algae bend or crumble while the corals stand firm, giving character to the scene and providing countless crannies in which other creatures can hide. Big sea stars of a bright blue color and two-inch darting fishes of the same unexpected hue rested in depressions where the tidal current did not reach them. And everywhere the corals rose toward the surface in myriad forms and a full spectrum of pastel shades.

A few of the hexacorals follow a solitary existence and retain almost as much independence as a sea anemone, for if currents change and the water shifting with the tides brings less food the animal may desert its limy support and move to a new location, there to secrete a new support. The mushroom coral (*Fungia*) thrives in this way, often attaining a diameter of five inches or more as a single broad polyp from whose brown or greenish body the tentacles extend outward two or three inches more. Hidden by the soft polyp, the saucer-shaped support bears dozens of radial ridges resembling the gills below the cap of a large mushroom. The living body rides over and between these ridges, modeling and enlarging them, and spreading beyond their outer limit in a thin, narrow skirt from which new individuals may bud off and separate.

Colonial hexacorals ring the changes on forming skeletal supports in concert. Some flare out over the edges of the cup-shaped depressions occupied by individual polyps, and secrete so much lime that the polyps themselves seem almost isolated on great stony bosses no ordinary wave can harm. Others occupy shallow cavities so close together as to have walls in common. Brain-coral polyps live in rows, joined together in sinuous grooves that are fringed on each side by a continuous row of tentacles. These capture food for a series of separate mouths at regular intervals.

Often the same kind of coral makes knoblike, rounded colonies where the wave action in storms is severe and branching masses which resemble antlers where more protected. At greater depths, flat vanes and treelike structures are more common, holding the polyps against gravity while at the same time shedding any sediments that drift down upon them from surface waters. Some polyps cast off particles of debris by expanding in their little cups and shaking from side to side. Most corals simply coat the unwanted material with a film of mucus, and shift it by the concerted action of hairlike cilia until gravity will carry off the waste.

While seeking for the secrets that have brought success to the stony corals of today, we marvel at their rapid rate of growth, their richness of variety and the features other than body form that seem to match their proliferation into solid reefs. A brain coral measured near Australia's Great Barrier Reef grew from 30 to 74 inches in diameter between 1890 and 1913. East Indian reefs more than fifteen feet below the surface built upward as much as four inches a year. Because navigable channels can fill in so rapidly with coral, sailors in reef water distrust any chart more than twenty years old.

All living reefs of stony corals occur in warm water, chiefly between latitudes 30° North and 30° South. Those along the Florida Keys, now protected in Coral Reef National Park, and those around Bermuda are exceptions made possible by northward currents of warm water in the Gulf Stream, extending tropical conditions a short distance beyond. Gaps in the distribution of reefs within the Tropics match cold currents and also the mouths of great rivers, where fresh water and silt make life impossible for the polyps.

Every reef with living polyps is near enough to the sea surface for sunlight to illuminate it every day. This, and the pastel colors of the polyps seen by divers, draws attention to algal partners that are abundant in every reef of stony corals. The colors are in the single cells, which appear to be captive dinoflagellates, carrying on photosynthesis unharmed within the digestive cavity of the coral animals. Apparently the polyps depend upon the algal cells to absorb carbon dioxide and to dispose of other wastes, particularly those rich in nitrogen and phosphorus. With this assistance the populations of colonial polyps reach uncountable proportions. So does the number of worms, crabs, fishes and other creatures that associate themselves with reef corals. More mouths get food each day in the densely crowded community of a reef than anywhere else in the sea or on land.

Going into partnership with algal cells may well have been the extra adaptation that let early hexacorals gradually replace the older tetracorals and tabulate types. None of these extinct kinds shows evidence of algal partners. Merely to succeed in defending themselves against gravity by secreting limy platforms was not enough for survival into modern times.

As we explore the reefs and examine the patterns of hard supports built by these soft-bodied creatures, we think of urban mankind living in high-rise apartment houses. We remember that Nietzsche said: "In the architectural structure, man's pride, man's triumph over gravitation, man's will to power, assume a visible form." But should we now go the extra step and imitate the successful corals? From them we could learn that defense against gravity is not enough to give us power for survival. We might build into our urban architecture an added wealth of plant partners to clean the air and give us extra food. Perhaps rows of wheat plants and a potato vine should join the geranium flowering on the window sill, as a first step in the right direction.

chapter eight

The Allure of Armor

WHENEVER we don masks and fins to snorkel our way into the lives of the sea creatures inhabiting coastal shallows, we grow particularly impressed with the variety of animals that feed on motes of food too small for us to see without a microscope. The mollusks in particular show extraordinary adaptations to filtering out the bacteria and plankton or to scraping and probing for the particles they eat.

We find oysters fixed for life to a rock or to one another. We look among mussels tethered like blimps or barrage balloons by dozens of tough fibers secreted and cemented in place by a tongue-shaped foot. We notice burrow-making clams in hard clays and soft rocks, furrow-making clams in muddy bottoms and sandy shallows, scallops and file shells as bivalves that swim to escape capture by predatory sea stars. All of them filter from the water they inhale the microbes they need for food.

Slipper shells, secreted by strangely contorted snails, hide owners that carry on filtration while clinging to whelks or horseshoe crabs that haul them from place to place. Limpets with shells like coolie hats, periwinkles in squat spiral shells, chitons armored with eight limy plates hinged together, all creep over the rocks and coarse seaweeds while scraping off particles of food. Deeper in the muds and sands of the bottom, tusk shells extend their sensitive, sticky tentacles to capture hidden plants and animals of microscopic size. We discover the smaller open ends of tusk shells projecting from the sediments, and know that the tubular tapering shell curves obliquely downward. From the larger, buried end the animal extends its powerful digging foot while searching in all directions for food it can bring back to its mouth.

At the slightest disturbance any of these mollusks pulls back its soft body into the safety of its shell. Even while active, the animal is slowed down by its portable armor—a burden from which it can never escape. To match its own growth, the creature must husband the lime it can absorb and add new zones to its shell. But whether it produces by eccentric additions a single piece, or a pair of valves, or the eight transverse plates that overlap on the back of a chiton, the shell consists of calcium carbonate. Columnar crystals at right angles to the surface make up most of the thickness. Across their inner ends, the mollusk secretes a thin layer of flat crystals all parallel to the surface. They reflect light in so many colors that they are known as "mother-of-pearl," and are the same material of which real pearls may be formed. Often the outer surface of the shell bears a layer of horny protein (conchiolin) which resists abrasion and prevents acids in the adjacent water from etching the lime crystals and weakening the armor.

Any animal that depends upon external protection of this kind must continue concentrating calcium from the surrounding water or salvaging it from its food. Its inheritance must guide it to add the hard material at a rate that makes the armor neither too flimsy nor so heavy as to become a burden. Some mollusks reach this ideal balance as they grow by dissolving away earlier internal parts of the shell. By using the same materials to enlarge the shelter around their open doorway, they diminish the rate at which the dead weight increases. Without some adaptation that buoys up the shell, no animal can haul around a really massive covering. Sea snails, for example, appear unable to grow larger than the kind called a horse conch, which attains a length of about twenty inches and a weight of a few pounds while preying on smaller shellfishes along the Atlantic coast from North Carolina to Brazil. Only the sedentary bear's paw clam of the South Pacific is a larger mollusk. It spends virtually its whole life embedded in a coral reef supported by the limestone, able to do no more than open and close its ponderous valves.

For 500 million years, the clams and snails and chitons have had a place in the fossil record. Yet a few of the chitons and some of the snails proved versatile enough to do away with a shell and survive unarmored. The chitons without shells live only at depths greater than sixty feet in the sea, and lack a common name. They feed on hydroids and coral animals, apparently immune to the nettling cells of their prey. The shell-less snails are slugs and sea hares, some attaining a weight of fifteen pounds and a length of fifteen inches on a diet of seaweeds. Perhaps the most highly adapted and widespread of all is the little sea slug *Glaucus eucharis,* which creeps along in search of microscopic food on the under-side of the surface film over the open oceans. Its deep violet-blue color camouflages it from sea birds looking down into the water.

One other great group of mollusks started out in Cambrian times, with an inherited pattern that took the weight off their backs. They evolved into some of the most spectacular sea creatures the world has ever known —the cephalopods or "head-footed ones," with grasping arms and a chambered shell. Indeed, the records for length and for diameter of armor among invertebrate animals with shells are held by the giant *Endoceras* of Ordovician seas, with a straight conical shell as much as fifteen feet long and twelve inches in diameter at the larger end, and by *Pachydiscus* of the Cretaceous, which produced a longer cone coiled into a flat spiral six feet eight inches across. To have reached these dimensions, the animals themselves must have lived where prey abounded within easy snatching distance.

The chambered shell that gives cephalopods an extra lift is a result of the animal's periodic moves as it grows. It extends the cone of its limy armor, then slides into the new larger parts of its covering and walls off the older smaller quarters with a crosswise partition. Only a slender stalk continues to connect the body to all of the previous living spaces. Through a wonderful adaptation, the animal uses the living tissues of this stalk to alter the amount of lime in the vacated chambers and to quickly adjust the buoyancy of the shell by replacing gas there with water or water with secreted gas.

Only during the Paleozoic era did the cephalopods produce straight shells. Later, all of them secreted their armor in the spiral form that continues today in the four different kinds of chambered nautilus inhabiting deep tropical waters from the eastern part of the Indian Ocean, past Australia to Fiji.

By adjusting their buoyancy the straight-shelled species should have been able to aim their limy cones in almost any direction, pointing directly at the zenith, slanting upward at an angle, or even hanging vertically below the body. Apparently the animals reached their food only in one way, by extending their arm tips downward to the bottom while the end of the conical shell rose straight up. Scientists see this as the only explanation for the fact that colored bands and other decorative features, which have been preserved in great assortment on the outside of these straight-shelled fossils, show no sign of wear on one side or indication that any part of the cone was habitually in shadow.

Modern cephalopods rarely attempt to retain a foothold in the bottom mud. Instead, they progress freely by jet propulsion. They take in water through slots around the head, then use the head as a stopper to close the intake ports while forcibly expelling the liquid through a small nozzle. The water goes one way, the cephalopod the opposite. Whenever the animal is in a hurry, it jets backward—in the direction of its shell. When frightened, it clouds the water behind it with a squirt of India ink. This brownish-black pigment is secreted into an ink sac. In times past, these sacs were harvested carefully for human use from cuttlefishes in the Indian Ocean, hence the name.

More than 10,000 different kinds of mollusks have followed this way of life since the production of chambered shells began. Almost all of them show a single pattern in armor which uniquely retains its shape despite increase in size. Mathematicians delight in the logarithmic course of this "equiangular spiral," and point to it again in the partitions between the chambers of the modern chambered nautili. It is a pattern that keeps down the weight of the shell and economizes on lime. But it makes the animal vulnerable, for it is attached to its armor over a minimal area.

Nautiloids held sway as the dominant predators of coastal seas into Silurian times, then declined as fishes with jaws invaded their habitat. It takes little imagination to think of a hungry fish seizing the exposed tentacles of a nautiloid, giving a vigorous twitch, and jerking the whole animal out of its shell. Only a few kinds of nautiloids survived, probably by following the daily cycle of chambered nautili today—descending with their armor into dark depths while the sun shows above the horizon, withdrawing into the shell while fishes with large mouths are hunting for edible shellfish, then rising each night to feed at the surface where fishes have plenty of softer prey among the small crustaceans that browse on the drifting, microscopic plants.

The principal survivors among the cephalopods were near kin called ammonoids, which had a better grip on the spiral shell. Each ammonoid produced partitions that appear to have been the work of an imaginative pastry cook. The surface is wrinkled, meeting the shell itself in a line that curves and recurves time after time to match the complex pattern of hills and hollows. The need for more and more surface to cling to seems to have governed the gradual changes in the inherited specifications of ammonoids. Beginning in the great Coal Ages (Carboniferous times) about 300 million years ago and continuing into the Age of Reptiles, the wrinkling of the partitions grew fantastic, the junction lines between partitions and shell became as tortuous as the switchbacks on a mountain road. So long as food was plentiful, this adaptation paid off. But toward the end of the Mesozoic era, when prey grew harder to find, the shells of the ammonoids seem to have dragged them rapidly to extinction. The wrinkled partitions added so much to the inertia of the shell that its owner was encumbered, even though buoyed up by seawater. Jet propulsion could shift so ponderous a bulk only at a slow pace. Stuck securely in its heavy armor, the ammonoid could not travel to new feeding grounds fast enough to match its appetite.

The point at which an armored covering passes from being a protection to being a hardship is seldom clearly defined. Yet that point has been passed many times in the shifting patterns of life on earth. The tendency to secrete too much mineral material remains a threat. Today it threatens humankind. When our arteries become heavy and brittle with deposits of calcium carbonate, our personal survival becomes precarious. We are challenged with finding a way to escape this hazard.

The cephalopod mollusks evolved an alternative. And as though this great group of mollusks ran a relay race, the torch of triumph passed from the nautiloids to the ammonoids, then to the ancestors of modern squids and octopuses. Almost all of the cephalopods that survive today are free-swimming, active animals that outgrow their shells without losing the benefits of buoyancy. Their safety lies in speed instead of armor, in muscular bodies so firm and so well supported by bars and rings of cartilage that it is hard to credit them with being mollusks—a word from the Latin *mollis,* for soft.

Only the cuttlefishes continue to wear a buoyant remnant of the more complex shell. It is the cuttlebone that hangs in bird cages, a porous limy structure which the living animal wears under its mantle on its back like a life jacket covered by an overcoat. The oldest (and smallest) chambers of the cuttlebone lie farthest from the head, each completely filled with fluid. Newer, larger chambers contain a gas whose release and absorption can be adjusted, supporting the animal approximately horizontally at whatever depth proves advantageous.

The world of the squids takes on a third dimension because they retain only the horny backing of the ancestral shell and vary their buoyancy by changing the quantity of a liquid filling their spacious body cavities. Being rich in ammonia, this liquid is significantly less dense than sea

Scalp of blue mussels, each attached by several slender threads; also a few acorn barnacles. Bar of Bar Harbor, Maine.

Acorn barnacles cemented permanently to a wharf piling, where each high tide brings a fresh supply of microscopic food.

water. It amounts to about two-thirds the total weight of a live squid. By discharging or secreting the liquid, the swimmer can dive deeply where pressures are great or rise to the surface after prey, without suffering from any equivalent of "the bends." With no gas bubbles to expand uncontrollably in shallow water or to shrink until their buoyant effect is negligible in the depths, the squids have a far larger territory in which to hunt than other cephalopods.

So active are squids in modern seas that no one can estimate reliably how many of them there are. The smaller kinds prey on still smaller fishes, and show by their abundance how rich the sea pastures are. At certain seasons, seals live almost exclusively on squids. Larger fishes hunt the smaller squids, as New England fishermen long have noted. "Plenty squid, plenty cod," they say. Their catch for the year in North Atlantic waters largely depends upon the supply of squid for bait. In other parts of the world, squids vie with octopuses as food for man.

Giant squids are too big, too strong, too fast and too deep by day for fishermen to meet. Sperm whales routinely dive to catch the giants. Sometimes, when harpooned and in their death throes, they regurgitate large, recognizable pieces. Whalers have saved so many samples that scientists can estimate the size of giant squids no one has seen alive: a body 20 feet long, with arms reaching ahead another 35 feet; eyes 14 inches in diameter; and a weight of several tons. No other animal without a backbone for support has ever been known to approach these dimensions. If size is a criterion, the adaptations that took the place of armor have paid handsomely.

Despite the conspicuous success of squids and their kin, this way of life offers relatively little variety. Counting every depth of all the oceans, the world supports only about 400 kinds of cephalopods today. By contrast, more than 30,000 species of snails find distinctive places to live. Some 11,000 kinds of bivalves maintain their separate styles of existence. Even the chitons show more variety than the cephalopods. For nearly 45,000 different species of mollusks, armor still holds its old allure.

The sea has its masqueraders too, each secreting its own distinctive kind of shell or moving freely without armor while fooling the skin diver and the beachcomber into believing he has found still another kind of snail or clam. As though the spiral shell and the bivalve covering were models too attractive to protect mollusks alone, other types of animals produce hard coverings in these shapes. They keep the coastal naturalist alert to know which is mollusk and which is not. They test the specialist on fossils, for with only the armor to go by, real detective methods must be applied to tell the look-alikes apart.

Along coasts of the North Atlantic Ocean, sharp-eyed visitors often notice what appear to be tiny snail shells cemented by one side of the flat spiral to seaweeds washing in the surf. Few of these coiled tubes attain as much as a quarter of an inch from side to side, and all are grayish-white as though some blight had killed every snail in its infancy. On cloudy days and at night, a tuft of fine threads usually protrudes from the open doorway. If touched, they vanish too quickly for the eye to follow. But after a while, if nothing more disturbs their owner, the threads slide out again and separate like the immersed bristles of an artist's brush.

These strange threads are the head plumes of a segmented worm which is a distant kin of earthworms and leeches. They serve it both as gills and feeding organs. Displayed upon their surface is a mucus as sticky as old-fashioned flypaper, which captures bacteria and other nourishing particles from the water. The loaded mucus is propelled by cilia toward the mouth and folded into a continuous rope for swallowing. This kind of worm, or ones producing a limy tube in a coil with no distinctive differences, has followed the same way of life since Ordovician times, perhaps 450 million years ago.

When we visit warmer waters near or within the Tropics, we find quite an assortment of far larger sea worms building gently curved tubes or highly irregular ones. Often they conform to the sides of wharf pilings, the hulls of sunken ships, and blocks of coralline limestone. If we do not disturb the worms, we see each inhabitant extending from the larger opening of its tube so many slender, plumelike organs that its common name of "feather-duster worm" seems most appropriate. Often the plumes bear bright bands of red and yellow, white or purple. Other "dusters" could be mistaken for the spreading tentacles of an anemone or a solitary coral. But at the slightest commotion in the water or a shadow cast upon them, every one of these creatures jerks backward into its tube. Slowly it emerges again in a minute or two, spreading its plumes with all the symmetry of a steam cloud puffed out by an active volcano.

A stroll along the beach leads us to other trophies. If we wade and watch through shallow water over gritty muds we are likely to find graceful, tusk-shaped tubes that project from the bottom. They are not tusk shells, however, for each is composed of sand grains and inhabited by a pink- or yellow-bodied worm. It burrows, head down, for half its length. Some call it a "trumpet worm" and wonder if the two antennalike projections from its head show it to be the larva of an insect. But the trumpet worm is already an adult and changes into nothing else. It uses the outgrowths from its head in conjunction with its mouth to select building materials with great care. It fits small sand grains in a single layer at the small end of its tube, and large grains at the large end. Storms sometimes wash out the worms, tubes and all, and roll them along the bottom. Unless the animal can get its head end into the mud again, a fish is likely to gobble it up or waves to throw it high on the beach. We find the empty tubes there, or ones with a shriveled owner dried in place. Only the grillwork of stiff golden bristles on its head suggests how the mummified worm looked in life.

From the same beaches, storms often undermine and toss ashore the limp, yellowish tubes of parchment worms. These soft-bodied animals secrete against all sides of their U-shaped burrows a heavy mucus that hardens, preventing collapse of the walls. A parchment worm has no need for extra stiffening. It has the whole world for a shell. It need only sway rhythmically to propel water past its body, in one doorway and out the other, bringing oxygen and particles of food to be caught in a net composed of a thinner type of mucus. Just the tips of the parchment tube project, revealing where the animal has its inconspicuous hideaway.

Sedentary sea worms move freely back and forth within the shelters they have built. Most of them can turn end and repair a modest amount of damage to their armor. But if the creature is induced to desert its tube, it rarely can find its way back again. Nor does its repertoire of inherited activities include the ability to replace a complete sheath of secreted lime or of sand particles cemented together or of mucus that will harden into a new parchment tube. Although the animal has no physical attachment to its armor, such as between a limpet and its shell, it is virtually helpless without it. Only once, in its first spring of youth, can it begin the house it must have for life. Thereafter, house and worm grow larger and older together, each utterly dependent upon the other, each matching a single way of living. Fortunately for these worms, the environment in which they fit so well has remained virtually unchanged for an immensity of time. It seems likely to be available to them indefinitely.

For continuity in way of life and in a body build to match it, both the first prize and the second go to creatures seldom met in the Western World, although they are sought for food along sandy coasts of the Orient. These winners in the long contest for living space are brachiopods whose two-part covering could easily be mistaken for the armor of a clam. Like the tube builders among the worms, the brachiopods found a place to live with an indefinite future. Two genera have become famous in scientific circles for their astonishing longevity: *Lingula,* which dates back to early Ordovician times almost 500 million years ago, and *Crania,* which can be traced to late Ordovician—still 450 million years into the past.

Modern members of the genus *Lingula* stand erect in vertical burrows, often between tide marks, along coasts of the Indian and Pacific Oceans. If disturbed or exposed by the receding water, they pull out of sight by contracting the slender muscular stalk with which they burrow and stay anchored in the sand. When covered by quiet water, a *Lingula* extends slightly above the burrow opening, exposing a body shaped like a paddle blade, both sides faced with a horny shell that may be pale yellow or various shades of green. The two valves are held together by several sets of muscles, and in relation to the body of the animal, are a top valve and a bottom rather than a left and right as in a clam. To feed, the creature rotates one shell past the other, forming a narrow V atop the stalk and exposing passageways through which enters water with microscopic food and oxygen and then returns to the sea. *Lingula* keeps its burrow from collapsing by coating the side walls with mucus secreted by the stalk and the edges of the body around the rim of the opposed shell valves.

Little *Crania* has survived into the present with no stalk at all. Producing a reddish chocolate-brown shell, it cements the lower valve to a rock or other hard object on the sea bottom and grows there for the rest of its life, attaining slightly less than half an inch in diameter. Eccentric lines of growth mark the surface of the exposed shell, which is almost circular in outline. Beyond its edge, where the water enters and leaves, stiff bristles extend for ⅛ inch or more, keeping sand and other large particles from reaching the little white body inside. To find these sedentary creatures in the West Indies and along the Florida Keys, a skin diver has to go more than 120 feet from the surface. But farther north along the Atlantic seaboard they live in shallower water until, around Greenland, they can be waded for along rocky shores just below low tide mark. With different animals as neighbors in these remote localities, *Crania* follows the same way of life its ancestors used so many millions of years ago. Its magic is in the combination of adaptations that include habits and function and structure, not merely ability to produce a bivalved shell of a characteristic shape.

Another style of armor produced by related animals that have changed more over the millennia and live mostly in deeper water suggested the name "lamp shell" for all brachiopods. Barely two hundred species of them survive today, out of more than thirty thousand known from fossils. Their empty shells often resemble the oil lamps of ancient Greece or Rome, like the stylized "lamp of wisdom," because the lower of the two unequal valves has a small hole suggesting the one where the oil flame burned. In life the animal has a sturdy stalk projecting through this hole, supporting itself from a rock or from the bottom. These are the "hinged lamp shells" which appear to open and close their valves like clam shells, although two different sets of muscles produce the movement rather than just an elastic ligament along the hinge, apposed by muscles that close the shell, as in mollusks. The structure of each shell is distinctive too, having the layer of flat crystals next to the outer protein layer and the columnar crystals next to the soft body tissue that secretes it. Often a lamp shell consists of calcium phosphate rather than calcium carbonate, or some mixture of the two with or without horny material. The lamp shells appear to have tried every combination, and to have found a number of different inherited recipes that come out right.

Attached by their flexible stalks, the lamp shells have clung to a far smaller part of their world than have the clams and other mollusks. Brachiopods today seem to be a dying breed—a mere token left over from former days of greatness during the early part of the Paleozoic era. In the continued contest for food particles suspended in their liquid environment, the lamp shells have lost ground. Nor is there any evidence that in the past they ever invaded fresh waters. By contrast, the coterie of clams includes as many living species as there are fossils from all earlier times. In their shells of calcium carbonate, lined with mother-of-pearl, clams compete successfully with more kinds of life today than in any earlier period. To a large extent, their adaptations have given them a flexibility the brachiopods never had, and have let them inherit the food resource that once supported lamp shells in such great abundance. Little *Lingula* in its well and *Crania* cemented like an oyster to some stone are the famous exceptions in a world that seems somehow to have passed them by.

Obscurity often brings with it safety. But rarely can a prolonged program of remaining inconspicuous lead to the kinds of progress that appeal to the human mind.

chapter nine

The Odd Animals

O F all the treasures the oceans cast upon the shores, none captures
the imagination of a beachcomber so immediately as the clean
bleached shell of a sea urchin or a live sea star. Their five-parted symmetry puts them in a special category, utterly unlike any animal on land.
Nor are relationships more obvious among their next of kin, the brittle
stars, sea cucumbers, feather stars and sea lilies. Each of these is so different from humans that it might have come from another world. Yet of
all the animals that lack a backbone, these creatures of the sea have
more in common with the vertebrates than any others. To us this is
perhaps the greatest paradox in all nature.

Aristotle puzzled over live sea urchins along the shores of Asia Minor.
"Urchins are devoid of flesh [muscles]," he wrote in his *History of Animals*. "And this is a character peculiar to them. . . . Singularly enough,
the urchin has what we may call its head and its mouth down below . . .
in a position well adapted for getting at the food. . . . The urchin has also,
five hollow teeth inside. . . . Next to this comes the esophagus, and then
the stomach, divided into five parts, and filled with excretion, all the five
parts uniting at the anal vent, where the shell is perforated for an outlet.
Underneath the stomach, in another membrane, are the so-called eggs
[ovaries], identical in number in all cases, and that number is always an
odd number, to wit five."

Along the west coast of New Zealand just north of Wellington, we chatted with four young men and a girl who had just brought ashore several bushels of live sea urchins from the cold waters. "We Maoris are very fond of urchins," they told us. And without waiting to dry themselves or get out of their wet bathing suits, they began opening the urchins with a screwdriver to reach the clear liquid inside the shell. Tipping up the shells as though they were cups of delicious punch, they quaffed the contents. "In spring," the Maoris added, "the urchins are much better. Then at least half of them are full of bright yellow eggs. They look like rice and have a wonderful taste."

Sea gulls like urchins too, and they search out those that fail to move into deeper water as the tide recedes. The bird tears an urchin free, carries it aloft over some large rocks or a convenient road. There it drops the urchin and swoops down to gorge on the contents spilled from the shattered shell. Unlike Aristotle and the Maoris, the gulls do not disdain the urchin's digestive tract which is full of small pieces of seaweed undergoing dissolution.

Sea otters in Pacific and Arctic waters are said to dive for sea urchins and to reach the edible internal organs by smashing the shell between two stones—one a flat anvil balanced on the recumbent, floating otter's chest and the other a round stone used as a hammer in its paws. (Some day, from a Californian or Alaskan shore, we hope to watch a sea otter perform this trick. Only then will we finally overcome our skepticism which remains despite hearing and reading the story so often from sources that seem reliable.)

Each sea urchin wears its limy armor just under its skin in the form of ten double rows of plates. They fit together closely, but allow the animal to grow slowly without changing much in shape. Rarely can this skeletal support be seen while the urchin is alive, for the skin is opaque and, beyond the skin, the urchin usually wears a formidable covering of movable spines. These give the creature the appearance of a pincushion and show why the Greeks used the same word *echinos* for both sea urchins and hedgehogs. A modern scientist knows sea urchins and all of their relatives as echinoderms—the "spiny-skinned" ones.

Along five meridians of its somewhat globular body, an urchin extends its most useful appendages—slender, soft tubefeet in double rows. Each tubefoot ends in a suction cup under muscular control, and the whole appendage can be moved about with remarkable coordination. Muscles in its walls contract or relax while a watery fluid inside the tubefoot keeps it taut with controlled hydraulic pressure. Ordinarily an urchin holds to some solid object under water so firmly and flexibly, with so many tubefeet at once, that wave action does not displace it. Yet it can move along slowly, taking hold with some tubefeet while letting go with others. It uses these appendages to police its body and sometimes to hold a bit of seaweed or a piece of coral like a parasol against the sun.

Often a sea star (starfish) feels almost as firm as an urchin. It may break apart if bent forcibly by human hands. But when a sea star exerts its own muscles to bend its body rather than to resist, the limy nodules below its leathery skin allow surprising flexibility.

A good way to see a star display its superb muscular control is to place one of these echinoderms on the bottom of a tide pool or an aquarium, mouth upward and all of the grooves filled with writhing tubefeet exposed to view along its arms. Some kinds will right themselves in two minutes, whereas other take ninety. The star may slowly rise up mouth first from the bottom by bending all of its arms away from its mouth until it topples from instability. Sometimes, before this stage is reached, the extended tubefeet on one arm or on two adjacent ones gain a firm grip. They support the star as though in a balancing act while it turns in slow motion and spreads out flat on the bottom, with its mouth downward in the normal position. Or the animal may bend all of its arms in the opposite direction, raising them around its mouth like the petals of a flower, until the center of gravity is high enough to create instability and lead to toppling. Whichever two arms then lie along the bottom will curl at the tip and let their tubefeet take hold, supporting the animal as it performs its slow somersault.

A great many sea stars could show a West Indian limbo dancer still fancier flexibility. When placed mouth up upon the bottom, they curl just the tips of one or two arms (usually two adjacent ones) under and away from the mouth side of the body. As soon as the tubefeet gain a grip, the star proceeds to walk under itself, bending in succession every region of its body, perhaps all the way to the tips of the opposite arms, and never raising itself more than two thicknesses of star away from the surface on which it rests.

These acrobatics find frequent use in the life of a sea star while it scavenges for large pieces of animal food or preys upon the bivalved mollusks such as clams and oysters. Scientists used to assume that a star poisons its living victims, anesthetizing them until they can no longer hold their valves together. Other scientists, after failing to find any anesthetic chemical in seawater gathered close to a sea star that was attacking a clam, suggested that the star merely pulled at the clam until the victim's muscles grew fatigued and the shell opened. But until 1956 no one really knew how a star uses its muscular body and its tubefeet to open a bivalve and reach the meat inside.

To learn the secret, Dr. Marcel E. Lavoie while a graduate student at Syracuse University cleaned an empty clam shell, drilled matching holes in the two valves, and placed a piece of clam inside. He then slid a strong bolt through a washer, then the two valves facing one another, then another washer, and tightened a nut with a wrench. The bolt would not get tired no matter how long a sea star worked, and the shell seemed more tightly locked than any clam could manage. But a star took hold of the bolted shell, turned it around in the customary way, hunched itself over the shell on the side opposite the natural hinge, and took equally firm hold on the two valves with its tubefeet. The shell began to gape, the limy valves actually bent by the force applied. When a slot about 1/16 inch wide appeared, the sea star slid its tissue-thin stomach through the narrow space, turning itself inside out to this extent through its own mouth and through the slot between the valves of the clam shell. Then it relaxed and let the clam shell clamp down on its own stomach! Soon it applied force again, causing the shell to gape while juices rich with nourishment from the digested clam flowed back into the sea star. In installments the star completed its meal, removing every bit of meat from inside the bolted shell. That a sea star could deform a clam shell had never been suggested. When measured, the force of the animal proved to reach seven to ten pounds per square inch, all by muscles in the armored body wall, in the tubefeet, and in the hydraulic system that operates them. Without being able to maintain the rigidity we feel in a sea star's body, the creature could never perform this routine trick in feeding.

According to the fossil record, sea stars have been predators with tough skins for at least 500 million years. But their free-ranging habits keep them exposed on rocky and muddy bottoms of the sea where only occasional individuals die under conditions that favor fossilization. By taking the offensive, sea stars prevent bivalves in particular from becoming abundant no matter how rich the marine environment is in food particles suspended in water near the bottom. At the same time they avoid competition with sea urchins, sea lilies, feather stars, brittle stars and sea cucumbers, all of which swallow particles too small to see with the unaided eye.

Coral reefs in the West Indies are rich with sea stars, sea cucumbers and golden feather stars, as well as featherduster worms.

A gorgon star from moderately deep water off the New England coast, where it gathers detritus as food with its many branched arms.

Sea lilies have always seemed to us the most unbelievable of echinoderms. They grow side by side in regular gardens, erect as Easter lilies
between the reef corals at a depth of thirty to sixty feet, or from the
bottom muds far down into the great abysses. Many of them are bright
green, yellow, brown or red. They appear to have roots, whorls of narrow leaves, and a single upright flower—with a mouth at its center. So
thin and transparent is the skin over a sea lily that the limy rings and
plates of its white skeleton show through conspicuously, almost as though
they were on the outside.

The part of a sea lily that suggests a cornflower is actually the body
of the animal atop its supporting stalk. Arms arise at five points around
the body, each dividing promptly into two. Often the arms branch again,
and every one of them bears a large number of side branchlets giving the
appearance of a double-sided comb. Slowly the sea lily waves these
branching arms through the water, collecting bacteria and other minute
particles in the film of mucus that coats the branchlets. Hairlike cilia beat
to propel the loaded mucus toward the midline of each branchlet, to
enter a groove there and continue down it to the supporting branch, to
the undivided arm, and eventually up a little cone like a miniature volcano into the mouth where the crater would be. Inside the body the digestive tract makes a U-turn, emptying its wastes through an anus atop
another small cone-shaped projection.

Few creatures attack sea lilies, for the body and branching arms are
well armored with limy plates. The heavy rings of lime in the single
stalk are even heavier, like Life-Saver candies of double thickness with
a smaller hole. But accidents happen, and each sea lily is ready to repair
the damage, however extensive. A broken arm is dropped and replaced.
If the upper surface is harmed between the five arms, the sea lily may
cast off a large part of its body wall, the whole of its digestive tract
including mouth and anus, and even other organs from the body cavity,
and may then regenerate all of these anew. If the brittle supporting stalk
gets broken, the sea lily shows still another ability. The whorls of narrow leaflike extensions below the body and on whatever stub of stalk
remains attached all become active, dragging the body to a new location
and raising it erect in the bottom mud; new rings of stalk and further
whorls of leaflike appendages (cirri) can be installed to raise the body
and its branching arms to a level where they can collect food from the
gentle rain of particles that continually sifts downward from surface
waters. If the amount of food decreases, the sea lily may even amputate

its own stalk and go traveling to a new location, walking on cirri and arms for some distance before raising itself on a new stalk.

With so much known today about sea lilies, it seems incredible that until a century ago only their fossilized remains had been found. Thick layers of limestone in Russia, Belgium, the United States and the island of Timor in the East Indies contain vast numbers of stems from sea lilies, and a smaller number of the bodies with arms. Scientists who knew about the fossils believed these animals to be extinct. Then, from 1872 to 1876, came the pioneering voyage of the British research ship H.M.S. *Challenger* starting the study of the oceans—oceanography. Up from the sea bottom came the mangled remains of sea lilies that had been alive until the heavy dredges caught them and hauled them to the surface. But not until later, when engineers learned to grapple for submarine telegraph cables and bring them to the surface for repair, did anyone see a live sea lily in place. The first broken cable to be raised aboard ship from the deep sea had sea lilies clinging to it, their clusters of cirri still grasping the man-made cylinder of armored wire. Since the invention of skin-diving equipment, undersea explorers have found sea lilies growing in shallower water. Thirty feet, however, seems to be their upper limit, perhaps because they cannot survive the wave action that reaches into lesser depths during severe storms.

We had heard that in the Mediterranean Sea a small-bodied sea lily with very long, branched arms sometimes separates from its short stalk and comes swimming to the surface, ponderously sweeping its feathery appendages. Otherwise it clings firmly to the bottom by means of strong cirri around the scar where the stalk used to be. A number of similar creatures, called feather stars, are mentioned in the scientific literature. But somehow we never expected to meet one unless we got skin-diving equipment and learned to use it skilfully. Great was our excitement, then, while snorkeling in the West Indies, to see feather stars spreading their golden brown arms on coral reefs we could dive to by holding our breath. Determined to touch this rarity, we swam down time after time. Yet so firmly did the feather stars hold to the reef that our attempts to free one for closer study seemed likely only to tear its arms to pieces.

We borrowed a hammer and cold chisel and set about cutting off the coral mass to which a feather star clung so securely. Maneuvering ten feet below the surface with flippers and one hand, while the surges from waves above us dragged us in every direction, we could manage only about two hammer blows per dive. The water slowed the hammer, absorbing the force we strove to apply to chisel and then to limy coral. Lungs clamoring for air, we persisted. Finally the rock broke. And in that instant, the feather star let go, transferring its grasp with amazing speed to a human finger. As we bobbed to the surface, the animal held on, pressing its cluster of half-inch cirri into the soft flesh with a grasp so utterly different to the touch from any creature we had met before that we are confident we could recognize the sensation in the dark, on another planet—just anywhere we might chance to be. Spiny, strong, yet too dull at the tips to break through human skin, the cirri held us with the grip of ages—more than half a billion years. That grasp was the secret of not being tossed ashore by waves in a modern sea. It held at least as securely since Cambrian times, while trilobites flourished and went extinct, while dinosaurs appeared and disappeared, while the center of gravity of life itself shifted from the seas to the shores and into the drying sunlight in air.

Staring at our prize, we thought of its cousins the sea lilies at greater depths; of the 5,000 different kinds of sea lilies known from the fossil record and the mere 630 species including both sea lilies and feather stars today; of the cystoids and blastoids that were near kin of these animals in Paleozoic times but that had too weak a grasp on the future to save themselves from extinction. Gently we touched the tiny tubefeet along the food grooves in the branches of the golden arms and marveled that, with extra adaptations, these appendages provide the propulsive power for sea urchins, sea cucumbers and sea stars.

Only the brittle stars (known often as serpent stars) possess tubefeet as tiny as a sea lily's. And brittle stars, like these other relatives, travel freely with their mouths against the bottom muds. Back in the Paleozoic era after the end of the Cambrian some 500 million years ago, brittle stars followed a more secluded life. Each one buried itself mouth downward at the bottom of a well of its own making. Its five slender arms bent in a right angle at the small disc-shaped body, and extended up the sides of the vertical well to spread out over the surface of the silt and pick up food. Violent waves might expose a brittle star. They might also suddenly smother it in a great mass of debris, perhaps fossilizing it in its plugged burrow.

Recently, in shallows around the coral reef that fringes the principal island in the Fiji archipelago, we found brittle stars hiding in crevices while extending four of their five arms to capture food. They seemed so much more vulnerable than similar stars in New England tide pools which hide under rocks or seaweed from the light of day. We wonder what change in the ancient environment led the brittle stars to emerge from their wells and to creep about freely in the dark of night. Any irregularity is enough to grasp as they hurry along by snaky movements of those agile, fragile arms.

Wherever we find a brittle star we can understand its readiness to escape by shedding the tip of any arm we seize. Since the very earliest days these were exposed parts of its body—expendable parts that could be replaced quickly when damaged. Each arm appears segmented, with every segment the same. As though the stiffening were mass-produced, it consists of four thin limy plates under the thin leathery skin, one plate above, one below, one on each side. Another mass of lime occupies a central position within each "segment," being convex like a vertebra on the surface toward the end of the arm and concave toward the body. Each pair of blocks forms a ball-and-socket joint operated by four muscles. The joint provides spectacular flexibility and serves also as a place where the arm can break easily, only to be regenerated in a few days.

At least since the "Age of Fishes" in Devonian times 400 million years ago, brittle stars have used their flexible arms in this same way to gather particles of food that settle like manna to the ocean floor. Today their competitors are often sea cucumbers which harvest the same kind of nourishment in a different way. Thrusting out soft tentacles that arise around its mouth, the sea cucumber pushes forward into the surface sediments, accumulating a load of whatever will adhere to the sticky mucus on each tentacle. One at a time, the animal slides a loaded tentacle into its mouth and strips it clean, like a boy with jam on his fingers. Indigestible material goes right through the digestive tract and is voided at frequent intervals. Sometimes it accumulates in conspicuous heaps. The late Professor W. J. Crozier of Harvard University estimated from cones of debris in one region off Bermuda that the sea cucumbers on each acre of sea bottom passed between one hundred and two hundred pounds of sand annually through their bodies while digesting out the organic matter.

Of all the echinoderms, the sea cucumbers manage with the least skeletal support. Whatever strange little plates and burs of lime they do produce in their leathery skins remain disconnected. Lying on the bottom or creeping slowly over seaweeds, the sea cucumber maintains its body form in a novel way: by inflating itself with water. Instead of armor, it produces a poison that repels fishes or kills them, depending upon the amount released. In the South Seas, native people on fishing expeditions often carry with them one or two of the larger sea cucumbers. Arriving at a tide pool in which edible fishes may be hiding, a man wrings a sea cucumber like a laundered towel and waits until its poisonous juices diffuse through the waters of the pool. Every fish comes to the surface in such distress that it can be caught easily by hand. For man, the poison has no effect on the flavor or edibility of the fish.

Sea cucumbers recover from being wrung, and from other similar insults. Among their disconcerting adaptations is a distinctive mode of self-defense when attacked by a crab or other creature at the posterior end. It is there that most sea cucumbers seem most active, inhaling and exhaling sea water through a large cloacal opening while inflating or deflating their branching, internal breathing organs. (These are strange counterparts of gills known as respiratory trees.) If bitten in this region of the body, a sea cucumber quickly responds by turning partly inside out. Streaming out long strands of intensely sticky secretion, it wraps the attacker in its own inverted respiratory trees. It frees itself from its cloacal rim, casting loose even the last part of its digestive tract, and creeps away with its body cavity widely open to the sea, to repair the damage at leisure.

The Italian scientist F. Bertolini was the first to suspect that these strange animals react to other, normal changes in their environment by the same self-mutilation. He noticed that in late autumn in the Bay of Naples virtually all of the common large sea cucumbers known as *Stichopus regalis* were regenerating their intestines and respiratory trees. More recently, in each month from September to March, Dr. Emery F. Swan hauled up from waters of Puget Sound in Washington dozens of a related species. In November, every one was regenerating. In early September and after late December, none were in the midst of this process. Apparently all of them eviscerate themselves in October and take from one to three months to rebuild their digestive tracts into functional condition. Like a rite of autumn or an air-raid drill, they replace their organs annually, giving their powers for meeting an emergency the severest test.

Between echinoderms and any of the other invertebrate animals there is scant resemblance. Indeed, each echinoderm embryo starts developing as though it were going to turn into something much like us or some other vertebrate. After establishing a right-left symmetry, it suddenly turns aside to install the special adaptations of the echinoderm line, including the odd five-parted symmetry that puzzled Aristotle. It produces its hydraulic system of tubefeet and expands on a radial design, following an inherited distinction established perhaps a billion years ago. This unique assemblage of adaptive features makes these creatures resemble nothing else in the sea and nothing at all on land. They are the oddest animals we know.

chapter ten

More Portable Protection

W HEN we hold in our hands a live crab or a grasshopper and watch its movements as it strives to get free, we never feel that the creature is imprisoned within a nonliving, articulated box of its own making. The animal never pulls away from its armor as though merely glued to it. It cannot shrink back, like a worm inside its tube or a snail within its shell, for the muscles are attached directly to the external skeleton by way of fine, tough fibrils that extend right through the skin.

Each muscle attached to the shell of a crab or grasshopper is a discrete band under individual control. By tightening, it regulates the relative positions of the skeletal parts to which its two ends are attached so firmly. Some muscles are opposed only by the natural elasticity of inner organs or the pressure of the blood. Others work in pairs on opposite sides of a hinge joint, where small knobs and sockets fit together between adjacent parts of the skeleton. They allow lever action and limit movement to one plane. The closing of a crab's claw demonstrates the powerful possibilities of this leverage, while the pulsating of a honeybee's abdomen shows how its body telescopes inward under muscular compulsion. By telescoping, the insect expels air from fine breathing tubes, only to have elastic recoil extend its body and draw in a fresh supply.

In these days when electronic engineers are seeking to understand how messages travel through the nervous system of a bee or a lobster, a great

93

many people realize how compactly the body of these familiar creatures is organized. Every one of them is a marvel of miniaturization, a model for man to imitate in his design of devices useful for civilization. Yet, when we stop to think about it, we see that the skin of any crustacean, insect, spider or similar living thing is equally wonderful. Softer than a single thickness of facial tissue that has been soaked in water, it nevertheless secretes the firm skeleton in three-dimensional contours, providing every feature that we use to identify these arthropods. Nearly eighty percent of all the kinds of animals in the world owe their visible differences to products of their arthropod skins!

Equally distinctive of these creatures is their habit of growth—molting their external skeletons from time to time and profiting from the chance to start anew. Many of them molt several times before they escape from the egg shell. This too is programmed in their inheritance. The same program calls for a little change or a big one in body form as the old external shell is shed. For this reason the hatchling may differ greatly from later stages of development, and show no resemblance at all to the adult.

We quote the old couplet:

> And what's a butterfly? At best,
> He's but a caterpillar, dresst.

But we know better. Between the day the caterpillar sheds its final skin and exposes its pupal armor, and the time the pupal covering splits releasing the butterfly within, the substance of the caterpillar has been converted completely. Not a larval cell remains in the winged insect that emerges. The wings, the legs, the compound eyes, the watchspring "tongue," the sex organs, all begin as growth centers which digest the caterpillar from within and transform its raw materials into a butterfly. All of these changes are parts of the program enabling an arthropod to take the fullest possible advantage of its environment.

The skin of each arthropod is just one cell thick. Yet this single layer produces a great variety of different secretions, all contributing to the external skeleton or its replacement. First comes a thin, flexible layer of inert proteins and fats. Below this outer cuticle the skin produces an inner layer composed chiefly of chitin—an insoluble carbohydrate akin to cellulose. Particularly among crustaceans and millipedes, the inner cuticle is often hardened by addition of mineral matter, most notably calcium carbonate and phosphate. But through both thicknesses of cuticle, the skin leaves slender open channels. These conduct additional secretions at the time of molting: a waxy material that waterproofs the outer cuticle and limits absorption or loss of moisture, and phenolic solutions that tan the proteins of the cuticle until it will harden into armor when exposed to the oxygen of the environment.

Following inherited instructions in the most exquisite detail, the skin varies the thickness and the form of the cuticle it is secreting, producing inflexible plates joined by thin zones which permit movement. Each leg or other appendage on an arthropod consists of a series of tubular segments linked by membranous joints. The word arthropod merely signifies "jointed legs." A similar sequence of flexible membranes encircles the body, enabling it to bend and telescope to some extent.

The cuticle conforms to the soft skin over its hills and valleys more faithfully than the lines in two dimensions that follow the coast on a map showing the ocean boundaries. Each sharp infolding of the skin leads to formation of a sturdy peg or a vane of cuticle, increasing the area of attachment for muscle fibrils and showing externally as a dimple or a crease. More complex contours and delicately adjusted rates of secretion produce the hinges between hard parts. At intervals, larger cells of the skin extend through holes in the cuticle as the living lining for sensory hairs and pegs. They help the animal remain aware of chemicals in its immediate vicinity or of the touch of external things that may become important.

The skin of an arthropod extends part way into the digestive tract from both ends, and there too secretes a thin cuticle protecting the creature from anything rough in its food or its fecal pellets. Every bit of this cuticle is shed, along with the outer covering of the body, at molting time. By then the animal has grown so much that its armor confines it. Its digestive tract, muscles and other internal organs would suit a larger size. At some subtle signal that has yet to be identified, chemical messages begin to flow with the blood throughout the body. The skin cells react by producing a digestive enzyme, secreting it between themselves and the cuticle until—despite the tightness of the external skeleton—a thin space filled with liquid separates the two layers. Into this space the skin begins laying down a new cuticle, soft and wrinkled as it has to be. Along special lines the old armor seems more susceptible to digestion from within, and these become zones of weakness. It is there that the cuticle splits when molting begins. Only then do the fibrils from the muscles lose their connection to the old jointed shell.

Most arthropods seek out some secluded place to molt, for their vulnerability then reaches a peak of helplessness. Almost the only muscles that can still operate effectively are those that control the path of circulating

Trilobites were among the commonest small animals of coastal waters during the Paleozoic Era, but they died out completely with no descendants.

blood and the movement of material through the digestive tract. Usually the creature lets the blood drain back into its body from every appendage, making the projection slender enough to slip like a finger out of the glovelike hard tubes of armor. At the same time, it ordinarily swallows as much water or air as possible, distending its body to the utmost and broadening the gap of every split in the old shell. Through one of these gaps the bulging animal escapes. Immediately it assumes whatever pose will stretch its skin and soft cuticle to the limit, and waits motionless while the new armor hardens. Time is needed to make the covering portable.

Parents of small children who outgrow their clothes might wish for a way in which new, bright coverings could be obtained with such regularity. The size-6 arthropod, bursting from the split seams of its size-5 shell, swells up to size 7 and holds on until the new "suit" hardens. It is still a size-6 individual, and will grow inside its size-7 shell until this too is inadequate—on a size-8 body. Then it will be time to molt again to the size-9 armor which will afford plenty of room for a while. If a child grew at the rate that is common among arthropods—doubling in weight by the time they swell into a new soft cuticle and hold still for it to harden—buying new clothes would indeed be a problem.

The renewable, disposable skeleton had its origin far back before the beginning of the Paleozoic era, for the first rocks of Cambrian age contain fossils of many different kinds of trilobites, several types of crustaceans, and remains that probably represent the ancestors of horseshoe crabs. Each of these animals seems to be well adapted to scavenge along the sea bottom, propelling itself with many pairs of jointed legs. No doubt some of the early arthropods in search of food pushed themselves like bulldozers through the soft, topmost layers of sediments. Others surely swam, although feebly. Very few fossils suggest creatures that might have floated, drifting near the surface of the oceans, but this may only mean that planktonic species had little chance to be preserved.

We keep hoping that a modern expedition ship, loaded with oceanographers, will haul aboard from some unexplored part of the sea bottom a few live trilobites. Supposedly all of these creatures have been extinct for 250 million years. But until the little mollusk *Neopilina* was discovered among specimens hauled from deep water in 1957 off the west coast of Central America, no animal with this style shell was known to have existed more recently than the Ordovician, perhaps 450 million years ago. Nor have scientists quite forgotten the great surprise of 1938, when a large fish weighing 180 pounds came to light from more than one thousand feet below the surface of the Indian Ocean and proved to be a living representative of a group believed to have been extinct for 70 million years! Live trilobites are not impossible. As a scientific prize they would be hard to surpass, for during the early Paleozoic the trilobes dominated the sea bottoms—more abundant in kinds and individuals than any other inch-long animals in the fossil record. A few of them attained a length of 27 inches, but most were shorter than 3, and a number became mature while barely 1/25 inch long.

The name trilobite always seems strange to us, for the three lobes it refers to are the left side, the middle of the body and the right side, marked off from one another by lengthwise grooves. No other type of animal we can think of has been named for features from side to side— not even crabs that sidle in these directions instead of moving (as trilobites did) forward and back. In outline most trilobites are oval, rather like the small flattened crustaceans called sow bugs, pill bugs or wood lice, that hide under fallen logs and in other moist places on land. The body of each trilobite, behind its broad flat head, is divided crosswise into a large number of nearly identical segments and suggests the slats of a venetian blind when they are closed and overlap a little.

Atop the head on each trilobite fossil can be seen the special seam, called the facial suture, that opened at molting time to let the animal escape and grow to a larger size. It is a broadly U-shaped groove, extending across the front of the head and curving to the sides at its back corners. The bulging top of the head and everything between the two big compound eyes raised up like the hood of a modern automobile as the trilobite freed the thin rim of its "cheeks," drew its paired feelers (antennules) from their old sheaths below the head, separated from its many pairs of creeping and swimming appendages and slithered forth to freedom.

For the 100 million years of Cambrian times, the trilobites grew ever more diverse and numerous, despite the increasing numbers of nautiloids and other cephalopod mollusks which preyed upon these arthropods. Then the toll began to show and trilobites became more specialized, adapted in ways that reduced attack. One change came over most of them: they developed the ability to curl up into a ball, tail to head. Perhaps this quick action helped them slip from the arms of hungry cephalopods. Almost certainly it aided them in getting back on their feet after being turned upside down by a wave, a neighbor or some accident.

Horseshoe crabs, *Limulus polyphemus*, living fossils along the New England coast.

The habit of enrolling upon the slightest provocation may have become so routine that trilobites reacted in this way even when they bumped into one another.

New trouble for them spread into the seas from fresh water early in Devonian times, about 400 million years ago. Down the broad rivers came fishes with jaws, some of them sharklike and others supported by a bony skeleton. Fishes that could tolerate the saltiness of oceans found trilobites to eat. At a nudge, the victim curled into a compact sphere, making it as easy to swallow as a wet vitamin pill. As rapidly as the population of fishes in the sea increased, the numbers of trilobites shrank. So did variety among the survivors. By the end of the Paleozoic, so far as we know, not one of these ancient arthropods remained—not even any offspring that had evolved into other types of animals.

Crustaceans escape a similar fate largely by adaptations of other kinds. A great many of these creatures remain small, drifting among the minute algae on which they feed in surface waters. Others find refuge in nooks and crannies or so close to shore that large fishes cannot follow them. Still others develop strong pincers as formidable weapons of self-defense, merely by additional growth of the next-to-last segment of the walking legs, forming a claw against which the final segment closes like a thumb. These crabs and lobsters take advantage of the quick changes possible in body form molt after molt. Their eggs hatch to tiny larvae, all legs and spines, that browse among the plankton. Step by step the individuals that survive grow larger in the body and add the features familiar among adult animals of these kinds. With added weight, they settle to the bottom and become scavengers.

When the tide receded and left sand bars or mud flats exposed to the hot sun and dry air, a great many of the ancient arthropods in shallow water must have buried themselves, much as young horseshoe crabs do today. Their skeletons withstood abrasion, even when the returning waves beat down upon the beach and vigorously pounded the sand grains. Even if the shell got scratched where it was thin and transparent over the eyes or where it was thin and porous, sleevelike, around the sensitive bristles and pegs that served the senses of smell and touch, it would be renewed perfectly at the next molt.

The ancestors of horseshoe crabs were there, scavenging about near shore, devouring sea weeds, various worms and clams small enough to push into the mouth between their armored, jointed legs. And as today, we can think of those ancient animals occasionally hurrying along the bottom like a heavily loaded airplane ready to take off, then zooming upward in a loop that no aircraft can match, to swim along upside down by rhythmic flapping of the paired legs and the plates of thin armor that protected the delicate gills. Tiring after a while, these homely creatures settled to the bottom, still back downward, and righted themselves by raising the long, stiff tail spine that projected almost as long as the body. These habits have not changed in more than 300 million years. Only the number of different horseshoe crabs has shrunk, so that now there is one kind along the Atlantic coast of America from Maine to Yucatan and three kinds in Oriental waters from India to China and the central islands of the East Indies. With ancestors of almost identical form that can be traced back through fossil record to the Silurian period about 425 million years ago, the four surviving species have every right to be regarded as "living fossils."

Horseshoe crabs find mates and creep ashore at high tide in early summer to lay their eggs in sandy beaches where the warmth of the sun will speed the development of the embryos. About a month later, when the waves again beat upon the sand, the egg shells break and little tail-less young emerge. In many ways they resemble trilobites. But soon they molt again, gain a tail spine, and seek out microscopic particles of food among the sediments on the bottom of coastal lagoons. Rains and droughts on land that dilute seawater near shore or make it more concentrated have little effect on these animals. Among their adaptations is a tolerance for changes of this kind. Inside their hard shells, they maintain the amount of water they need for normal life.

This ability is far from new. It is a pattern that allowed survival for a number of different groups of animals that spread into fresh water as soon as microscopic green plants began growing there—at least 600 million years ago. But conditions seldom were right for preserving fossils of creatures in fresh water, and much mystery still surrounds the ancestors of sea scorpions, the spiders and their kin, the insects these found for food, and the fishes that began the great trend toward animals with a supporting backbone. Each of these styles of animal life appeared first in fresh water. Their forebears and those of many mollusks and crustaceans had also inconspicuously reached the rivers and streams, lakes and ponds, long before life of any kind dared brave the sun and dry air on land.

The name "sea scorpion" refers to fossils found embedded in sediments that were consolidated from old mud flats and sand bars at the mouths of ancient rivers, where the tide slowed the current and let suspended matter settle. Each of these animals tapers to a sharp tail spine which could be turned up over the back as a dagger and used to kill prey held in the powerful pincers on the front legs. Today neither part of the name seems suitable, for the bodies are believed to have been washed down stream to the sea, and the tail spine is known to have carried no poison comparable to that of a land scorpion. Yet sea scorpions must have been dangerous predators. A few of them became the largest arthropods that ever lived, with a length of almost nine feet and a somewhat flattened pear-shaped body as much as two feet broad. Perhaps they depended upon being buoyed up by water, for at the close of the Paleozoic when the climate on the continents suffered from prolonged drought and cold, sea scorpions became extinct.

Somewhere in the ancestral line of sea scorpions a branch evolved with adaptations that later made possible the invasion of the land and survival despite extremes of heat and cold, flood and drought. This branch, which is represented today by only a handful of fossils, led to the land scorpions, the land spiders and the tiny ticks and mites that specialized still more in body and in habit. Similar changes on quite different animals in fresh water let the ancestors of centipedes, millipedes and insects become air-breathing inhabitants of the land. By Devonian times, some 400 million years ago, when all of these creatures first became terrestrial, the distinctions between the various types had already been well established.

No animals on earth have benefited as much as insects from the arthropod style of skeleton. It offers more strength and waterproofing than any other covering, even when thin and lightweight enough for a body less than ⅛ inch in length. It has aided insects in invading and colonizing successfully more different places to live than any other group of animals. They continue to exploit the land and the fresh waters of the world. Alone among animals without a backbone, they have developed adaptations that enable them to fly.

During the 65 million years of the Carboniferous period (the "Coal Ages"), when insects suddenly appeared and rapidly diversified according to the fossil record, a few of them attained dimensions greater than are known today. Among the dragonflies were some with a 29-inch wingspan. The giant owlet moth of Panama and northern South America holds the modern record, spreading its gray wings about twelve inches at the maximum. We once found one in the rain forest on Barro Colorado

Island in Gatun Lake, almost within view of ocean-going ships in the high-level part of the Panama Canal. The moth rested on the bare trunk of a tall tree perhaps two feet in diameter. Its wings, stretched on either side, almost clasped the trunk, their small black markings making the creature only slightly less conspicuous. We tried to capture the insect by suddenly clamping a long-handled net over it, but the reactions of the moth saved its life. Instead of rising in fright from the tree straight into the fine net, the insect slithered sidewise where the metal frame left a thin gap on each side. Flapping vigorously, the moth flew off into the forest as two pairs of human eyes tried to keep it in sight. Someday we hope for another chance to see the giant owlet (*Thysania agrippina*) at closer hand.

In those same dense thickets we did handle a four-inch scarab, a beetle that seemed the insect equivalent of the cartooned Superman. It flew with a great buzzing sound like some mechanical toy, its heavy forewings stiffly spread to give added lift while the membranous rear wings beat rapidly, providing both propulsion and hovering power. We heard the insect coming, then saw it just as the sound stopped and the beetle plummeted to earth among some undergrowth only a few feet away. Quickly we raced to the spot in time to see the rear legs assist in folding the tips of the membranous wings where they would be concealed and protected as the forewings came together and clamped down. The fitted doorways that conceal the landing gear in the belly of an airplane work no more smoothly.

Knowing that the beetle's only means of defense were its armor and the small strong jaws that met from side to side below its head, we picked it up. Frantically it waved its six legs; and then the middle pair caught on our fingers and shoved so vigorously we could not maintain our grip. Never before had we been pushed around by an insect!

The heaviest of flying insects live in the Congo rain forests and weigh six to eight ounces—as much as a full-grown rat. There, one day in July, we had our interpreter ask members of a nomadic group of pygmy people if they could catch for us one of these goliath beetles (*Goliathus giganticus*). The spokesman for the group replied that he knew the beetles well, but the season was wrong. He talked and talked, gesturing enthusiastically by drawing horizontal circles in the air with his forefinger. Translated, his story told of pygmy youngsters tying the giant insects with flexible fibers from a plant to the end of a stick. The beetles would fly in circles, buzzing without getting anywhere. Yet the pygmy insisted that the children always released their living toys. The beetle itself is too heavily armored to be edible, but they do lay eggs in rotting wood. There the pygmies dig at the proper time of year to get gigantic grubs, each C-shaped and, to a pygmy's palate, delicious to eat either raw or lightly toasted over the camp fire. Plenty of grubs get overlooked and mature into the biggest beetles in the world.

Beetles, incidentally, come in more than 280,000 different kinds. They account for more than a third of the known species of insects, outnumbering in variety everything in the animal kingdom that is not an insect. Nor, if the suspicions of botanists are correct, has this burgeoning of beetles failed to influence the other living things on land. During Mesozoic times, between 230 and 65 million years ago, as beetles evolved and increased their attacks on terrestrial vegetation, one inconspicuous group of seed plants developed a new adaptation giving them some protection. It consisted of folding the leaf on which the seeds were borne to form a beetle-proof cover. These became the "covered-seeded" plants—the angiosperms. The "covers" ripen as the seeds inside mature, and are called fruits. They may be dry like the wing on an elm or maple seed, helping it spin in the wind away from the parent tree; or dry like a poppy pod, shaking out minute seeds like oversize grains of pepper; or fleshy like a strawberry, an apple or a watermelon. The armor against attack by beetles is immensely valuable to the plant as well as to man. By developing it, the descendants of those Mesozoic kinds of vegetation now include more than two-thirds of all the species in the plant kingdom. They are the flowering plants so familiar to everyone. The flowers that give them distinction combine a host of later adaptations, mostly aiding the plants by encouraging insects to share unwittingly in the process of pollination.

Just as in the sea the small crustaceans serve as go-betweens by transforming the nourishment of microscopic drifting plants into food for fishes, so too on land the insects consume the vegetation and convert its goodness into bite-size pieces enjoyed by larger animals. Insects form the principal food of frogs and toads, reptiles of many kinds, a great variety of birds, and a surprising number of mammals such as bats, shrews and skunks. Ever since insects became numerous in Carboniferous times, they have provided a reward for insect-seekers in and on the soil, on and inside the plants, and flying through the air. They may have lured early vertebrate animals into adopting a terrestrial life, and made it worthwhile later for some of them to become winged. It was only when insects began their spectacular diversification that air-breathing fishes developed legs, instead of fins, transforming from aquatic tadpoles to insect-eating amphibians. The first reptiles and the first mammals seem all to have been insectivorous. The first birds may have been feathered flying reptiles with teeth, useful in eating small fishes caught in shallow waters. But most land birds today raise their nestlings on an insect diet, even if later they will change to meals exclusively of seeds and fruits.

Among the great innovations that made the living world what it is today, few outrank the hard cuticle, to be molted time after time, evolved by the ancestors of arthropods. Nor is there any sign that this pattern that aided in survival has run its course or is about to wane. Immensely adaptable, it seems ideal for animals that are large enough and sufficiently long-lived to profit—as beach hoppers, butterflies and horseshoe crabs do —from setting their own courses by the sun and stars. It is equally ideal for insects such as fruit flies that are small enough to pass through several generations in just a few weeks when food is temporarily abundant. Testing their adaptations and evolving a little at each new generation, insects and other arthropods have already out-evolved most of their competitors. Now many of them compete with the cultural evolution of modern man.

chapter eleven

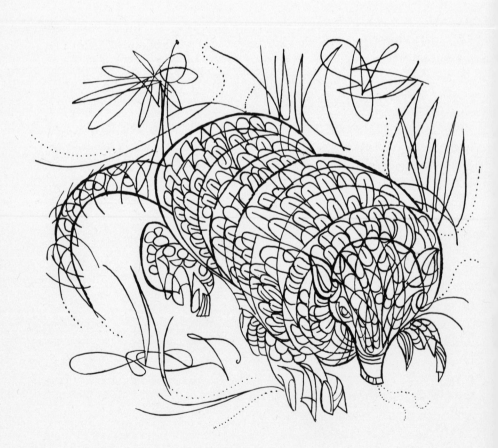

Valuable Adaptations
That Are Only Skin-deep

THREE hundred and fifty years ago the English author John Davies wrote one line that brought him fame: "Beauty's but skin deep." Today we know that skin is far more than just a decorative wrapping around the animal. Its adaptations have gone a long way to make vertebrates the successful creatures they are.

Seldom do we stop to realize how much of what we know comes to us through sense organs in the skin. Our understanding of the world began in infancy through the sense of touch. Patterns detected through our eyes and ears became meaningful in terms of what came in contact with the sensitive skin of our fingertips and lips. Later we learned to rely increasingly upon vision and hearing to save us from harming the skin with flame or sharp tools, to tell us that rain was falling without getting wet, to interpret wind and snow without getting cold, to recognize the shadeless noonday sun as a source of burning heat. And still we like to confirm our impressions by touching things: soft fur, keen edges, hot cups of coffee, wet paint.

Much of our heritage we take on faith, confident that most scholars tell the truth as they sense it. We know that these men continually push back the frontiers while scanning their personal horizons to maintain perspective. They stride ahead on facts, leaping often from one to the next without waiting for the road between to be solidly paved. We can follow them, crediting our own senses wherever the evidence comes into view. We need to see only a few dinosaurs reconstructed in a museum display to become convinced that live dinosaurs existed in immense variety and astonishing dimensions. A few remains of fossil men suffice to let us think of our own past and to make us appreciate the considered conclusions of specialists who have handled all of the available evidence.

Sometimes, as we rely upon the ideas gained from the study of fossils, we feel like Jack the Giant Killer descending the beanstalk, carrying a fortune gained in never-never land. We can climb down our own family tree, rich with the discoveries and interpretations of fossils that science has gained in less than a century and a half. These feats of detective work allow us to visualize how the mammals of today diversified during the last 65 million years.

All mammals, and our own species too, came from four-footed animals with five flexible fingers on each hand and five similar toes on each foot, but with pointed heads and many teeth that seem fitted best for catching and devouring insects. Modern tree shrews—small, bushy-tailed creatures of the Oriental tropics—resemble most closely the ancestral mammals from which the human line slowly evolved, a few adaptations at a time.

It was a nonliving product of the skin—a fur coat—that distinguished the first mammals. All of them were rat-sized during the last days of the Mesozoic era, while the dinosaurs and other great reptiles were heading for extinction. Fur shielded them from the cold and let them be warm-blooded, active without regard for weather, with a tolerable expenditure of energy. While scale-clad reptiles remained torpid and insects were slowed down by morning chill and winter cold, the mammals could share the land with the birds, which had an equivalent adaptation from the skin as a coat of feathers.

Still earlier, during the stressful transition between the Paleozoic and the Mesozoic, the common ancestors of mammals, birds and reptiles can be found among creatures with a multitude of teeth. At first glance it might be guessed that their bodies belong to some kind of crocodile. With short, powerful legs and a long, strong tail, they showed adaptations that gave them a grip on the land far more secure than that among any of their amphibian forebears. No reptile has to return to a pond, stream, swamp or other wet place at mating time, as amphibians do to this day. Instead, each mother reptile encloses every egg in its own armor coat: a shell. It can be left in some place of concealment such as the soil.

Within the shell the embryo grows on its yolky food, surrounded by the "white" of egg which is its private pond. It breathes through the shell by means of a special adaptive extension of its skin.

We used to believe that the chief reason for giving so much attention to the skulls of fossil vertebrates was that these hard parts had a statistically better chance than other parts of the body to be preserved and later discovered in sedimentary rocks. While this is true, the fact remains that in the pattern of bones that comprise the skull, a good anatomist can recognize more about the nature of the beast than in any other part of the skeleton. He can follow a meaningful sequence of changes back through time from a mammal skull to a reptilian one, to an ancestral amphibian, and then to an armored fish. The location of the nasal openings, both outside and into the mouth, tell a consecutive story. So does the hinging of the jaws, the mode of attachment of the teeth, and the pattern in the bony plates that originate in the skin but sink down to become skull parts.

The message in the skulls might never have really impressed us if we had not left our warm beds before dawn to go with a game warden up a long lagoon that fingered into the Natal coast from the Indian Ocean. At the head of this lagoon we hoped to see and photograph one or both species of African flamingo as these long-legged birds waded and fed in the shallow water. But as daylight spread into the papyrus marshes that lined our route, we saw from our little boat dark objects about two feet long, floating like pulpwood logs on a river. As the outboard motor drove us onward, each "log" sank silently, without a swirl, at our approach. Every one of them was the head of a watchful crocodile, its eyes protruding, its nostrils flaring to keep it aware of events above the water surface until we came too close.

It did not help to remember Kipling's story of the elephant child who got his nose pulled out of shape by inquiring too closely what the crocodile had for dinner. Our curiosity stopped short of learning whether the many teeth in a crocodile's mouth are just larger or more numerous than the twenty along each side, top and bottom, in a baby alligator. Instead, we wondered whether a crocodile longer than our boat—and there were plenty of them—could tip us over. Which was stronger, if we collided with a monster, its skull or the bottom of our craft? Every crocodile that ignored us, continuing to bask with its mouth agape on the shore, reminded us of the huge reptiles we could not see in the murky water below our boat.

The tree iguana of tropical Latin America feeds on foliage high above the rain forest.

Those two-foot heads with their rows of sharp teeth haunt us whenever we visit a museum where skeletons of prehistoric animals trace our own ancestry. Except in details, the skull of a crocodile or an alligator appears remarkably similar to the corresponding parts of early reptiles, still earlier amphibians, and the large air-breathing fishes from which, supposedly, they descended. Every tooth, like every scale, is a product of the skin.

We can trace this story back through the eons of Paleozoic time to the "Age of Fishes." And before that we find armored, jawless fishes that had large, thin, bony plates deep in the skin instead of overlapping scales. These fishes of Ordovician times are the earliest vertebrates known. Among the abundant fossils from the preceding period (the Cambrian), not a single bony plate or tooth or other hard part has ever been found. We can only believe that the Ordovician fishes had Cambrian ancestors, but that these were unarmored, untoothed and uncommon. Almost certainly they lived in the seas, as though waiting for that extra adaptation to let them spread into fresh water and find success.

To review our remote ancestors in the light of the present is like reading the last paragraphs of a continued story before starting at the beginning. We know how it turned out until today. But how will the characters that remain alive in the current installment react next week, next year, next millennium? What features should we notice as portending their future, determining which will be able to survive the challenges they meet? Clues to the past are far easier to pick out, because we see what actually happened.

In its context of early Ordovician times, which is Chapter Two in the fossil record, we can appreciate the armor on those jawless fishes. These first of all known animals with a backbone possess just the kind of protection that, once added to the inheritable features of a previously thin-skinned ancestor, would allow it to emigrate from the oceans that had been its home. The hard plates of bone just below the delicate skin would block any dangerous inflow of water as that ancestor proceeded from the sea into an estuary with a body adjusted to a salty environment. Microscopic algae and other kinds of life in minute sizes already thrived in lakes and rivers. Enough small invertebrates were feeding on them to provide prey for the first sea scorpions. The armored, jawless fishes joined in feasting on this bonanza, and grew diverse to better match the many variations in the fresh-water environment.

Scientists call all of these early, jawless fishes the ostracoderms—the "shell-skinned" ones. Uniquely among animals, they held on by means of their sucker mouths while drawing water in and expelling it again through a row of gill openings along each side of the throat region. Or they slithered their tapering tails into the bottom sediments near shore, anchoring themselves while taking water in at the mouth, filtering the plankton on which they fed, and routing the water out through the gill openings. Some of them improved the process a little by developing inside their armor a new adaptation: vertical bars of stiff cartilage between the gill openings. These provided a firmer attachment for the muscles whose contractions controlled the flow of water. At the time this extra feature may have seemed a small step. Later the gill bars led to additional improvements including the origin of jaws, ear bones, voice boxes and the delicate bones that support a tongue.

During the 75 million years of the Ordovician period, some of the ostracoderms gained other adaptations with a great future. Outwardly they grew more flexible through a reduction in their bony armor or even its total loss. Part of this change came through increasing the thickness of the skin, making it many layers deep and a good barrier in its own right even without plates of bone beneath it. An alteration deep inside seems equally important: the kidneys grew more complex and efficient, able to handle a larger amount of water that entered through the skin or with food. They removed the moisture from the blood and discharged it as urine. Some of these unarmored ostracoderms continued with few further changes into the present day as lampreys.

Among both the armored and unarmored ostracoderms, a new adaptation arose in a few species and spread rapidly because of the success it allowed. The front pair of gill openings arose so far underneath the head that they finally joined to create a single gash—a new mouth. The bars of cartilage in front of and behind this opening joined at their lower extremities to become the first jaws. The muscles that earlier had served to control the gill openings now gave biting action. The old sucker mouth disappeared. The transformed ostracoderms included many still in plates of armor; scientists call them "plate-skinned" fishes—placoderms. Hordes of them spread downstream into the oceans where they could find trilobites and other food on which to exercise their jaws. Unarmored fishes with similar jaws joined in this rush to the seas. There they became the sharks and rays, whose skeletons contain no bones but whose bony teeth may represent ancestral bits of armor transformed for a new use in the skin around the rim of the powerful jaws.

The dramatic increase in the number and variety of marine fishes during Devonian times, making this the "Age of Fishes," came largely through further adaptations. Most of these swimmers, both in the oceans (which teemed with them) and fresh water, developed more efficient kidneys and improved the arrangement and size of armor in the skin. Some gained flexibility by reducing the bony plates into a mosaic of pieces butting together below a leathery covering, in patterns still followed by the sturgeon and garfish which somehow appear antiques. Others folded their skins in such a way that the thin scales overlapped, each outside the one behind like shingles on a roof. A few in tropical waters retired within an almost solid box, while a similar number began slithering through the water in the manner of an eel with no scales or plates of any kind.

Through sheer abundance and diversity the marine fishes of the Devonian tend to steal the show. They distract us from noticing continued changes of greater, later significance in the shallows of fresh water. There a few large fishes with heavy heads and overlapping scales can be imagined as drifting at the surface. For oxygen they rely upon air forced into two-lobed pockets in the floor of the throat. Their nostrils, located just above the end of the snout, are not blind like those of other fishes but open into the mouth and are equipped with valves. Each fish keeps its mouth shut, opens the nostril valves, lowers the floor to increase the cavity inside; then closes the valves and raises the floor, thus pressing air into the short tube from the throat and inflating those elementary lungs. These same fishes have mouths as full of teeth as do crocodiles, and they have a different style of paired fins, like a compromise between paddles and legs. Both the front pair and the rear pair of fins are thick and muscular next to the body and contain a number of bony blocks. They make the fin sturdy as well as powerful in laborious movements that can propel the heavy fish from one pond to the next.

For a reason we still fail to understand, the slender spines that support the thin vane portion of each fin are hollow. Scientists find such ease in recognizing the whole fish by its hollow spines that they call the animal itself a "hollow-spine" (coelacanth). Or they emphasize the nostrils, which are so like those of modern amphibians, and call the creatures "nostril fishes" (choanichthyes). Among these denizens of fresh water 400 million years ago were the ancestors of *Latimeria,* the modern lobe-fin from the depths of the Indian Ocean, and of the amphibians that hunted insects through the swamp forests of Carboniferous times.

Those first amphibians were big animals, several feet in length, with armored heads but few scales over the rest of the body. Known as the "roof-heads" (stegocephalians) or known from their teeth as labyrinthodonts, they thrived in the swamps where shallow water, shade from the sun and insects to eat were all abundant. But at the end of the Paleozoic, when drought became more frequent and widespread, the amphibian way of life could be followed only by small creatures, benefiting from local areas of high humidity and from ponds in the spring of the year. Some went underground, becoming the legless coecilians of the tropics which burrow through the soil like earthworms in search of insects and other prey. Many remained four-legged and long-tailed, as small salamanders, swimming in temporary ponds, hiding among the fallen leaves, or digging down and becoming dormant during long periods of dry weather. Some inherited the ability to wait through a long juvenile growth as legless tadpoles, feeding on microscopic plants, before developing legs and hopping out on shore; these became tail-less frogs and toads, which catch insects by flicking out their sticky tongues.

The skeleton of the first reptiles is so like that of the roof-headed amphibians that only an expert would know which is which. But how many little details had to be modified at once to produce a reptile? No longer does the animal depend upon mucus secreted from its thin, glandular skin to protect it from the dry air. Instead, a reptile's skin is like our own in gaining its tolerance for low humidity from a thin covering of dead cells, each reasonably waterproof. Even when supported from within by a pattern of bony scales, the outer layer is renewed and the old dead skin shed, usually more than once a year. From most reptiles the molting process recurs at irregular intervals. The skin pulls free in a single piece and is discarded, like a tan-colored coverall which, in snakes, includes clear convex shields that protect each eye.

Through its dry skin a reptile cannot absorb oxygen from the atmosphere to charge its blood, as amphibians do through their moist surfaces. Nor, apparently, can a reptile ventilate itself sufficiently by using the floor of the mouth as a bellows, pumping air into its lungs. They breathe, instead, by muscular movements of their ribs. They inhale and exhale by expanding and contracting the body cavity in which their lungs lie. This process gains in efficiency through another inconspicuous adaptation: the lower ends of most ribs are hinged to a breastbone, making them more effective levers. Only in snakes and turtles is this ancient improvement replaced, in the one by hinging the ribs to the crosswise scales

Large antlers on buck fallow deer of northern Europe seem bigger than ever while still covered by the hairy skin ("velvet") within which they develop.

The antlers on a bull elk are shed in winter, then replaced by a new pair, which are still larger if the elk is young and healthy.

with which the serpent creeps, and in the other by special muscles inside the boxlike shell to which the ribs are fused immovably.

The armor around a reptile's egg, whether leathery and flexible or calcified and hard, protects the developing embryo from mechanical damage, invasion by microbes and loss of its limited supply of water by evaporation. Yet its success depends upon still more adaptations, all of them in harmony. No reptile embryo in its private pond makes use of gills, like those of an amphibian or a fish. Instead, until it hatches, it purifies its blood by pumping this precious liquid through special vessels to a thin extension of its own body that is spread just inside the shell, as close as possible to the air outside. Without those membranes connected to it only by a slender umbilical cord which contains the blood vessels, the reptile embryo would suffocate. The egg shell and watery albumen are contributions from the parent, due to inherited instructions about how to make a good egg. The membranes that come to line the shell are produced by the growing embryo, following its own inherited directions about how to survive through embryohood. Further directions induce the unhatched reptile to grow a "hatching tooth" on the skin at the end of its snout, as a tool with which to open an escape route into the outside world. Without all of these adaptations simultaneously, the ancestral line of reptiles would have vanished by extinction long ago.

As we think about the little reptile growing within the seclusion of its egg shell, taking fats and proteins from the yolk and water and protein from the "white," we realize how thriftily it uses its resources. If people around the globe would make a similar effort to avoid waste and pollution, many chronic problems would disappear. By the time the reptile hatches, all of its water and albumin have been absorbed and its small amount of remaining yolk is carried along, tied on at its belly button like a plastic bag full of thick soup.

Every reptile embryo has one adaptation an astronaut might envy in his space capsule. It has no need to drink water to flush wastes from its kidneys, for these organs produce only insoluble crystals of uric acid in a gentle stream of slippery mucus. Instead of a liquid urine, the reptile produces a thick paste which glistens when light strikes the faces of the white crystals. Neither the waste nor the mucus can pollute the "white" of the egg, and both can be stored conveniently in a minimum of space. This adaptation, so valuable inside the egg shell, becomes a way of life for reptiles even after they have hatched. Birds, too, followed this mode of waste disposal when they evolved from reptiles. They benefited greatly from it since it reduced the amount of weight in water which each flier had to lift off the ground.

Birds and mammals have roamed the earth for less than 180 million years. For much of this time, most of them remained small and insignificant, dwarfed by the giant dinosaurs in the "Age of Reptiles." With modest requirements for food and an independence of weather made possible by feathers or furs combined with an ability to adjust heat production according to body temperature, they survived the cruel days at the end of the Mesozoic era.

No one is quite sure what trick of fate doomed so many successful types of animals, including all of the dinosaurs and all of the ammonoid mollusks, making available their places on earth to a new assemblage of living things. Evidence can be cited to show that cold weather struck the temperate zones and adjacent seas, paralyzing the reptiles for much of the year and slowing the movements of predatory mollusks offshore. But what hurt the tropics and the warm oceans under an equatorial sun? On chilly days the hungry birds and mammals may have dug out reptile eggs or even attacked lethargic monsters, eating them on the installment plan—like a steer or deer from the deepfreeze. Again no single explanation seems to fit all parts of the earth and seas.

Recently scientists offered a new suggestion. They could interpret the record in the rocks of Mesozoic time as showing that no new mountain building took place for nearly 200 million years. If the erosive forces of water and wind almost leveled the continents by the middle of the Cretaceous period, rainfall would dwindle, rivers diminish and meander, floodwaters rarely renew the land with fertilizing sediments. Vegetation on land would decrease in productivity, and coastal waters would also suffer a serious loss in mineral nutrients since so little was coming in rivers from the continents. General starvation could be predicted on land and in the oceans. Surely no greater disaster than this would be needed to account for the extinction of so many kinds of life, weeding out all but the small and outstandingly versatile species.

Certainly the few large reptiles and members of ancient groups that have survived since the close of the Mesozoic era are holdouts. They inhabit swamps, seas and remote islands in warm parts of the world, where time seems to have passed them by. Yet all of them are small by comparison with some of their relatives in the days of the Jurassic and Cretaceous periods, when hordes of reptiles ruled the lands, swam in the seas and flew about on leathery wings.

In many ways the turtles have won this prolonged race. Plodding over the continents or paddling through the oceans, they continue a tradition in armor that began at least 215 million years ago. Unlike other reptiles they have retained flexibility only in the neck, tail and legs. Their ribs and hip girdles now join with bony plates beneath the skin, and their skulls have fused into a single massive bone. Often the skin produces a further barrier against the world, in the form of horny scales that fit together in a pattern with no correspondence to the bones underneath.

Some day we hope to meet the largest of these ancient beasts: the leatherback turtle which swims remote from land in warm seas. There it often attains a length of 8 feet and a weight of 1,200 pounds, devouring the seaweeds that drift by and whatever fishes tarry within reach of its powerful jaws. It is the only surviving member of its genus, its family, and its section of the old order of turtles. When we do encounter a leatherback, it will remind us of *Archelon*, a giant from the great inland sea that covered much of the American West during the late Cretaceous. *Archelon's* shell was leathery too, but fossils of it are twelve feet long, indicating a weight of close to three tons.

The green turtles we have admired in pens called "turtle crawls" close to the restaurants of Key West, Florida, are the favorite source of soup and steak. Free, they roam the Atlantic and Pacific Oceans on both sides of the equator to about 35° latitude—Cape Fear, North Carolina to Buenos Aires, Argentina; San Diego, California to Santiago, Chile—with occasional individuals ranging still farther. Eating chiefly the succulent parts of coarse seaweeds, they grow rapidly. On a generous diet, captives have added about a pound a month until, at an age of almost three years, they reach maturity. The larger, upper shell is 8 inches long at the end of the first year, 16 after the second, and by 9 years may be 44 inches long and enlarging much more slowly. The record for size and weight is barely over 46 inches, at about 850 pounds.

On land the giants are club-footed tortoises with every appearance of being relics from the ancient past. Half a world away from one another, one species once flourished in isolation far out in the Indian Ocean while a second enjoyed equal freedom from competition on the similarly volcanic islands of the Galápagos Archipelago in the Pacific Ocean six hundred miles west of the coast of Ecuador. Both have been threatened with extermination ever since the sixteenth century when they were discovered by sea captains who put ashore to replenish their ships with water and whatever food could be found. Galápagos is the Spanish word for tortoise and commemorates the regular raids conducted to haul living animals aboard ship as a source of fresh meat, where they remained alive for months without food or water.

Charles Darwin arrived in the Galápagos aboard the British exploration ship H.M.S. *Beagle* in 1835, and despaired of the future in store for the huge beasts. Between 1831 and 1868, whalers in the Pacific were harvesting the tortoises at a rate far greater than reproduction could match. The logbooks of whaling vessels examined recently by Dr. C. H. Townsend showed a total of more than 10,000 large "turpin" collected during just 189 visits, averaging more than 52 per visit. Darwin, in his diary entry for October 8, recorded the English vice-governor of the islands as saying that he had seen several tortoises "so large, that it required six or eight men to lift them from the ground; and that some had afforded as much as two hundred pounds of meat." This may not, in itself, indicate a great age, for two small specimens which weighed only thirty pounds each when brought alive to the Brookfield Zoo near Chicago, grew to nearly four hundred pounds apiece in 26 years. Their high-domed upper shells were then of the size routinely used as bathtubs by people on the Galápagos Islands.

It is one thing to watch some of these giants (*Testudo elephantopus*) from the Galápagos as they take their exercise penned up in a zoological garden, and quite another to walk along beside them on the well-worn trails they make in their native haunts. Darwin measured the speed of a giant on one island as sixty yards in ten minutes, which translated into "four miles a day,—allowing a little time for it to eat on the road." Many of them marched from the high scrub forests where they fed on cactus and other vegetation to springs about eight miles down trail near the coast. He described near the drinking places "these huge creatures, one set eagerly travelling onwards with outstretched necks, and another set returning, after having drunk their fill."

Similar tortoises on Aldabra, the Mascarene Islands and the Seychelles of the Indian Ocean are isolated by hundreds of miles of open water, but appear to be different races of a single species which justifies its scientific name of *Testudo gigantea*. The record length for an upper shell is 49½ inches, measured in a straight line from front to back. From most of the islands where they were discovered three hundred years ago, they have been exterminated for meat and oil and by introduced dogs, pigs, and rats (which destroy the eggs and young). Knowing this, we were astonished and delighted while on the island of Zanzibar in 1963 to learn

The African pangolin is well armored against attack. It can crush biting ants and soldier termites between the plates if they creep into the crevices.

The loose quills on the tropical tree porcupine of Latin America are barbed and pull out easily from its skin. They tend to work into the flesh of any attacking animal.

that we could visit an island where some of the giants still plodded about. Out into the Indian Ocean we sailed to "Prison Island," a limestone platform perhaps twenty feet above sea level and fifteen acres in extent. We counted 22 tortoises, none less than two feet long and many almost four feet from front to back. In their armor they had no difficulty crashing through the harsh vegetation. Their well-worn trails went everywhere.

Except for the tortoises, a caretaker and his few goats, Prison Island is deserted today. A century ago it was a place of infamy, where Arab traders brought their Negro slaves to be examined and auctioned off to the captains of slave ships. The frame building with its cages for human merchandise and its auction block still stand. Near it are cement buildings intended to have greater permanency. For a while they served a leper colony, then the victims of other contagious diseases, and finally the prisoners of the Sultan. Now the cells are empty, but the tile roof remains intact, its gutters gathering any rain that falls and conducting it to cement cisterns at each end. The spigots have been broken from the bottoms of the cisterns, and whatever water enters at the top floods out at once into rectangular basins where people once came to drink.

No drop of rain had arrived for weeks, and the tortoises were thirsty. Several giants hung around each of the rectangular basins, now and then walking over to lower an outstretched head into the place where only dust remained. Nowhere else on the island could they get a drink, and none of the vegetation within reach offered a succulent stem or a leaf with moisture evident. From time to time a tortoise explored below an avenue of frangipani trees. Every blossom that faded and fell went down a tortoise's throat. We plucked a few branches with fresh flowers and proffered these to the great beasts. They sniffed the blossoms but declined them. Perhaps the perfumed petals are poisonous until faded, with milky juice like that dripping from the severed stems.

Determined to help the tortoises if we could, we explored their limited world more thoroughly. In a small shack, probably built by some fisherman, we found an empty can. With a pocket screwdriver we repaired a pump that remained connected to a deep cistern under the abandoned cookhouse. To our delight the system worked. But when the first canful of fresh water went splashing into the cement basin, we had to jump aside. The tortoises crowded in to get a drink, each crunching its heavy armor against its neighbor. And others at a distance came marching, their dull eyes directed at the spot where the precious water had been spilled. It was impossible for us to believe that they had not heard it splash, although Charles Darwin had satisfied himself that deafness afflicted all of the similar tortoises in the Galápagos Islands. These in the Indian Ocean hurried at the same slow pace, pausing only momentarily when one of us climbed to perch precariously atop its heavy shell.

Bringing more water, we tried to push aside a giant whose mouth was still gulping in great draughts and blocking access to the rectangular basin. We might as well have heaved against the cement wall of the prison itself. With a shove that would have started a steer or a horse on its way, we budged the tortoise not a fraction of an inch. Never has the weight of armor so impressed us, nor the needs of the ancient animal inside affected us more. We could not be sure whether the creature was 15 years old or 150. With scarcely a change in its way of life, it and its ancestors had yielded no more to neighbors while the dinosaurs came and vanished, while the whole continent of Gondwanaland (or Lemuria) sank and scattered in the Indian Ocean leaving only a few islands to mark its place. And we wondered how long the giants could continue in a world of men. Neither their old-style armor nor the seclusion they once enjoyed hold much promise anymore.

In the course of evolution, giant size generally implies a mistake. It gambles too much food and too long a life on each individual, as though a big body could do more than a small one for the good of the species. Except through accidents of chance, which allow some creatures to continue unfaltering and essentially unchanged for many generations, the brightest hopes for survival go to the small and the quick. The adaptable rarely rely upon a hard exterior that weighs them down. Instead, the darlings of fate are the daring who travel without encumbrance.

The fastest turtles today are those with soft shells, a pointed nose that can be used like a snorkel to breathe while hidden under water, and small, beady eyes watching in all directions. Until they were wiped out of Europe by glaciers of the Ice Ages, they were common there. Now the soft-shell of the Nile lives in ponds and streams from Asia Minor to the Congo basin, and other kinds find suitable places to live in southern Africa, southern Asia and North America.

Far more conspicuous are the pond turtles which emerge to bask in the sun. While letting its warmth spread through their bodies, helping internal processes (such as digestion) proceed more efficiently, they remain alert and ready to dive as quickly as any mammal could, to hide out of sight in the mud on the bottom. Somehow they escaped the glaciers, and now include nearly half of the kinds of turtles in the Northern Hemisphere, including the common pond turtle of Europe, the spotted, the painted, the red-eared and the map turtles of America, all of which can be found by the dozen at hatchling size in almost any pet store. If a reliable measure of an animal's assurance of a future can be found in its readiness to share man's home, his hamburger and thin slices of cold hot dog, then these turtles are the true candidates for a long posterity.

Once we tried to make a pet of an armored mammal we had heard about but never before met alive. Accepting the armadillo the way the Texan held it out to us—dangled by its powerful tapering tail—we realized at once that below the hard armor protecting its back and sides from head to thighs were muscles of tremendous strength. The animal must have been about full grown, for it weighed just over fifteen pounds. Although its brawny legs bore stout, sharp claws and several dozen small teeth showed between its tense lips, it made no attempt to kick or bite. Instead, it repeatedly curled into a "J" and straightened suddenly, throwing its weight downward so abruptly that we needed constantly to renew our grasp.

Released inside a closed room, the armadillo set out to explore the walls. With more intelligence than we had suspected, it identified the door but could not push it open. Time after time it wandered away, only to return to that one place where only wood stood between the animal and freedom. We watched, motionless, hoping that the armadillo would forget our presence and show us that its armor had uses other than to ward off attackers while rolled into a ball.

After about twenty minutes the animal exceeded our wildest dreams. Trotting for about fifteen feet straight away from the door, it stopped. It turned about. All at once it dashed back the way it had come, at top speed. About three feet short of the door—and without slowing in the slightest—the armadillo tucked its narrow nose between its front feet and hunched over sharply, converting its body into a projectile about the size of a basketball. CRASH! The quarter-inch paneling of the wooden door splintered and almost gave way. Hastily we caught the armadillo before it could repeat its trick and freed it out of doors. Left to itself, we felt sure, it would have broken through in one or two more tries. We didn't ask the carpenter to confirm this, but when he came to fix the panel he took one look at it, one at us, raised an eyebrow and asked: "Armadillo?"

Solely in the New World have mammals tested this particular type of armor as an aid to survival. But according to the fossil record, they began this unplanned experiment in their time of greatest challenge and opportunity. Right after the close of the Mesozoic era, when geologic forces expressed themselves by heaving up the Andes and the Rocky Mountains, the Alps and the Himalayas, and by elevating all the continents, spilling off the overlying seas, armadillos of various kinds appeared in South America. By the time climatic changes brought on the Ice Ages, giant armadillos as much as fifteen feet from head to tail roamed as far north as modern Texas. They must have weighed two tons or more. Today the largest exponent of this way of life feeds on carrion as well as snakes and insects in eastern South America, where it attains a weight of 130 pounds and a length from tip of nose to end of tail as great as sixty inches.

In the Old World too, armor plates for mammals have had their day. They once shielded the bodies, legs and tails of many species of pangolins. Today only four different kinds survive, all of them in Southeast Asia or in Africa south of the great deserts as far as Swaziland. We met one of these strange creatures early one morning in the Orange Free State, where it was using the hooked claws on its powerful forelegs to rip into a termite mound. Intent on its breakfast, the pangolin did not see us. Most of the time its eyes, nostrils and tiny openings to its ear canals remained tightly closed, shutting out the termites which scurried from their ruined galleries over the pangolin's head. Its long slender tongue darted snakelike into the narrow passageways, capturing the insects with a sticky saliva. Counterbalancing and bracing itself with its long tail, it stood mostly on its back legs while reaching with the front pair ever deeper into the termite nest.

We touched the pangolin's outstretched tail, and jumped away—needlessly. The animal sought only to protect itself by quickly bending its head against its chest, clasping its arms over its unarmored snout, and curling itself into a tight spiral with its scaly tail on the outside. Since we made no further move, the pangolin slowly relaxed. A dull black eye peered out from behind its arm. Seeing nothing to alarm it, the pangolin unrolled completely, stood up, fanned out its scales (each more than two inches across) and shook itself, then returned to its attack on the termite mound.

Resembling only a giant, animated pine cone, each pangolin ordinarily hides in a burrow or a hollow tree during the day and emerges to hunt for insects at night. Biting or stinging ants or soldier termites that crawl down between the overlapping plates of armor are simply crushed by squeezing the hard pieces together, and then are ejected when the pangolin shakes itself. According to local people who have taken time to watch these strange creatures on many occasions, pangolins can wash themselves with their long tongues, much as a cat might. But sometimes they let ants do the work. Settling atop an ant hill, the animal spreads its scales and waits until the insects have scavenged thoroughly in every crevice. Going directly to an adjacent stream or pond and submerging itself, the pangolin uses the water to float out the ants, and emerges from its ant-and-water bath cleaner than it has been in a long time.

The solid scales on any pangolin add significantly to its total weight. Those on a large specimen of the biggest species in Africa measure almost three inches in each direction, grading in thickness from about $\frac{1}{8}$ inch where they join the skin to $\frac{1}{16}$ inch at the free edge, and overlapping nearly half their length. The largest of these armored creatures weighs just under sixty pounds, with a tail equal in length to the body and head combined, reaching as much as six feet tip to tip. The tree-climbing species of equatorial Africa reaches only a third this weight and half the length. But its armored tail is prehensile, and its scales rimmed with sharp teeth which help the animal cling to the trunk or branches while ripping with its front feet into a nest of ants or termites high above the ground.

Even after a person has become acquainted at first hand with pangolins and armadillos, it seems strange to see a mammal armed with scales and horny plates that overlap. Protection of this kind is so much more common among reptiles and fishes that we tend to be surprised when the same adaptation of the skin turns up elsewhere in the animal kingdom. But according to anatomists, hairs evolved in association with scales on the bodies of ancestral mammals. Generally the scales have been lost, perhaps as an unnecessary burden. On the tail of a rat, hairs and scales persist in just about the same arrangement as during the remote past when dinosaurs were still the conspicuous animals on land.

Yet hairs need not be soft and flexible. They too can provide an armor for mammals, either joined together into stiff solid spines as in hedgehogs or separate, hollow, barbed near the tip and easily detached as in porcupines. Now that we have encountered both types of animals in their widely separate homelands, we find each adapted as dramatically as the other. Since few predators can get past the defensive hairs, both hedgehogs and porcupines might be expected to live to a ripe old age, produce many offspring, become exceedingly abundant and be represented by many species all over the world. Yet with all the insects and worms on land available to them as food, barely more than a dozen different kinds of hedgehogs manage to survive, and some of them live in virtual isolation. Twenty kinds of porcupines find the plants they like to eat in the Old World, and twenty-three kinds in the New. Rarely are two individuals found together except at mating time, or until the young of the year are weaned. Could it be that a body covered with prickles goes with an unsociable disposition? Or, once safely behind a barrier of sharp spines, did these animals cease to be pushed on toward further evolution?

Hedgehogs remain widespread in the Old World from the British Isles to eastern China, including northern Africa and, circuiting the rain forests of the Congo basin, southward to Angola. Members of most kinds attain a length of about ten inches. A female may produce her first litter when she is a year old, and more babies every six months afterward. But while four offspring is a common number and seven a possibility, only one may be born at a season or none at all. Families as small as this ordinarily correspond among animals to an unusually low rate of mortality, and often to individuals reaching a great age. Yet a hedgehog six years old appears to be a patriarch, perhaps losing its spines and then its life. Baldness is fatal among these animals. Once their armament hardens, a few hours after birth, they rely upon it completely.

One reaction serves to save the hedgehog's life when it is frightened by a touch or a sudden noise. (It prepares itself in the same way for sleep during the day or for dormancy during the winter or a dry season.) Arching its back and constricting special muscles that pull its strange coat around it, the animal partly erects its spines and purses the armament into a prickly ball, slightly longer than wide or high, with only a narrow slit below through which to breathe. Legend holds that foxes roll hedgehogs into any nearby pond or stream and seize the victim by its unarmed undersurface as soon as it unrolls to swim. Remote from water the hedgehog is safe, its white-tipped chocolate-brown or black spines pointing irregularly in all directions.

European children find hedgehogs hiding for the day under vegetation and in shallow burrows. They learn that the little animals are harmless and somewhat helpful, eating beetles, grubs, slugs, worms, mice and young rats, as well as occasional newborn rabbits, birds' eggs and hatchlings that are on the ground, and sometimes garden fruits or vegetables. Hedgehogs often visit the back porch of a house in which a cat lives, to drink whatever milk is left in the pet's plate and to eat the cat's food. Cats look on with obvious annoyance. A dog may bark furiously at the

The mudpuppy *Necturus* retains its gills when it develops lungs and remains aquatic, breathing air only when summer droughts make the water foul.

On remote islands in the Indian Ocean, as also in the Pacific off the coast of Ecuador, giant land tortoises have survived from ancient times—an endangered type of life.

intruder. But friends showed us how to boost a hedgehog with a broom, or to pick up the animal gingerly by taking hold of several spines together between thumb and forefinger in each hand and lifting it. (We have had these experiences also in New Zealand, to which hedgehogs were introduced repeatedly since about 1890 and where they are still spreading in orchards, gardens and tussock country.)

Hedgehogs climb poorly and rarely inhabit woodlands or forest areas. Instead, among the trees, the prickly mammals are porcupines. These large rodents are native to Africa from the Cape Province in the South up the west coast to countries along the southern fringe of the great deserts, and eastward in suitable areas of Asia Minor, Asia south of the Himalayas, high into Nepal and down the Malayan Peninsula to Sumatra, Java and the mountains of Borneo. In America other porcupines are distributed from Alaska and Newfoundland to the rain forests of the Amazon. All of these animals have powerful jaws and chisel-shaped incisor teeth with which they cut through the outer bark of trees to reach the nutritious layers underneath. Their large molars grind up the wood pieces, as well as the foliage and fruits they eat. But their sharp, stiff quills merely add a defensive armament on an animal that wears a rather ordinary coat of fur. Unlike a hedgehog's spines, the quills are hollow, barbed and loosely attached in the skin. Unlike a hedgehog itself, a porcupine may take the offensive to discourage its attacker, driving its quills so firmly into the face or paws of a dog or curious cow that the weapons can be removed only with pliers in a strong hand.

Traveling from tree to tree chiefly at night, porcupines remain active all through the year. They swim across small streams, dog-paddling along while buoyed up by their quills. If frightened on land, a porcupine in the open may gallop clumsily—but with surprising speed—to the nearest bush or pile of stones into which it can thrust its defenseless snout. With quills erect, the porcupine waits, always trying to keep its tail and its haunches and back with their long weapons toward an attacker. At the slightest touch on these parts of the body, the "quill-pig" backs up quickly, swatting its tail from side to side and often driving home a dozen quills or more. So firm are the short quills on the creature's tail that they will penetrate the hard wood of a broomstick.

The giants among porcupines live in West Africa. Perhaps their weight, as much as sixty pounds, makes climbing precarious, for they rarely leave the ground. The one species of porcupine in North America attains the same body length—about thirty inches—but only half the weight, and spends much of its life among the upper branches. Like a cat, it clambers up the nearest tree to escape danger. But woe betide any animal that follows the porcupine. With tail switching from side to side faster than a pendulum, the porcupine backs down on its attacker, forcing the pursuer to jump or be stuck full of quills like a pincushion.

Sometimes a porcupine becomes impaled with its own quills or those of a neighbor. We recall seeing one of these creatures with half a dozen quills projecting from its wrist. Every few minutes the porcupine took time off from feeding to scratch vigorously at the irritated area. But it could do nothing to remove them. Nor were we equipped to give first aid there in the rain forest on the island of Trinidad. Within a week or two, according to Dr. Albert R. Shadle of the University of Buffalo, those quills would work right through the animal's wrist between the bones and emerge harmlessly on the opposite side. Dr. Shadle had the courage to test this on himself when an animal he was handling accidentally drove a quill more than a third of its one-inch length deeply into his forearm. Just two days later, guided by the needle-sharp tip, the quill worked out of his arm on the other side and was pulled out easily. It caused no infection, real discomfort or disfiguring scars, whereas dragging it from the flesh against the holding power of the multitude of microscopic barbs would have produced agonizing pain.

Dr. Shadle maintains that any informed person can capture a North American porcupine barehanded, providing he has a way to securely hold down the animal while reaching under its tail. Seizing the animal from below at the base of its tail, a man can get a good grip where only long hairs are present. If these, and the tail inside, are grasped and pulled firmly, the animal makes no attempt to back up. Nor will it try to turn and bite, although its formidable incisor teeth could sever a finger. Instead, the porcupine strives only to drag itself away in the opposite direction. By the base of its tail, it can be lifted off the ground and carried from place to place without harm.

Left to themselves, American porcupines mate in autumn and females produce a single offspring. (The offspring is so well developed that it ordinarily weans itself and wanders off to become independent within a week. If a human infant weighed as much at birth in proportion to its parent, it would tip the scales at better than eighty pounds!) Only an animal with a fine means of protecting itself can afford to reproduce at so slow a rate. No doubt this explains why a single species of predator—the big tree-climbing weasel known as a fisher—can hold a population

of porcupines in check. We can scarcely regard the quills and the behavior that goes with them as being a particularly successful adaptation.
Rather than wonder why no more kinds of mammals follow this way
of life, rattling around in armor, perhaps we should marvel that as many
have found it suitable.

Most other mammals seem to gain more by escaping from danger
through speed and flexibility. If they must turn to defend themselves,
they use their teeth, claws, nails or hoofs, all of which are products of
the skin that are important in many other ways. Similarly, the horns
that gradually enlarge on sheep, bison, cattle and antelopes, or the antlers that grow afresh each year on caribou, deer, elk and moose, become
weapons only as a last resort. While arming the head for defense of the
individual or the herd, they provide marks of special significance to other
members of their own kind.

Almost everyone has had experiences that reveal this multiplicity of
roles. Often the incidents seem unrelated. A child plays with a kitten and
the kitten responds playfully. Then the pet is on its back, being tickled
and apparently enjoying the attention. Suddenly it tires of the game and
brings up its two rear feet together. Extending their claws, the kitten
reacts in a way that some day may save its life. With all its youthful
power, it rips those feet backward against the child's hand, and can easily
draw blood. These are the same claws and leg muscles with which the
domesticated cat climbs a tree or pounces on prey of its own. The animal's reactions differ little from those of wild cats, which also use their
claws as a last resort in self-defense and as tools with which to grasp.
Usually those claws reach their target an instant before the teeth make
contact, whether in the furious charge of a tawny lioness from the sun-
drenched grass of an African savannah, the unheralded leap of a striped
tiger out of the impenetrable darkness of an Oriental night, or the plunge
of a mountain lion from some American point of vantage onto the neck
of a hapless deer.

Those few hard products of the skin, when used precisely according
to inherited reactions, make the difference between life and death for
many a mammal. We'll not soon forget the evidence of battle shown to
us by a game guard on one of the great reserves of equatorial Africa. We
knelt with him beside the carcass of a full-grown lion. Why had the
animal become so gaunt and died? Its jaw hung in two pieces, although
the flesh over the wound had healed. Some hoofed creature—perhaps a
fat zebra or a lanky giraffe—had kicked in exactly the right direction at

the ideal moment. It had used all the force in its leg to drive its armored toe tip against the lion's head. The big cat may have been stunned by the blow, but it survived to die somewhere else, unable to eat without a way to use its teeth effectively.

On those same African savannas we finally saw in the horns of antelopes a significance that made their distinctive features understandable for the first time. Each kind of animal wears a style of horns at least as unique in pattern as the color markings on its head, body, legs and tail. Why, we always asked ourselves, should animals that face the same predators show such variety in the armor on their brows? Surely some few types must excel as weapons with which to drive off a lion, a cheetah, a wild dog or a hyena. The reason escaped us as we examined the wonderful details of habitat groups in major museums, seeing families of one kind of antelope after another. Nor did we ever ask our question in a form that brought a satisfactory answer from sportsmen who had stalked many kinds of antelope and whose home walls seemed to us a mausoleum of taxidermied heads, each from an animal that had worn it proudly until felled from a distance by the hunter safe behind his high-powered rifle. That each mounted trophy was a record for size, or at least a runner-up, did not explain why these hard parts on the head differed so greatly while the hoofs or the teeth of the same animals were so much alike except in size.

The answer dawned on us as we tried to see over the tall elephant grass that grew right up to the roadside, along twisting dirt roads that wound like canyons across the high country of East Africa. Always we felt apprehensive that a herd of antelopes or Cape buffalo or elephant would suddenly cross in front of us, materializing suddenly from the forest of grass stems. At intervals we stopped our small rented European car and raised our heads and shoulders through its sun roof while peering over the grass tops. This position elevated us by the height of the car's floor boards, and the car gave us some protection on all sides. Quite often from our movable observation post we saw the heads of antelopes as the animals stood on *their* hind legs and looked about.

We realized that each pair of horns could be identified as its owner turned in various directions. That the rest of the antelope remained hidden among the grass mattered not at all. And if we, with limited experience and only curiosity to impel us, could recognize a topi, distinguishing it from a sassaby, a lechwe, a kob or the several kinds each of wildebeest, reedbucks and gazelles, surely the antelopes themselves could do better. Seeing another of their own kind at a distance, they could head for it even while foraging among the grass. How better could these animals keep their herds together without constantly voicing some distinctive call which would invite predators from all around?

The elephants appear to have no need to raise themselves to see others at a distance. The grass, which is a kind of millet, grows only as high as an elephant's eye. Like gigantic boulders, the gray backs of elephants bulge above the grass, and their great ears flap in the open like doors blowing in the wind. If the animal hears anything suspicious, it raises its trunk like a periscope and sniffs the breeze. The faintest clue may induce the pachyderm to charge through the grass, ready to skewer an enemy with its tusks or crush it under bended knees, still holding its trunk high and trumpeting its displeasure.

When undisturbed, an elephant employs its tusks for many other purposes. They are digging tools for loosening roots, and may well have given man the idea for the first digging stick—evolving eventually into the plow. We have seen elephants standing beside a tree, as though for a noonday siesta, resting their tusks on a horizontal limb and hanging their trunks over the tusks. Until man began to covet those giant teeth for their ivory, and to kill elephants for those hard parts alone, the multiple uses of tusks may have served their owners well. Now they have become a liability which may drag the pachyderms themselves into extinction.

Somehow we are less impressed by a pair of ten-foot tusks together weighing 226 pounds on a 13,000-pound elephant, than by a pair of five-foot antlers weighing about 20 pounds on a 1,000-pound elk. Those on the elephant enlarge gradually over a period of nearly fifty years. Those on the elk are produced, discarded and replaced every year by an animal that seldom attains an age greater than eighteen years. With its armament it dashes through the forest, its antlers catching on low branches. With them it can leap over a ten-foot fence.

In the high country of Wyoming we found and weighed a discarded elk antler with five points, then calculated the amount of lime it contained. Suddenly we realized how efficient an elk must be to extract this quantity of calcium from the food it eats and to secrete the material in its antlers of the year. Even if the elk browses on foliage containing twice as much lime as is in lettuce leaves (a rich source for man) and manages to gain fifty percent of the calcium present, which is a generous assumption, it would have to eat the equivalent of 50,000 large heads of lettuce annually—150 heads per day! Just to produce antlers of these dimensions adds to the cost of living. Antlers must be really important to an elk to make worthwhile the effort of secreting in the skin a new pair each year.

Antlers have become a status symbol, their size a measure of dominance. The elk with the largest rack held defiantly above his head has the right to more mates than any lesser male. Whether by battle or bluff, he wins a larger share in posterity.

chapter twelve

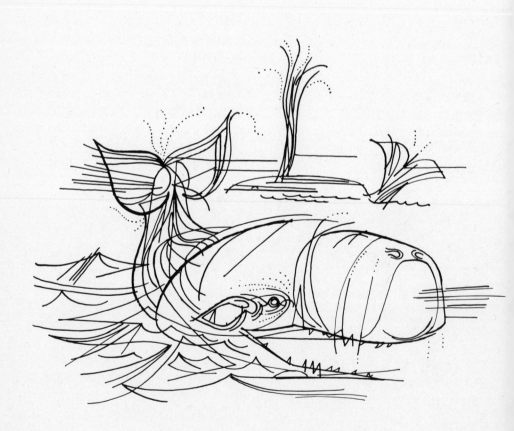

Life on the Fringe

THE place could have been a park in Merrie England instead of New England. The date might have been 1491, when only a forty-year-old captain from Genoa was dreaming of a royal grant for exploration, and no one had heard of Christopher Columbus or a New World. The stringed instrument would have been a lute instead of an electric guitar connected to a public-address system. But the song was the same. It told of Sir Patric Spens, who drowned "Wi' the Scots lords at his feet" on his mission to "Noroway," all because he ignored the warning of a superstitious seaman:

> I saw the new moon late yestreen
> Wi' the auld moon in her arm;
> And if we gang to sea, master,
> I fear we'll come to harm.

No one knows who wrote the ballad. But as the singer raised her young voice above the plucking of the strings, the new moon hung in the western sky above the audience and the loudspeakers. Back to our eyes came sunlight reflected from the earth to the "auld moon." Straight to our eyes came sunlight glancing off the thin crescent of the new moon itself, making it brighter than any star visible through the pale twilight sky. Did anyone wonder why the time of new moon brings special hazards for men who go down to the sea in ships? Or to creatures that live along the fringe of the ocean waters? No other time of the month tests so regularly the plans of men and the adaptations of unthinking kinds of life.

With a new moon always on the same side of the earth as the setting sun, the two pull together at our planet with all the force that keeps the moon and the earth in their distinctive orbits. The earth pulls equally in the opposite direction, and geologists can show that the strain deforms even the solid rocks and the plastic central core. But only the liquid water in the oceans and the greatest lakes is free to move enough to show. It piles up toward the moon and sun, producing a high tide greater than at any other time in the 28-day lunar month. Water floods over the land, opening passageways for boats and swimmers, drifters and flotsam, that will not appear again until once more the silvery crescent holds "the auld moon in her arm."

The water that makes the tide high at any time of the month comes from a quarter of a world away around the earth from the moon, lowering the level there enough to be recognizable as a low tide. On the side of the planet opposite the moon, where the pull of the earth's only natural satellite is least, the oceans maintain a more normal depth, described as a high tide of lesser magnitude. Around and around the globe the two high tides and the intervening lows circuit, due to the rotation of the earth, as the largest and slowest waves noticeable in water. The higher of the two highs each day comes a few hours after the moon attains its highest point in the sky, delayed this much by a combination of inertia, friction against the bottom, and obstacles to free flow provided by the continents and major islands.

About six hours and six minutes—a quarter of a lunar day—both before and after the highest tides under a new moon, the water ebbs away from the land more than ever. Mariners have reason to fear these low tides, for shoals block many navigable channels. Living things on rocks and in mudflats face exposure where otherwise they receive only the constant caress of the sea.

Tidal changes show least in the great lakes and around small islands far out in the great oceans. They become most dramatic where the continents restrict the flow of water and channel it into passageways that narrow toward the northeast. There the rotation of the earth tends to pile up the water, as it does along the French coast of the English Channel, in the Minas Basin of the Bay of Fundy and in the Leaf Basin of Ungava Bay. At the French port of San Malo and in Truro, Nova Scotia, the difference at new moon between low and high tide is often greater than fifty feet. This change in water level is at the rate of 8.3 inches *per minute.* A periwinkle snail would have to hurry to creep down and up this fast to remain at the surface. Swirling currents would tug at its shell most of the time.

Ocean water does far more than merely buoy up the creatures that live in it. It protects them from cold, never chilling below the 28° F. at which a floating roof of sea ice forms overhead. It saves them from excessive heat, rarely warming to 90° even in a tropical lagoon. It filters out the actinic rays of sunlight, particularly the ultraviolet, shielding plants and animals from sunburn or other chemical damage due to the radiant energy. Year after year it acts as a great balance wheel, smoothing out the changes in temperature day and night, summer and winter. It yields an abundance of water as a raw material for life, and affords at least some of every known chemical element. But to receive all of these benefits, each denizen of the sea must stay covered even when the new moon brings the lowest tides.

Only along the seacoasts do people need to take the tides into consideration. Otherwise we time our lives by the rising and setting of the sun and can justify our high esteem for its light by pointing to the seasons and to the fact that all of the energy used by living plants and animals comes from the sun. If we notice the moon, it is to see in its reflected sunlight an inspiration for romantic thoughts or, when its bright face shines toward the earth, a poor substitute for the sun to guide our feet at night. Yet, for all its size and radiance, the sun is 388 times as far from the earth as the moon and only a third as influential in changing the level of our oceans. For coastal people and living things close to shore, the moon is a potent force never to be overlooked. The paradox lies in the fact that when the moon disappears—the "no moon" stage of new moon—its effect is added to by the slighter gravitational pull of the sun, and the tides then become most impressive.

Few indeed are the sea creatures that can afford to ignore being exposed by the ebbing tide. As soon as the water grows shallower than about three inches, gulls are likely to alight and wade about, stabbing with strong beaks at anything that moves. Fishes of small size that remain in isolated pools can rarely elude the persistent, sharp-eyed birds. Worms that continue to expose themselves are snapped up. Thin-shelled clams may be swallowed whole or, if too large, carried aloft over the nearest coastal rocks or paved road or parked car with a steel roof, there to be dropped and smashed open. Even young horseshoe crabs in

Replacement of a lost large pincer with a small one, and of the smaller one with a new large pincer, changes right-handed fiddler crabs to left.

Ghost crabs, *Ocypode albicans,* change color, being pale when warm and dry or in daytime, and dark at night or when wet and cool.

their armor risk their lives if they keep on plowing like miniature bulldozers through the oozy surface coating a mudflat or sandbar once the
tide ebbs away. A gull can flip the crab on its back and break through
the thinner covering of the under surface. Yet, until recent years, small
fishes in nursery shallows and horseshoe crabs lost their lives at low tide
too infrequently to threaten them with extinction. Now the population
of gulls has increased enormously, nourished on wasted food in garbage
dumps. Man welcomes this free disposal of garbage and the policing the
gulls do for stranded fish along the coasts. But with the growth of this
aerial armada has come a marked decline in coastal fisheries and a growing scarcity of horseshoe crabs. Unless the fishes and crabs alter their
ways to avoid the gulls, they may disappear forever.

Most living things along the fringes of the ocean are already well
adapted to escape when exposed to air at low tide, to resist it, or even
to benefit from the periodic change. Crabs and other small crustaceans
hide below the limp hanks of seaweeds until the waves return and once
more buoy up the tethered vegetation. The dark blue mussels simply close
their shells tightly, each individual held to a solid support of some kind
(often another mussel) by fine threadlike fibers that fan out from the
creature's hidden foot.

Often during a low, low tide we visit the coast and clamber over the
rocks that are exposed to air only at these times. We used to be surprised
to find so many chitons and limpets clamped in place, heated and dried
by the direct sun. Why had these mollusks not moved fifteen or twenty
inches to the nearest tidal pool, or at least hidden under the rockweeds
instead of remaining so completely exposed? All of them were free to
move, if only each would relax the suction by which its foot held on so
firmly. Then we began marking individual chitons and limpets with waterproof paint, and revisiting the scene at other times of the tidal cycle.
Every animal, we discovered, ranged for several feet in different directions while under water, grazing on the thin film of green algae that
coated the rocks. Somehow it managed to return to its own favorite
place whenever the tide would soon expose the inch-broad area, or when
storm waves began to assail the coast. One site alone is home, even
though it is there that the water violently bangs the mollusk time after
time against its support. Whenever the tide is in and the rock is covered, the mollusk is almost sure to be dining elsewhere, its resting place
still recognizable by an elliptical groove worn into the hard substratum
by repeated impacts between limpet shell and rock.

As we explore this intertidal world, the greatest hazard is in slipping and tearing our hands or other exposed skin against the ash-white acorn barnacles. Their limy shells, resembling small, sharp-edged volcanoes, coat virtually every outcropping and boulder that resists the waves. In the crater of each cone, paired, limy doors are locked securely. They shut out the dry air and hold in whatever moisture the animal has space for. These doors open widely when the tide covers them, allowing the barnacle to reach out rhythmically with its six pairs of jointed legs to snatch for food. The motion can be imitated if a person whose wrists are taped together, palms facing one another, grasps quickly for a double handful of cranberries from among a hundred or so floating in a pail of water. The barnacle grasps for particles of food, then scrapes its catch out of the basketlike cluster of legs by means of the first pair of mouthparts, passing the particles to the jaws to be chewed and swallowed.

Many of the barnacles are cemented to the rock where they are immersed regularly only at high tide, perhaps for two hours twice a day. Below this their neighbors tend to be smaller, crowded, partly atop one another. Although they have more hours daily underwater to compete for food, they are in real danger of being smothered by others of their kind. Yet in many parts of the world, the densest populations of barnacles live above mean tide, where they are immersed for less than half of their lives. Toward the level of the lowest low tide, their numbers thin out drastically, and young individuals with a precarious future exceed the mature ones that have managed to survive. Barnacles face different dangers in the two directions, and succeed best when on the borderline between the devil of desiccation above and the predators of the deep blue sea below. Wherever the tide covers them with quiet water for too many consecutive hours, they are attacked by certain sea snails, some kinds of starfishes and a number of different fishes with jaws adapted to the crushing of limy shells.

As a barnacle grows it adds new layers of lime to the plates of its shell. But it is fixed for life to the site it chose while barely beyond the hatchling stage, still a free-swimming creature rather like a young shrimp. Apparently this sedentary habit in maturity began about 170 million years ago, and the juvenile barnacle is still repeating in its own way the transformation in habits that arose while dinosaurs were in style. Special adhesive glands develop at the tips of the swimmer's antennae, and the creature begins to express its inborn urge to settle down by seeking a suitable site. Within hours after it affixes itself, its armor of limy plates begins to form, its compound eyes degenerate (or actually drop out), and the barnacle has become the extreme specialist described by Louis Agassiz: an "animal, standing on its head in a limestone house and kicking food into its mouth." More than ever before in history, the world's rocky coasts support acorn barnacles in immense numbers, often more than ten thousand to the square foot and at least half of them mature. Their adaptations have made this an Age of Barnacles. Additional kinds are found attached to almost all floating objects, to the skin of whales and to solid supports even in deep water.

It is easy to see why, until well into the nineteenth century, everyone assumed barnacles to be a type of mollusk. Today, the part of the barnacle's body that secretes its limy shell is still called its "mantle," just as it would be if the animal were closely related to snails and clams. Yet in 1829 the British biologist J. Vaughan Thompson worked out the strange life history of barnacles and discovered them to be crustaceans masquerading in limy shells. Unlike other crustaceans, they molt only the armor covering their under surfaces and paired appendages, retaining their limy shells and merely enlarging them.

Thompson's discovery was only two years old when the young Charles Darwin boarded H.M.S. *Beagle* for the voyage around the world that was to keep him seasick and out of touch with scientific thinking for almost five years. It is most unlikely that he knew of the free-swimming larval stages of barnacles until after his return. Yet barnacles captured Darwin's attention in 1834 while he was exploring the coast of Chile, because he regularly found one kind growing atop another—and nowhere else. This association so intrigued him that he began an intensive study of all barnacles, and in eight years he made himself the world authority on these animals. On the basis of countless dissections, Darwin published two thick books and two thin ones between 1851 and 1854, describing all of the known kinds of barnacles more fully than anyone had ever done before. These monographs established Darwin's reputation as an independent scientist. From leafing through the volumes, we tend to think of barnacles now as "Darwin's animals," a sentiment that comes to mind when we see billions of these creatures along a rocky coast or find a bit of flotsam (such as a corked, empty bottle) supporting a dozen goose barnacles, each attached by its flexible rubbery "neck." Darwin's work comes to mind too when we straighten the papers on our desk, where the four-inch shell of a giant barnacle Darwin named *Balanus nubilis* serves as a paperweight. We collected it in Puget Sound, near

Vancouver Island, where Indians have long harvested the living animals for food. The shell shows how successful a barnacle can be where particles of nourishment are really plentiful in the waters that swirl by in every tide.

Along seashores with a softer bottom, whether compacted of muds or sands, a host of burrowing creatures pull down out of sight and away from the air as soon as their world is exposed by the receding water. Many of them are sedentary worms, some as much as an inch in diameter and three feet long. A few kinds of sea anemone inhabit vertical burrows and withdraw into them when the water drains away. Others in the intertidal zone are clams, ranging in size from the little coquinas to the giant gweduc.

Coquinas, known also as butterfly-shells and pompano-shells, delight anyone who stands barefoot where gentle waves wash up the sandy beach from North Carolina south and around the Gulf of Mexico. As the fringe of a wave passes shoreward, and the water clears momentarily, these half-inch pink or yellow shells lie strewn about where they have been washed out of the sand. Suddenly from between each pair of valves comes a pale tongue-shaped foot. It reaches into the sand and quickly pulls the little clam down out of sight. By the time the wave drains back to the sea, not a single coquina is visible.

On stormier days, the five-inch razor clams respond in the same way where waves expose them in beaches from Labrador and Scandinavia into the Tropics. From the end of the slender shells, the agile foot emerges, catches hold, tilts the razor clam vertically, and drags it down inch by inch before the next wave strikes.

The spectacular gweducs, found along the coast of the North Pacific from Oregon to Alaska, are the largest of the world's burrowing clams. The strange name, pronounced "goo-ee-duck" and often spelled "geoduck," comes from the Nisqually Indian word meaning "to dig deep." Adult clams are most numerous four feet down in the mud where the bottom is exposed only by the lowest tides. Each gweduc continues to exchange water from which it has filtered out all particles of food for a fresh supply through a four-foot "neck," which protrudes slightly from the muddy bottom unless touched by air or some animal that might attack. Then the big clam withdraws its "neck" (siphon) and waits.

During one low tide at Gig Harbor, Washington, we joined an energetic family from Tacoma who were using all their wiles to harvest the legal limit of three big gweducs per shovel before the tide returned. As the water reached its lowest level, the children scouted for shallow pools where a gweduc continued to spout like a miniature fountain. When they found a big one the father placed a V-shaped wooden frame gently as a whisper, to deflect any further water draining down the wet slope, keeping it out of the hole he was about to dig. No vibration of the mud must alert the unsuspecting clam until the gweduc hunter was ready to shovel at top speed. At the first touch of his tool to the mud a foot away, the spurting siphon vanished. Cutting out an imitation of a cylindrical post-hole, the digger avoided its center and cleared away the mud as the sides continually caved in. Two feet down. Three. And then the short-ened "neck" of the big clam came into view. Two inches in diameter at the tip, a foot in length, it expanded in a rapid taper as though to a pair of shoulders where it reached the body itself. The gweduc is far too large to be covered by its two limy valves, each of them eight inches long and four wide. Instead, its appearance suggests a headless, legless chicken with clam shells in place of wings. This illusion remains unharmed where the shells meet at the hinge line along the back. It gapes widely where the "breast" of the clam (its mantle edges) protrude—smooth, plump, firm, colored like a roasted fowl, and grading gradually into the wrinkled "neck."

Young gweducs have almost no shell when first they settle from a brief swimming life and burrow into the mud. Fishermen often mistake them for sea worms. Perhaps most of those that begin their sedentary existence where the daily tides expose them for an hour or more each day get caught by gulls and other birds. Certainly the survivors are rare above low-tide mark, and live mostly along this fringe of ocean at its tem-porary lowest. Like the far smaller quahogs and little-necked clams of the Atlantic shores, the gweducs may slowly work their bodies deeper into the mud as they grow. But they lose their lives if exposed by some change in currents or a particularly violent storm that transports the bot-tom sediments. Only while very young have they the body form and the inherited reactions to let them dig a new home. Thereafter they are as fixed as a barnacle, as dependent upon the vagaries of food supply in this final site, and as ready to shut off connections with the outside world when threatened by disturbance or desiccation.

On some of the islands in Puget Sound, excavators have uncovered evidence of a different hazard to burrowing clams. In the exposed earth lie hundreds of gweduc shells, every one upright in its normal position, exactly where the big clam died when the sea above it unloaded a great thickness of sandy gravel. The addition must have come in a matter of days or weeks, too fast for the clams to move vertically upward and retain connection through their extended siphons with the world of water. Entombed in these strata, they became fossils, only discovered many years later after local movements of the earth elevated the whole area to form the islands in which man now digs cellars.

So many changes in the world must affect creatures hidden in mudflats and tidepools. They depend upon the regular return of the sea water and are endangered if anything interrupts it. A storm, throwing up a sandbar, can isolate a lagoon for a week or a month. Summer's sun and dry air will evaporate much of the water, concentrating the brine until it becomes poisonously salty. Summer's thundershowers may dilute the lagoon waters until they are almost fresh. For this too, most sea creatures are ill-adapted, unprepared. They die, leaving the lagoon to be colonized by different kinds of life. Or it may wait, as a place of death, until once more the sea sweeps away the sandbar and lets a new assortment of marine life move in while the tide is high.

Few indeed are the animals that emerge from their burrows at low tide and sleep while the water covers them. Most of them are fiddler crabs, which scavenge by the hundreds, always alert to run for the nearest hole at the appearance of a gull or a person. The "fiddle" is the oversized pincer that each male brandishes on one side, as a counterpart for the small pincer (the "bow") on the other. Males wave their big pincers like semaphores, signaling their maleness, their species and their readiness to mate. Females, which have two small pincers and use both like hands to pick up particles of food, recognize males of their own kind and the message the "fiddles" convey. If a fiddler male is pursued, he sidles this way and that, always holding his big pincer ready as a weapon. Many a dog has come too close and been seized by the nose, only to have the crab lock its pincer in place and shed the whole appendage. While the dog yelps and strives to free itself, the fiddlers make good their escape. At the next molt, the male replaces the self-amputated "fiddle" with a new bow, and the small claw is replaced simultaneously by a new large one. A left-handed male has become right-handed, or conversely, and must change his habits accordingly. This adaptation is called upon so frequently that at any one time in every population of fiddler males, half are right-handed and half left.

Mated female fiddlers carry their developing eggs a while, then launch the hatchlings into the sea where waves carry them off for a period of wandering. As the survivors grow older they become large enough to dig their own high-tide shelters in some shore. At the same time progressive changes in their adaptations require them to leave the water. In the spe-

Young sea turtles, hatched in the upper beach, must reach the safety of the sea at night, before gulls can see to attack them on land.

A young wedge-tailed shearwater almost ready to take off on its own from the South Pacific island where its parents fed it in a burrow, then deserted it on schedule.

cial chambers at each side of the shell, their gills shrink to uselessness. To keep from drowning the fiddlers come ashore, letting the water drain from the chambers, which then serve like lungs in exchanging carbon dioxide from the blood for oxygen from the atmosphere. Twice a day, while the tide is in, each fiddler crab in its burrow gets soaked thoroughly, insuring that all surfaces of its gill chamber will be moist and active for gas exchange. If prevented from wetting itself in this fashion, the crab soon dies of desiccation. So intimately is the creature's way of life linked to the tidal rhythm that even the coloration of its body changes according to the interaction between the solar and lunar cycles. A fiddler is darkest for a low tide at night, and is pale as sun-bleached ivory while daylight penetrates a high tide at noon.

Along the world's warmer coasts at night, the fiddler crabs are joined in their scavenging by ghost crabs, many of larger size. Sometimes still larger crustaceans hurry from farther inland, rushing down to the water and then back where they came from. As we watch all these comings and goings in the light of a flash lamp, we see among the different adaptations the limitations of fiddler crabs and the reason why they are so tied to the intertidal shores of the world.

The oversize pincer on a male fiddler is a trademark with a penalty. It develops at an early age because the pincer enlarges, molt after molt, far faster than the body of the animal. On the largest fiddler crabs, which live in the Tropics, the "fiddle" on a full-grown male weighs seven-tenths as much as all the rest of the individual combined. To wave such a huge appendage at a female, or to brandish it in self-defense, becomes a juggling act which threatens constantly to get out of control. A larger fiddler, with a still bigger claw, can scarcely be imagined.

Ghost crabs carry pincers of more nearly equal size, which grow barely faster than the body. These animals dig U- or Y-shaped burrows in the dry beach, and actually hibernate among the dunes at the northern limit of their range. The larger the crab, it seems, the farther it can go from the sea. Within its bulky body it carries a greater load of water, while exposing scarcely more surface from which to lose moisture by evaporation. Yet active ghosts must visit the edge of the tide once or twice a night, to wade into a wave that comes high on the beach and wet the empty gill chambers they use in respiration.

Land crabs of the Tropics grow still larger and become emancipated even from a nightly dunking. They climb the humid mountains on small islands, thousands of feet above sea level, and return to the coast only when the females bear eggs that are about to hatch. Then the sea-beach at night becomes a congested thoroughfare. Clattering and rattling against one another, the shoreward contingent comes, clambering over obstructions rather than going around them. Once in the water, each female lowers her apronlike abdomen. Within seconds the minute, shrimplike young burst from the eggs and swim away. Back to the hills goes the parent. And months later, when the babies have reached crab form and larger size, they too leave the ocean for the high country, night after night, slowly and silently, noticed by few people in the darkness.

A surprising number of marine creatures migrate for great distances in the opposite direction, approaching the land or actually coming ashore briefly to place their eggs or bear their young along the fringe of the highest tides. Mackerel and herring draw near to shore to mate and lay, but remain where the water shows its full salinity. In the Southern Hemisphere, a wide-ranging relative of the mackerels—the snoek—arrives each spring along coasts of Australia and South Africa to unload eggs or milt. These fish have fasted for many months while readying themselves for reproduction, and are too thin to interest a fisherman as food. But as soon as spawning is over, they feed greedily in inshore waters. By December, at the beginning of summer, they are fat and well worth catching. For six months the snoek remain within reach, and then abruptly vanish into offshore waters, not to be seen again until the following September when the moon is new.

Caplins and grunions, both fishes of the smelt family, time their travels shoreward with outstanding precision. The caplins wait offshore at night for the highest tides of spring around Greenland and other arctic coasts of the North Atlantic. When the time is exactly right, hundreds of these eight-inch fishes swim with each wave right onto the shore. Loaded with them, the water strikes and spills onto the beach. In just that instant the fishes discharge and fertilize their eggs and turn with the same wave, to be carried back to sea. Sand churned by the wave settles again atop the eggs. But laymen and scientists who watch this amazing performance agree that, with so many fishes participating, the beach becomes a "quivering" mixture of sand and eggs—well worth the attention of hungry animals next morning. Yet millions of the embryos remain undiscovered, developing in the sun-warmed sand, readying themselves for the high tides that come two weeks later when every little fish must pop out into a wave and ride it into the cold seas offshore.

Along with thousands of other people, we have watched a similar spectacle along the beaches of southern California, when the grunions provide the free entertainment. On the nights following a full moon in March, April, May and June, these six- or seven-inch fishes swim into shallow water and, as the high tide begins to recede, let the waves throw them ashore in little groups. The central performer is always a female, who wriggles her tail into the wet sand until only the front third of her body is exposed. While she lays her eggs, several males arch themselves around her and flood the sand with their milt. By the time the next wave washes in, half a minute later or less, the eggs have been fertilized and all the grunions are eager to wriggle and swim out into the dark sea.

The lesser tides that follow may wash an extra layer of sand atop the buried eggs so that they come to lie four inches below the surface—not just two. There they are better protected from changes in temperature, desiccation, abrasion and the beaks of birds that probe the sand, as curlews and godwits do. Like the caplins, the young grunions grow rapidly toward their one chance, two weeks later, when the slightly higher tides of a new moon knock upon the beach and roll out a liquid carpet to the open ocean.

The fossil record tells nothing about the steps by which caplins and grunions achieved their modern ability to match their reproductive runs so perfectly to the high tides at night. The habit can be successful only along coasts where the highest tides occur in darkness, after birds that feed on fishes have gone to sleep. We can only wonder whether some quirk inherited by smeltlike fishes prepared these particular two species for taking advantage of the tidal movements they encountered. The quirk, if not the habit, must be older than the continents for caplins to act this way in the northernmost Atlantic Ocean while grunions behave so similarly along the eastern fringe of the Pacific. Perhaps these fishes developed their pattern of behavior as an adaptation that was necessary for survival when birds first evolved from reptiles and began patrolling the shorelines every day.

Armored animals can be credited with following a similar schedule for a far longer time. Fossil horseshoe crabs so closely resemble those of the present that their habits probably differed only in minor details. Today these creatures respond to spring by crawling out of deeper water toward the shore, there to pair up and continue feeding in the shallows until the appointed time. From Yucatan to Key West in the Gulf of Mexico, and up the Atlantic coast to the Bay of Fundy, the horseshoe crabs detect when a new moon floods seawater farthest up the beaches. Lumbering through the wavelets to the very edge, each big female "cow" crab drags her most successful suitor (a "bull") close behind her. With her hard shell like a bulldozer blade, she pushes into the mud or sand to excavate a crude nest. Into it she pours a generous batch of greenish-blue, translucent eggs, each about 5/64 inch in diameter. Her mate fertilizes them, and continues to cling to her shell while she moves on to dig again elsewhere. Only when all of her ten thousand eggs have been extruded does he forsake her. By then eels and other fishes may have gobbled up more than half of her output. Often they reach their heads right under the cow crab's shell and keep eating until they can hold no more. The crab pays no attention. By comparison with the antiquity of horseshoe crabs, soft-bodied fishes and birds are newcomers. They may become extinct before the crabs do, as did the trilobites, the nautiloid mollusks and the swimming dinosaurs.

From the Age of Reptiles only a token number of species remain to-day. Yet the survivors include turtles and snakes so perfectly adapted to life in the sea that they can swim across an ocean. The sea turtles pro-gress by languidly waving their flippers, each like a thumbless mitten. Inside the flippers are all the normal bones of fingers or toes, showing that the ancestors of these animals were creatures of the land. Periodically these marine reptiles swim to the surface to renew the air in their lungs, but only the pregnant females come ashore. The sea turtles pull and shove their bulky bodies high on the beach in the dark of night at the peak of high tide, and there dig a hole in the sand to be stocked with fertile eggs and filled level again. By daybreak the hidden nests and the broad tracks back to the sea mark this one brief visit of the year. Many weeks later the baby turtles work their way up through the sand and scamper as fast as they can go for the waves and open sea.

The sea snakes, which are close kin of cobras, appear to have evolved on the coast of the Malay Peninsula. They swam eastward to the limits of the Pacific Ocean, but apparently came too late to find a sea-level route into the Caribbean. Not since Pliocene times has there been open water separating the Americas. They spread westward across the Indian Ocean to the shores of Africa, and south to the limit of warm water.

Any new canal is likely to let the sea snakes through the land bar-rier posed by Panama. Any pause in the cold current northbound from the Antarctic may allow them to round Cape Agulhas and enter the South Atlantic. By either or both routes, these swimmers could find more tropical shores around which to scull themselves by means of a flattened tail, or to dive among coral reefs for small fishes, crustaceans and worms. Subduing a victim quickly with a potent venom and holding it in its jaws, the snake rises to the surface where it can breathe while swallowing its meal. Like cobras, the sea snakes seek out piles of debris for nesting sites. The females find suitable places just above the highest tide mark, where storms have tossed flotsam on the beach. Usually each pregnant snake places her eggs in darkness and returns unseen to the sea. After a month or two, baby snakes slide warily from under the flotsam drying in the sun and hurry to the water as though they had already spent far too long a time on land.

As we explore the coasts of the world, we grow increasingly impressed by the intolerance shown by the various living things that cross the tidal barrier to start new generations. None of the parents stays long in the ancestral environment to which they return so regularly. On the rocky shores of Alaska and the Aleutian Archipelago, the fur seal mothers scarcely wait until their pups are weaned before leading them into the ocean. The big bull seal is still standing guard, shrinking visibly from his prolonged fast and increasing thirst, but making the land a safe place to bear young. He will remain until the last of his cows has left to teach the offspring to catch fish and squid in the open ocean. Nothing on land interests him beyond protecting his harem from other bulls. Everything he wants comes out of the sea.

Similarly, the petrels and shearwaters converge almost surreptitiously from the far reaches of the oceans to make their landings and dig their nests in darkness on remote islands off chilly coasts. They come only if they have business to attend to—a solitary egg to be laid and two birds to attend it. Whether in the turf of a storm-swept rock off a bleak shore of the North Atlantic or on a tiny islet somewhere between Australia and Tasmania, these birds meet their reproductive responsibilities as though prisoners eager to escape. Each nightfall the parent birds change places. One with a full crop sings plaintively while navigating with extraordinary skill to reach the other bird in the burrow. The greetings are brief, the relieved bird departs, the arrived one settles down to incubate the egg or regurgitate much of its fish to stuff the single chick.

So much food is forced upon the baby petrel or shearwater that it becomes a butterball whose covering of down slowly sprouts the appropriate feathers. Somehow the parents judge when their youngster is loaded with enough nourishment to complete its growth untended. Thereupon they desert it. Eventually, when its body is ready and its hunger really insistent, it must find its way alone over the most terrifying precipices into the rough seas that churn below. Only its inherited behavior can guide it and afterward teach it to catch fishes and escape starvation. How much of these ordeals in its youth does the bird recall a few years later, when its inborn guidance brings it flying back with a mate to the same rocky island to repeat the performance for another generation? We wish we knew.

For any living thing to cross the tidal barrier and make itself permanently at home on the other side requires many an adaptation in addition to tolerance. Apparently the direct route from sea to shore has never provided to any plant or animal quite the right stimulus for it to add adaptations and gradually make the full transition. It looks so easy to rise with the tide and stick. It simply has not worked out that way. And we think of a comment by one of our favorite mentors, the late Dr. William Beebe: much of the intertidal zone is the "wildest place left in the world, the truest no-man's-land," where no one can stay for 24 hours at a stretch unless "anchored and in a diver's suit."

Whales seem unique in having moved in the opposite direction, escaping from predators on land into the seas of Eocene times, growing progressively better fitted for life at sea until they no longer had any need to return to land. Not only did they achieve this transformation, but they competed in their new environment with outstanding success. No creature of the seas strikes more terror into a seal or polar bear or man on an ice floe than one killer whale, unless it is a group of these sharp-toothed, intelligent, ferocious monsters. No hunter of the deeps excels the sperm whale, which dives to tremendous depths and catches giant squids despite their speed, their powerful sucker-studded arms and their formidable beaks. No animal on earth has ever grown so large (or so quickly) as a great blue whale, filtering its food from the open ocean. Perhaps whales would have been exceptional no matter how they invaded the world of water.

For other kinds of life, the avenue from and to the sea has been more circuitous. It has led through the brackish water of estuaries, where the salinity changes almost constantly. In this change has come the challenge that led to progressive adaptations, allowing marine life to invade the rivers, the lakes and then the land. Similarly, plants and animals from fresh water have spread into the sea and colonized it. An estuary tests tolerance in many directions, and offers its wealth to creatures that remain adaptable. It absorbs the tides and dissolves the fringe that elsewhere poses a barrier between the salt and the fresh, the water and the land.

chapter thirteen

The Tempting Land

S OME 400 million years have passed since our ancestors relinquished their aquatic way of life to gamble their future on the precarious land. But once firmly ashore, they clung to the soil and plants that grew there as tenaciously as any farmer. Today our imagination boggles at putting ourselves in their place. No matter how we peer through the surface of a sea or lake, a pond or running stream, the creatures we see swimming and creeping over the sunlit bottom are too different from ourselves. Yet to them, as to our ancestors long ago, the land remains a forbidding, tempting realm. It is swept by dry air and offers scant protection from the sun's rays or from devastating changes in temperature. Wherein lies its seductive charm?

High on many a lofty mountain, we can find little lakes as uncolonized by living things as were the rivers and streams, the ponds and other fresh waters back in Ordovician times. At intervals the burning sun penetrates the crystal depths of these alpine lakes, brightening white stones sixty feet or more below the surface but scarcely warming the icy water. Reflecting the swift-changing patterns in passing clouds, the lake remains perfectly clear right to its shores, where the biting wind snaps wavelets against the clean pebbles with a glassy clatter. Never does a green film of algae coat the rocky bottom. This meltwater from snow-fields, tarrying briefly before spilling down the mountain slopes, is too

153

pure to support life. Until it has associated a while with solid earth, trickling and splashing from rock to rock, it contains almost none of the dissolved salts that take the place of vitamins in the nutrition of all green plants. Without plants, the lake lacks animals, except for an occasional prospector such as a duck or a loon, a diving beetle or a waterboatman bug. Finding nothing to eat, they soon fly off again.

Fresh water is scarcely more hospitable to life than land. By the time it has dissolved the nutrients needed by green plants, it usually also carries so many particles of rock eroded forcibly from the land that sunlight can penetrate far fewer inches through most lakes and rivers than through the open sea. The green plants, upon which all the truly aquatic animals depend for food, get enough light for growth only near the surface. In Lake Michigan, for example, two-thirds of the plants and animals live in the topmost seven feet of water. The others are scattered through depths too dark for photosynthesis, all the way to the oozy sediments on the bottom, and include the bacteria that carry on decomposition there.

People who spend their days in a terrestrial world seldom realize how shallow are the depths to which daylight penetrates at intensities that allow green plants to grow. Not until 1865 did anyone devise a way to measure the transparency of water to sunlight. Then an Italian astronomer, Brother A. Pietro Secchi of the Jesuit order, began lowering from a small boat a flat disc like an imitation star. Painted white and eight inches in diameter, it hung from a cord tied to its center. From markings on the cord, Secchi read the depth at which his disc vanished from sight. Then he hauled it slowly toward the surface and read the depth at which the disc reappeared. The average of the two readings corresponds to the level at which the overlying water has absorbed or scattered about 95 percent of the sunlight, leaving only five percent to shine back from the Secchi disc. Measured in this way, the still waters of Oregon's Crater Lake reveal an astonishing transparency, almost equal to that of the Mediterranean Sea. The disc remains visible to a depth of 122 feet, whereas in most lakes it would vanish in fewer than 55 feet. River water, which is still more turbid, often becomes so full of suspended matter at flood stage that a Secchi disc disappears when a mere half inch below the surface.

Those topmost seven feet of water in big Lake Michigan are virtually the only productive part. Failure of green plants to grow well at greater depths is due to the existence there of twilight and night conditions while the terrestrial world has plenty of light. On cloudy days, or when the sun's rays strike the lake obliquely in early morning and late afternoon, the amount of solar energy penetrating the surface is far less than at midday, and a Secchi disc vanishes from sight at much shallower levels. Once a person realizes how long is the night, how short and shallow the day for aquatic life, he sees what a tremendous gain awaited the green plants of late Ordovician times as they tested various sets of adaptations that might permit them to survive on land. If anything could tempt a plant, rewarding it for change, it would be a longer growing season and more daylight every year.

Any change as vast as for aquatic life to colonize the air-swept shores has a comet's tail of inescapable disadvantages. Each plant and animal on land encounters these same challenges and softens their impact through its own special features. No two sets of adaptations may be identical, but each combination unlocks the same terrestrial treasurehouse, opening its own distinctive door.

Probably the first plants to colonize the shores were green algae of the simplest kind, mere specks of color between the sand grains and atop each embedded pebble. Today their descendants occupy these sites, secure in much the same way that Henry David Thoreau was on the shore of Walden Pond: "Rich in proportion to the number of things which he can afford to let alone." They still require an extra tolerance for the heat of the full sun, a shield against the disrupting effect of its ultraviolet radiations, an ability to shift quickly from active growth to complete dormancy to match the vagaries of weather bringing them useful water or denying it to them. But they set no store in cells that cannot profit by the opportunity to reproduce, and never rise above the earth.

In the water that runs over the ground after every rainstorm and major melt of snow, sand grains and pebbles overturn and shift position. They bury millions of the living algal cells, which soon die in darkness. Dying, the algae become food for bacteria and other agents of decay, which release into the moisture between the mineral particles a wealth of simple, soluble substances—just the kinds that are so important to the nutrition of green plants anywhere. In doing so, the decomposers convert the sand and gravel into a fertile soil, giving it a dynamic future built upon a routine past.

Vegetation of greater complexity has lived on land since Devonian times, when the first soils added a slight token of hospitality for terrestrial life. These larger plants reach upward toward the sun, each one protected, supported and serviced by a multitude of cells possessing new

Representing the most ancient of land plants, the whisk-fern *Psilotum* grows from tree holes and the rotting tops of bald cypress knees in southern Florida.

When disturbed, a millipede curls up like a watchspring, protecting its feet and mouth which are more sensitive and delicate than its armored body.

adaptations that confer special abilities but simultaneously make them mortal. Out of the mainstream of evolution because they contribute nothing themselves to posterity, the vegetative cells provide a continuous epidermis, a variety of centers for production and storage of food, a number of stiffening structures capable of resisting the force of gravity and of modest winds, and suitable tubes in which important watery solutions can travel rapidly in parts of the plant exposed to air.

The epidermis that serves as a skin over a land plant consists of a single layer of cells fitting snugly together, secreting over the one exposed surface a tough film of inert cuticle which prevents loss of water into dry air and also helps shut out the sporelings of fungi that might invade as parasites. Yet if the epidermis were truly airtight, it would block the exchange of carbon dioxide from the atmosphere for oxygen produced in photosynthesis, and it would reduce the rate at which a green plant could capture useful energy from the sun. By another adaptation most land plants risk invasion and carry out the exchange of gases through a limited number of special pores which, because of their shape, are called stomata —the Greek word for mouths. Each stoma opens and closes according to changes in the amount of sugar in the two distinctive epidermal cells that suggest lips pursing and flattening. When light and water are both available, photosynthesis in these paired, lip-shaped cells increases the amount of sugar, opening the stoma and allowing gases to diffuse out and in. The shade of a cloud suffices to close the opening part way. A shortage of water, which is needed to make the guard cells plump, causes complete closure, often accompanied by a general limpness of the vegetation—the first step in wilting. But throughout every night the stomata all shut tightly, sealing up each plant while it waits for another dawn.

Despite the automatic action of the two cells guarding each stoma, land plants discharge through their open pores fully nine-tenths of the water they take from the soil. To a farmer who must buy irrigation water for his crops, this release of water vapor seems to be sheer waste. It lacks even the display value that a fountain or a geyser of equal activity would offer. Yet the moisture has already served an important role inside the plant, carrying in dilute solution the traces of mineral nutrients required for growth. Nor can most land plants be called inefficient in using water generously. In their native environments they have never found water to be so chronically scarce that, without special adaptations to conserve it, they could not grow or reproduce. Instead, the raw material in constantly short supply is carbon dioxide, the plant's sole source of carbon for synthesis of organic compounds. Ten thousand cubic feet of air contain only three cubic feet of carbon dioxide. To capture enough from so little, a plant must keep its stomata open for most hours of daylight.

Knowing that Indian corn is among the most economical with water of all crops man raises, we have stopped several times beside a road in the American Midwest to marvel at this superlative kind of grass. The agriculturalists know that during the three or more months of its growing period, each corn plant discharges water vapor at an average rate of four pounds per day. A acre of corn releases into the air on an average day about 350 tons of moisture, while adding to its own weight about 200 pounds of organic compounds. These include substantial amounts of cellulose in cell walls, plus all the other carbohydrates, fats and proteins of the living matter inside those cells.

To us it seems utterly incredible that an acre of corn plants can capture from the atmosphere the eighty pounds of carbon actually going into those new molecules of organic substances. Yet virtually all of it enters the open stomata during daylight hours, still linked to oxygen as carbon dioxide. To get that much carbon, the corn plants process a stupendous volume of air. Even if they were 100 percent efficient, they would require 12,100,000 cubic feet of it, which is the amount in a segment of atmosphere extending vertically for 278 feet above the acre of ground. If 33 percent efficient (which is still astonishingly high), the corn plants would have to pass through their stomata during the day the amount of air in three times this height—to an altitude of 834 feet above the ground. Only because of air movements we overlook on a sunny day is this silent magic possible, all aiding the "ordinary" growth of a familiar plant. In vain we look for human engineering systems that can accomplish so much with only sunlight for energy and no more than 350 tons of water daily to keep the premises livably cool! Even if a potato plant needs almost twice as much water as a corn stalk, we cannot regard it as inefficient in acquiring the carbon it needs for growth.

For a corn plant to conduct four pounds of water from the soil to the growing regions of the stalk, leaves and flowers from which pollen and fruit will develop, it needs an inner organization of outstanding reliability. Four pounds of water is four pints—two quarts. Yet in any cross section of the stalk cut with a sharp knife, not a single tube can be seen that might carry this volume. The only openings down which a slender pin might be thrust are air channels, serving to distribute oxygen and carbon dioxide for the respiration of tissues—particularly those of the roots below ground level. Liquids are moved in a multitude of tubules so fine that they are visible only through a microscope. A few in each of several dozen vascular strands perform this service, in some cases moving water upward as rapidly as 7½ inches per minute. For an animal this would be slow. But for a heartless plant it verges so near to the impossible that we can only honor the adaptations that make it routine.

In every bud and in the tips of each growing root we can discover with a microscope how the wonderful conducting tubes are extended and then go into operation. At definite sites specified by the plant's inheritance, new cells produced by cell division grow long and slender while other cells all around them remain nearly equal in all directions. This pattern of elongation and maturation has continued with few changes for hundreds of millions of years. It calls for those cells that are to carry watery solutions upward from the soil to add ring-shaped and spiral thickenings on the inner surface of their cellulose cell walls. Then the living contents of these cells are replaced by water, which forms a continuous column of liquid from end to end.

So subtle, silent and strong is the rise of sap in these tubular cells that until recently scientists sought in vain to account for what they could measure. Each plant appears able to apply pressure to the liquid in the system at the end nearest the soil, compelling water to move upward against the force of gravity. The solution zigzags from one reinforced tube to the next, traveling with surprising ease through the thin portions of the cellulose walls between the strengthening rings and spirals. But while water is evaporating in the small air spaces under the epidermis where cells are carrying on photosynthesis, the discharge of the vapor through the open stomata is enough to raise more watery solutions through the conducting system—like oil rising through the wick of an old-fashioned lamp to ignite in the flame. So simply has the plant taken advantage of its structural materials and the physical nature of water (particularly the cohesive strength and high surface tension) that most of the time it need expend no energy of its own to raise water high above the soil.

The earliest of all plants to use this conducting system attained a height of less than four feet. Fossils in Devonian rocks show that these plants consisted only of thick, branching stems embedded in the mud, lacking roots, leaves, flowers and fruits. Virtually the only vegetation in the modern world that still follows this ancient way of life are the strange little whisk ferns of Florida and warm coasts around the Caribbean. We find them in the great Everglades swamp, thrusting into the half-light in the shade of towering cypress trees. They grow in knotholes of bald–cypress trees and from bits of soil that accumulate where a palm frond has broken from the trunk. Wind carries their spores to new locations, just as it did those of the first vascular plants so long ago.

Recently we made a sort of scientific pilgrimage to the Scottish village of Rhynie, thirty miles northwest of Aberdeen. There in 1917, skilled fossil hunters found the earliest known remains of plants with conducting tissues, buried in some cherty hillsides flanking a broad, shallow valley called the Strath Bogie. We tried to imagine the place as it was during middle Devonian times, when the only land vegetation taller than a moss was shrubby, leafless greenery. No root had spread into the shallow soil. No leaf had yet evolved. Yet, if a space traveler had visited the earth when those ancient plants were in their prime of life, he would have had to look closely to discover the distinctive slender cells in which they raised water above ground level. He would have had to be extraordinarily astute to realize that plants with this feature would, within a few million years, rise hundreds of feet tall, grow in dense forests. Gradually they would diversify until they became the dominant land vegetation on all continents, from sea level to snowline on mountain peaks, from open lake to driest desert. And we looked around the Strath Bogie wondering what feature of modern plants might be a comparable talisman of success 400 million years in the future.

We shocked some of the Scots we met by wondering aloud what native plants would clothe the humid slopes if no sheep grazed there. Scotland without sheep proved unthinkable. At the same time, the herders admitted that pasture lands once rich in grass were being invaded rapidly by heather and other heaths unpalatable to sheep. Scotland was changing fast—for the worse in the minds of anyone wanting wool and mutton. Though the transformation of the hillsides was damaging their livelihood at a pace they could see, many of these men blamed the heather, the weather, the atom bombs, rather than admit that the grasses the sheep cropped so close and trampled with sharp hoofs could no longer compete successfully with any plant the animals avoided.

Recognizing something after it happens is much easier than predicting it far in advance. Time itself becomes almost meaningless for most people when viewed on a scale as vast as that in the fossil record. Changes within a thousand years stagger the imagination, making the Dark Ages one millennium ago almost unintelligible. Only the gnarled bristlecone pines on the upper slopes of the White Mountains in California have withstood the good years and the bad for 4000 years. But it would take 100,000 lifetimes of these patriarchs to reach back into the time when their ancestors (and the ancestors of all other vascular plants) were leafless, rootless, branching shrubs like those fossilized in the Rhynie rocks.

During the 400 million years since the Devonian, no other adaptation permitting life in the longer days on land has arisen in the plant kingdom, allowing its possessors to challenge seriously the dominance of the vascular group which comprise the one phylum Tracheophyta. The club-mosses, the horsetails, the ferns and the seed plants, which outnumber the nonvascular kinds of vegetation by about five to two, are all descended from the one ancestral type.*

Animals were far more versatile in their invasion of the tempting land. Members of half a dozen different phyla gained their own unique adaptations that let them colonize the shores of fresh water as soon as plants lived in air, providing food and perhaps a modicum of shade.** But oxygen, not daylight, provided the lure, rewarding creatures as soon as they could make the change from a watery environment to a terrestrial one.

For animals, the advantages in a breath of air surpass every other gain to be found on land. To terrestrial life of all kinds, oxygen is at least 1500 times as available as to creatures whose adaptations confine them to an aquatic existence. No animal of any kind can provide the truly phenomenal amount of energy required to split water molecules and free the oxygen that accounts for almost ninety percent of their weight. Instead, respiratory needs in water must be solved using dissolved oxygen, and this never attains generous proportions. Except where water has recently come bouncing down a waterfall, tumbling through a rapids, or been churned repeatedly by wave action, it is never saturated with oxygen from the atmosphere. More usually, it shows a variation picturesquely called an "oxygen pulse," which matches the release of oxygen by water plants engaged in photosynthesis. Concentration rises above the half-saturation point to a maximum about three o'clock in the after-

---

* Of all the species of plants that have been given names, about 296,000 are vascular plants in phylum Tracheophyta, and 118,300 are nonvascular in eleven other phyla.

** The flatworms, roundworms, segmented worms, arthropods, mollusks and chordates.

noon, then sags slowly to a minimum about seven o'clock the following morning.

Temperature affects the availability of oxygen for aquatic life in a way that has no parallel for terrestrial creatures. Chilled to its freezing point, cooling many creatures to the verge of dormancy and reducing their needs for oxygen to the minimum, water holds at half-saturation about 73 parts of this gas in each million of solution. At 68° F., when most underwater animals become around four times as active and need at least four times as much oxygen, their environment contains only 46 parts per million at half-saturation. At either temperature in air, the proportion of oxygen is 209,500 parts per million, as the 21 percent we have come to expect in every breath of air we inhale.

We terrestrial animals gain too in having our exhaled air renewed without effort on our part. Aquatic creatures either depend upon natural currents to replace the solution around their bodies, or they work like a worm in a tube or a fish gulping steadily, to insure that new water flows past their gills. This difference reflects the physical fact that oxygen molecules diffuse from place to place, expressing their kinetic energy of heat, 3 million times as rapidly in air as they do in water. So quickly do the gases comprising the earth's atmosphere redistribute themselves by diffusion that no land animal can ever breathe fast enough to use up the oxygen near it. Without any wind or other turbulence to stir up the air mechanically, molecular movements maintain a uniform concentration, letting each new breath bring the animal a fresh supply of the oxygen it must have to live.

Like the psalmist who bid "every thing that hath breath" to praise the Lord, we tend to overlook the incredible number of different animals that live in the soil, absorbing their oxygen through moist skins without exerting themselves for respiration. The gas they need reaches them too, penetrating as far down as burrows and roots go below the surface. Earthworms and insects use the larger passageways every day. Thin films of water coat the smallest spaces. Twisting tunnels with a diameter of ¼ inch or more often show where roots once were before they died, decomposed and slowly dissolved away. Forest soil is particularly riddled by passageways, which together amount to between fifty and sixty percent of the total volume. After each rain these spaces become temporary watercourses through which the liquid flows to deep reserves. As it gurgles through the soil, the water compresses the air in them, helping to redistribute it through smaller spaces. All of these events contribute to the

High humidity is necessary for a sowbug to be active, although it is a crustacean well-adapted to life on land.

fertility of the soil, sustaining the welfare of the living things we see above ground as well as of the dwellers in the earth itself.

We know the earthworms are there, and realize that they manage without lungs or other special adaptations for respiration. In their skins, red blood circulates through a network of microscopic vessels, pumped by half a dozen pairs of hearts. Between the blood and the oxygen in the air of the burrow, only the thin cells of the vessel wall and the skin and a film of watery mucus intervene. Oxygen dissolves in the water of the mucus and diffuses through the cells to reach the blood, much as it does through the lining of a human lung. Indeed, the smooth, slippery surface of an earthworm is its counterpart of a lung. Instead of being protected inside the body, the respiratory surface of the worm remains shielded most of the time by the walls of its burrow.

In temperate lands these adaptations combine into a successful pattern for survival of earthworms that grow to be a foot in length and the diameter of a pencil. All across Eurasia, down through Africa, in the Americas, and in some parts of Australia, similar worms follow the same way of life. Only Madagascar and a number of smaller islands remote from continents lack these creatures that swallow soil, digest out its organic matter, and cast the residue behind them. Knowingly though inelegantly, Aristotle called them "earth's guts."

Near the equator some of these segmented worms grow far longer—to as much as ten feet—and a few much thicker, making them spectacular animals, native wildlife with which to amaze a visitor. A few miles from Kingwilliamstown, in Natal province of South Africa, our hosts introduced us to some of these giants without warning. They took us in their car to where the road passed through some of the strangest pastureland we had ever seen, and led us on foot across a ditch, over a fence, and out into a field. Walking proved difficult, for alternately we skidded down and clambered up a grassy surface that was all hills and hollows. Crests rose about three feet higher than the troughs. Only in the depressions lay small patches of level land, each an irregular area of hard mud floor with scanty vegetation, as though sediments dropped by rainwater had recently buried the short plants there.

Fist-sized masses of brown-gray soil stuck to the ground between the taller grasses on every slope and crest. A few of these irregular knobs had a dark color and appeared damp. Seizing one, we snapped it off, only to see something vanish down a burrow underneath. We tried to be quicker with the next one. This time we managed to glimpse fully two inches of segmented worm, at least an inch in diameter and flesh pink, before it too disappeared into safe depths.

With a shovel we cut into one of the hillocks and encountered a maze of passageways almost large enough to house a colony of American prairie dogs. Our hosts just sat and laughed at us. They knew that, although we might cut the tail from one of the big earthworms while it was extruding a mass of earth, the creature would hasten deep into its burrow and later repair the damage. To capture an intact worm, we might revisit the pasture after a heavy rain, when these animals desert their tunnels in large numbers just as do smaller worms in temperate lands. Or we could come at night with a red flashlamp, when the creatures reach headfirst from their burrows to search for mates by touch. (All earthworms appear insensitive to red light. Other parts of the spectrum visible to us send them into the continual night of their branching hideaways.)

Our hosts assured us that if we dug a few inches below the surface of any of the depressions in the field we would hit a large, flat piece of stone which prevented the worms from coming to the surface. Between the rocks the animals piled their half-pound castings and progressively raised up a mound of loosened soil. Recalling the flagstones that Charles Darwin investigated in his English garden, we inquired whether anyone could recall a time when these particular rocks lay scattered on the surface of the ground. "Yes, indeed!" came the answer. Local people remembered that this land had been eroded badly by excessive grazing until less than 25 years before, when a farmer put up a fence to keep livestock out. The worms may have been there all along. But like those that Darwin observed, they warm themselves in tunnels made below any flat rock heated by the sun, removing so much earth below it that the stone sinks slowly below the surface. Flagstones in an English garden sink about a quarter of an inch a year until they disappear under a layer of earth that shields them from the sun. Thereafter the rocks cease to attract chilly worms that seek warmth without danger from desiccation or attack. Burial of the flat rocks in the South African field might be expected to progress at a faster rate because the worms themselves are so huge.

Soil contains more roundworms and flatworms than earthworms. The roundworms of the soil are all small, able to squeeze through the narrowest passageways by wriggling like miniature eels. Their slender bodies may be half an inch in total length, each with a fine, tubular digestive tract from end to end, suited solely to a diet of microscopic particles.

Bacteria and single-celled animals are taken whole. Very small insects, spider mites, bear animalcules and other diminutive denizens of the soil, are cut to size by the three formidable jaws that meet in the worm's triangular mouth. Products of digestion, like oxygen that has diffused through the moist body wall from the air in the burrow, shift lengthwise in the worm, dissolved in a clear fluid between its digestive tract and the longitudinal muscles with which the creature contorts itself and moves along.

Desiccation is the mortal enemy of roundworms and flatworms, since oxygen can enter only through skin that is moist. In the Tropics where the humidity is constantly high, and in greenhouses where similar conditions are maintained, flatworms on land are sometimes quite conspicuous. Each of them absorbs oxygen through a film of secreted moisture over its entire upper surface, and the dissolved gas has only a short distance to travel to the tissues inside. Below its body a terrestrial flatworm produces a thicker sheet of watery mucus as a liquid carpet upon which to float, propelled by the continuous beating of myriad short, hairlike cilia. A creature of this kind has no need for blood or any body fluid to take its place. No simpler animal large enough for us to see easily ever explores the land and exploits the atmosphere.

Flatworms of the land often wear brighter colors than their close relatives in fresh water. Their bodies may be green, brown or black and may be striped with yellow, orange or white. Among the most spectacular flatworms is a giant we have met in Florida, California and the West Indies, although it probably originated in the Indo-Malayan jungles. Named *Bipalium kewense,* it was discovered first in the orchid house at Kew Gardens near London. We can just imagine a gardener rushing off to find his superior, carrying at arm's length a big, wet flowerpot around which one of these fourteen-inch flatworms was gliding. Its inch-wide body is gaudily striped, its expanded half-moon-shaped head edged with dozens of minute black eyes. Thin as a piece of ribbon, the animal seldom rears up from the substratum upon which it searches for small prey and bits of carrion. Its mouth, in the middle of the under surface, opens into a blind digestive sac with branches extending to all parts of the body. Products of digestion go almost directly to the cells that need the nourishment.

Far more complex organs than are to be found in the body of any flatworm or roundworm are fitted into the smallest of insects. Yet if the insect is big enough to require more oxygen than can diffuse readily through its skin, it respires by means of branching tubes that are a unique, inherited feature of arthropods. It inhales air through special openings along each side of its body, into tubes that extend forward and back, out into its legs, even into its slender jointed antennae ("feelers"). Without depending upon circulation through its slow-moving blood, the insect brings oxygen quickly to its active tissues.

Insects share this adaptation with centipedes, millipedes and some spiders. But none of these others seems capable of sustained activity comparable to the prolonged flights of insects—flights after which the creature's abdomen pulses silently, ventilating all parts of its body in the same manner as is used while on the wing. Similar exercise leaves us gasping and puffing, our hearts pounding, our blood vessels throbbing with a rushing torrent, to circulate the oxygen we absorb in the limited cavities of our lungs.

A system of branching tubes seems ideally suited to an animal smaller than a big beetle—usually much smaller—if it is to take advantage of oxygen in the earth's atmosphere while following a terrestrial way of life. Gas diffuses readily in small tubes of a size that match a really small body, whereas blood is too viscous to move easily with a load of oxygen through vessels as diminutive as a house fly could contain. For an animal larger than a frog—usually considerably larger—air tubes would be inefficient because of the distance between the body surface and the innermost organs. A land vertebrate has a large enough body to spare space for blood vessels of generous size, in which red blood cells can rush along between the lungs (where the cells move slowly in fine tubes while being loaded) and the needy tissues (where the cells slide equally slowly through another set of fine tubes while giving up their oxygen).

In a very real sense, by adding lungs and adaptations to help ventilate them, vertebrate animals with a good circulatory system gained a way both to become terrestrial and to grow larger. At the same time in history, the arthropods that developed branching air tubes and adaptations to use them in breathing achieved a means to live on land and to evolve into smaller sizes. Some modern insects, when fully grown, are tinier than many of the largest kinds of single-celled protozoans.

Maturing at small size, insects and their close kin among the arthropods require rather modest amounts of food per individual. They can complete many generations in a year when conditions are propitious, evolving a little at each new generation. For example, the wild fruit flies (that have provided so much information about inheritance) mate and

The astonishing "gold frog" of Panama can be a brilliant yellow marked with black spots because its skin is highly poisonous. No bird tries to eat a second gold frog.

One kind of tree frog has become specialized to life in calla lilies that grow wild in its native South Africa, using water that collects in the funnel-shaped spathe.

lay eggs which then develop into new adults ready to mate and lay eggs, on a schedule that produces three generations in a month. Since 1912, when the study of genetics in these insects began at Columbia University, fruit flies have gone through as many generations and had as much opportunity to evolve as mankind has in the last 48,000 years—a date far back into the Ice Ages. Small wonder, then, that insects have become so diverse. In species they outnumber by three to one all the rest of the animal kingdom combined. They live in more different terrestrial situations, eat a greater variety of foods, and show a broader spectrum of habits than any other life on land.

Representatives of several orders among the insects have reinvaded the fresh waters, although most of them managed in some way to get atmospheric air to breathe. Water-scorpion bugs and mosquito wrigglers thrust through the surface film a special breathing tube that repels the water while they inhale a fresh breath. Water-boatman bugs and diving beetles capture a bubble of gas below their wings and use it as a trap for oxygen. These and other aquatic insects emerge into air to mate and reproduce. Often they require bizarre adaptations to place their eggs for hatching underwater, since the surface film may be too tough or hazardous for a hatchling to penetrate unaided. Quite clearly the water insects of today had ancestors on land for a long time during the past 300 million years. All insects are primarily terrestrial.

During the eons before any insects began secondarily colonizing the fresh waters, the forebears of fishes and clams in streams and lakes were supposedly developing special ways in which to exploit the resources available there. Yet nothing halted the insects, once they turned their hereditary adaptability to the challenges of invading. Into the already populated world of fishes and clams they simply moved, taking the food they wanted, escaping from predators more often than they fell as victims, just as though they had lived there all along. With their breathing tubes and short life cycles, insects continue to demonstrate this same superlative vitality and evolutionary versatility. Most recently these characteristics have helped them become immune in just a few years to poisons spread by man to protect his person and possessions. Countless old-style, susceptible insects died while the newer, tougher types kept on.

Only the sea has so far kept the insects from gaining more than a foothold. To colonize it too they would have to give up breathing air, and perhaps give up some other gains made on the tempting land. The oceans remain the domain of 25,000 kinds of crustaceans and 30,000 different mollusks, plus a wealth of every other phylum of animals. Through fresh water as a highway, both the crustaceans and the mollusks have sent some colonists ashore. Land crabs scarcely count, since their offspring must develop in the sea. But the oval, armored creatures known variously as sow bugs, pillbugs and slaters have adaptations that free them from a need to find liquid water at mating time. They breathe air, so long as it is humid, and find it among the leaf litter in forests, under soggy decaying wood, in our basement corners, and in the open on dewy nights. Thin membranes between their plates of armor provide for part of their respiratory exchanges. Additionally, their gills have become adapted, either to form overlapping plates concealing a lunglike pocket below the body or to possess internal branching air tubes, somewhat like those in insects.

The only mollusks that have taken to land are snails and slugs, each with a single lung. Their relatives are abundant in fresh water, where the gas in the lung is used in the same strange way as the air bubble that diving beetles hold beneath their wings. Always the animal keeps a small part of its captive air supply in contact with the surrounding water. Through this area of contact oxygen diffuses as though descending a staircase of concentrations. The top step of the stairway is the atmosphere, with 21 percent oxygen. From this level, oxygen diffuses downward into the water, dissolving until close to saturation in streams and shallow ponds. Near-saturation is the second step in the stair. It is far above the concentration of oxygen in the gas held within a snail's lung or a beetle's bubble, where the level is close to zero because the animal is constantly withdrawing what it needs. This is the bottom step. Oxygen from solution escapes from the water into the captive gas, constantly renewing the supply for the snail or the beetle without effort. Slowly, however, the nitrogen in the captive bubble dissolves into the water through the same surface of contact. The lung gradually empties and the snail must journey to the top of the water world to replenish its trap for oxygen. Often we see these animals rise to the water film, press against it, and suddenly open the passageway leading to the lung.

When drought dries up a pond or stream, many a freshwater snail is forced into air. But although it can continue to breathe through its lung, it is usually too completely adapted in habits to tolerate any substitute for an underwater life. Generally these snails creep into places of concealment as soon as they can find no open water, and soon withdraw into their shells, sealing the doorway with a sheet of mucus and remaining dormant until a flood of water somehow awakens them. Their close relatives, the land snails, may be equally intolerant of immersion. They need no more than moderately high humidity to remain active, and they reduce loss of water into the air by secreting a thin film of mucus over all exposed soft parts of their bodies. Only during the driest part of the day or of the year are they forced to hide inside their limy shelters.

Slugs have dispensed with even this portable refuge. Some merely grow much faster than they build a shell, and the hard part becomes overgrown by the soft tissues of the body. Others follow their inherited pattern by producing a shell during development within the egg, but destroy it by digestion after they hatch as though producing a shell originally had been a mistake. Nor is a slug limited by its nakedness to be a minute creature, hiding from the air and light under fallen vegetation and a coat of slime. Some grow to be eight or ten inches long, gliding through shady forests in broad daylight. They abound in the temperate rain forests of Olympic National Park in Washington which capture the moisture of the Pacific Ocean. We have found them too among the luxuriant vegetation on the slopes of the Ruwenzori range in Africa and in the Congo basin, and we have found individuals of only slightly smaller size in populated areas of Europe and New England. A velvety black slug, more than six inches long, posed for its photograph above the spectacular chalk cliffs on the Danish island of Møn. A golden yellow one, spotted with black in a handsome pattern, turned up in our own back yard in New Hampshire and had its picture taken while creeping along a big carrot.

Only once have we seen a slug demonstrate its ultimate weapon. It was provoked into action by having a young robin, understandably inexperienced, peck suddenly at the four-inch body as though the slug were a big worm. Instantly the unarmored mollusk struck back, ejecting fine jets of milky slime upward and outward in all directions like a lawn sprinkler. Several of the jets struck the bird about the head and chest, soiling its feathers and probably spraying into its eyes, partly blinding the attacker. The robin flew off with a screech. We hastened to the slug and prodded it gently with a twig. Again it discharged its jets of slime, but for less distance and a briefer time. It was running out of ammunition.

As we broaden our acquaintance with the plants and animals on land and consider how their ancestors made the step out of the fresh waters into the longer days and more abundant oxygen, we realize how few styles of creatures took the opportunity: two phyla of plants—the lowly liverworts and mosses, and the vascular kinds; a few in one class of flatworms—all of them turbellarians; a number of different members of the roundworm phylum; part of one class of segmented worms—the earthworms—and of one class of mollusks—the lung-bearing snails and slugs; two class of arthropod animals—the insects and the arachnids—and a minor part of one order of crustaceans—the sow bugs, and part of one class of vertebrates—the amphibians.

Just two of these types of colonists found conditions in their new, airy world to be so stimulating that they diversified into additional styles of life, not merely into a greater variety of the original emigrant stock. The rootless, leafless vascular plants of the whisk-fern style responded to life on land by spinning off the clubmosses, the horsetails and the first leafy plants—the ferns. Some ferns developed the seed habit and, within 100 million years, were recognizably gymnosperms ancestral to cycads and conifers. Flowering plants came later. Another 100 million years and grasses appeared. Each of these changes left its mark upon the land, altering and extending it as a place where animals might live.

The ancestral amphibians that pursued insects in the swamp forests of the Coal Ages gave rise to reptiles, and the reptiles to birds and mammals in the Age of Reptiles. Still more recently, perhaps no more than 3 million years ago, a twig on the edge of the mammal branch took a two-legged stance on the ground as man. In ways that would have defied prediction, the descendants of the ancestral amphibians that ceased to be amphibians changed the world more than did those that continued to vacillate between ponds and land.

Yet without the abundance of insects on land, how many of these other types of terrestrial life would have fared so well? While the insects diversified in one general style of efficient body, they provided the reward for new adaptations in both plants and animals. Under attack by hungry insects, the seed ferns of the Carboniferous became extinct, but not before their progeny included the ancestors of cycads and conifers, ginkgoes and flowering plants, whose adaptations protected the all-important seeds. Still later, toward the close of the Age of Reptiles when insects evolved a pupal stage (letting younger individuals become better adapted to feeding without hindering the better adaptation of adults to traveling in search of mates and places to lay eggs), some of these plants began actually to welcome insects that could help in pollination. So well did this partnership fare that plants with flowers quickly became the dominant vegetation on the land.

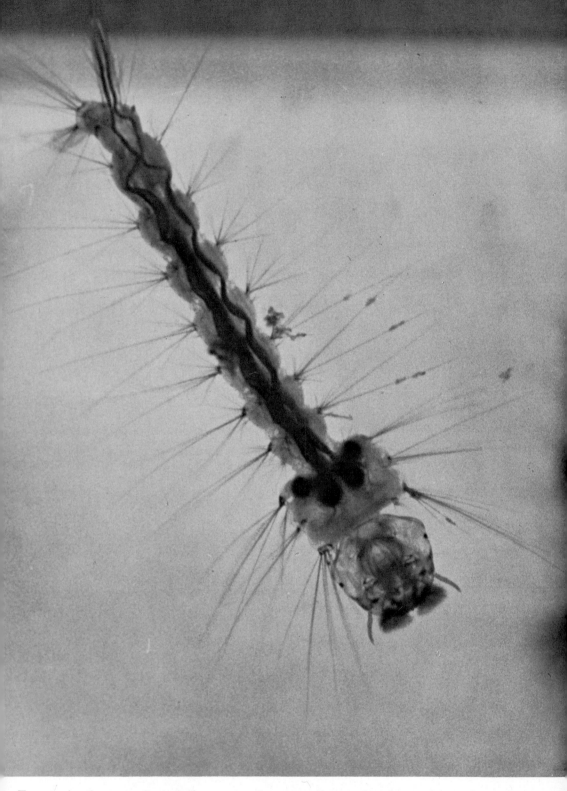

To get air, the mosquito wriggler must swim up to the pond surface and spread open there a breathing tube surrounded by water-repellent hairs.

How many arachnids—scorpions, spiders and their kin—would in-habit the world today if not for a profusion of insects as prey? How many terrestrial salamanders, frogs and toads would there be without insects for them to eat? Amphibians on land appear to have depended upon insects as prey, spaced out with an occasional earthworm, ever since they began their alternation between aquatic and terrestrial life. Without this plentiful food, it seems likely that amphibians would never have diver-sified on land enough to give rise to reptiles, and these to the birds and mammals.

Whenever we reconstruct the past and think of the interactions among living things as they colonized the tempting land, we grow more grateful for the small creatures around us. We can notice an insect—any insect—and admit to each other, "Without the ancestors of that little animal, ours would not have evolved. We would not be here." We feel sure that if insects had never found their myriad places and their immense suc-cess in terrestrial existence the course of history would have been far, far different from the sequence shown by the fossil record.

With so few styles of life in fresh water showing the versatility needed to spread into the open air, we wonder what substitute for insects might have been possible in the past if, for some physiological reason, fine branching tubes for carrying air throughout the small body had not been feasible. We cannot imagine a mollusk, a segmented worm, a round-worm, a flatworm or even a crustacean evolving on land into equal di-versity. None of these animals give insects or terrestrial vertebrates much competition. Only the roundworms in the soil and over the surface of plants in humid lands or wet weather stimulate vegetation to special adaptations. Only a few land snails and slugs attack the vascular plants to a degree that approaches the devastation insects can cause.

In a time when people on every continent are contemplating the uni-verse and admitting the likelihood that distant stars have planets much like earth, perhaps inhabited by sentient beings similar to man, we may need to extent our parallels to expect the existence of the counterparts of insects, too. Already the scientists are trying to devise a code that would have universal meaning, and ask themselves what messages would be most vital to beam across the vast voids in hope of receiving an answer after months or years. What discoveries of man might be worth sharing? Numbers? The wheel? The mathematical expansion of pi? The ratio of diameters among the orbits of planets cycling our sun? All these have been suggested, chiefly by men who can choose today whether $1 + 1 = 2$ or 10 and expect others to know what their symbols mean.

Perhaps we can reasonably predict that any cosmic conversations will be with creatures somewhat resembling man, on islands or continents below an equivalent of our atmosphere, living under conditions that some earthly inhabitants at least could tolerate. It may be too much to anticipate visiting back and forth across distances so great. But how reassuring it would be to learn that evolution there and here took corresponding paths because, as we suspect, it follows universal rules.

We are what we are because of past interaction between our ancestors and their living neighbors. This realization of the twentieth century leads us to assume that any counterparts of man with whom we might communicate have had a similar history. The more like us these distant correspondents are, the more probable it becomes that their distant world has its counterparts of insects and of plants with leaves, flowers, fruits and seeds. It may have its amphibian chorus around the ponds in spring, its songbirds, its bats echolocating their insect prey in darkness. These are all parts of the pattern that produced us through interdependent invasions of the land 400 million years ago.

chapter fourteen

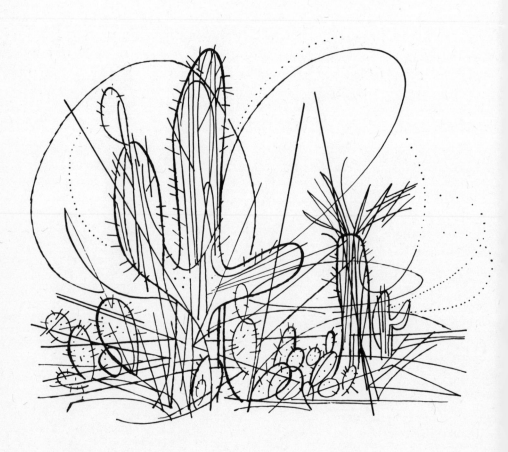

Green Ways in a Thirsty World

E VERY year we meet people who have returned recently from a trip to Alaska. With photographs to show as evidence, they enthuse over the huge size and delectable flavor of strawberries, tomatoes, even cabbages, grown in the long days of polar summer. "If only some way could be found to make the weather warm all year," they dream, "the Arctic would be a paradise!"

If some change in the heat budget of our planet let the polar lands warm up, the air there would suddenly become an invisible sponge, carrying off the moisture. At a chill 50° F., twice as much moisture is needed to saturate the air as at the freezing point. At 72°, the load of invisible water the air can hold doubles again. And if the temperature could rise to that of human blood, each breeze would take away ten times as much water as will saturate the air at 32°. With no increase in the rainfall to compensate for a rise in the average temperature during the growing season, the polar lands would become some of the driest deserts on earth.

So long as polar temperatures remain low, the cool air carries off only small amounts of moisture. Once saturated, it can pick up no more unless it passes across some area warmed by the sun. This feature of the earth's atmosphere, plus the poor drainage through frozen and rocky soils, accounts for the vast wetlands of the Arctic, to which incredible numbers of waterfowl migrate to raise their young. The annual rainfall is often less than ten inches a year.

In the wet woodlands on the South Island of New Zealand, as on New Guinea, giant mosses (*Dawsonia superba*) grow more than a foot tall.

A 40-foot tree fern towering overhead in the "native bush" of North Island, New Zealand, suggests the type of tree so common in Carboniferous days eons ago.

In London, England, the total rainfall is less than 25 inches. This amount of rain in most parts of the world would support a prairie but few trees. More rain falls annually on Lincoln, Nebraska, and on Algiers, Algeria, than on foggy London. This is why the official rule in the weather bureau in the metropolis states that "Fifteen consecutive days without rain constitute an absolute drought."

In America the effects of drought show more slowly. The United States weather services recognize a drought only at the end of a month with less than 60 percent average precipitation, or year with less than 75 percent. Native plants and animals on land rely on their own criteria. They live or die according to the suitability of their adaptations for benefiting when water is available at the average rate and for surviving when it is not.

For terrestrial life the most crucial alternative is whether wind brings water or takes it away. Sometimes addition is still in progress when sub-traction begins. The last raindrops from a passing shower may still be falling when the rays of the sun begin slanting under the black cloud, shining on a wet world and warming it, transforming the glistening moisture into invisible vapor for the same breeze to carry off.

Living things must manage with whatever water is left to them after the wind has absorbed whatever it can carry. For this reason the actual rainfall is less important to life than the amount that remains after the air is saturated. So long as actual precipitation exceeds evaporation about five times, the land will be wet. If the margin of excess shrinks to twofold, conditions will merely be moist. Dry is the only word to describe cor-rectly any land where potential evaporation equals or exceeds precipita-tion. These are the parts of the world that require special adaptations toward economy with water for survival of any plant or animal.

Few places on earth are uniformly dry. Dew forms during the clear, chilly nights even on deserts. Rain comes at intervals, and some of it percolates into the earth. Moisture flows deep underground and rises by capillarity between the particles of soil. Fog blows inland from many a coast. In any form, water brings an opportunity in dry lands for all living things that can seize and hold it whenever it comes their way. Yet, to survive, they must also be able to wait in dormancy until the next rain arrives, or to get what water they require for activity by some other means.

Of all the patterns with which life meets these needs, the simplest and most compact is the way of the mosses. Seldom do such lowly plants call attention to themselves, for few of them rise more than two inches tall and none bear brighter colors than leaf-green. Blackish and brittle when dry, greening up and growing soft as fur when wet, they spread over stones from crevices in which a little dust accumulates. With every warm rain they develop new branches, held closely to the rock or the soil by white threads that break under the slightest strain.

No one notices when moss plants discharge their spores, each a single cell, into the winds of the world. Borne by the air currents, these microscopic pioneers ride to every continent, bringing everywhere an equal chance that new plants of the same kind will take hold. Lodged in nooks too inhospitable for other kinds of vegetation or on soil too deficient to support most plants, the moss spores wait for a drop of rain or a pearl of dew to wet and wake them. As though loaded with "instant" protoplasm requiring only the addition of water, each of these single cells reacts to high humidity by dividing again and again. From the gaping wall of its spore coat, a slender finger of greenery extends itself, capturing radiant energy from daylight and synthesizing more of the organic compounds it can use in rapid growth.

Over all of its exposed surfaces, the sporeling secretes a thin cuticle. In hours after first emerging into the world, the little plant is ready to reduce its life processes to a minimum, to survive watered only by the dew and the humid air of dawn until rain comes abundantly enough to allow the growth called for in its inheritance. Usually, in temperate and polar lands, mosses grow so intermittently that they take years to branch extensively and become a better sponge for dew and rain.

No moss produces spores directly. Instead, when hormones diffusing throughout the interconnections of the plant signal that its nutritional resources are adequate, centers of growth in many of the branch tips respond by producing sex organs of characteristic form. Those that contain a single large egg apiece have the form of a flask, attached by a narrow pedestal. Those within which thousands of sperm cells mature are shaped like an upright punching bag. Ordinarily each branch tip with sex organs and sex cells bears one kind or the other and holds them ready, sharing in the frugal dormancy of the moss plant until rain begins to fall with exactly the correct vigor.

Around the sacs of sperms, the tip of a moss branch shows a further adaptation, matching rain drops of the proper size—neither too small and misty nor too smashingly large. Impressively simple, the tip consists of petal-shaped green plates in a rosette that forms a cup open to the sky. The green plates scarcely differ from those that suggest leaves on a moss, as they extend from the side of each branch. But grouped into a cup, they catch raindrops and use them, one after another. When a drop of the right size strikes squarely, it fills the cup, smashes down on the sacs of sperms, and spills out their contents. Splashing immediately upward and outward into a miniature fountain of tiny droplets, it sprays those sperms over a circular area as much as five inches across. Each sperm has a chance to alight on the open end of a flask containing a ripe egg and to swim down to it through the neck, which is filled by a slender column of secreted liquid. Fertilization of the egg takes almost no time. It calls forth the next slow steps toward production of countless spores that can safely ride the winds.

Depending upon the supply of moisture, a moss plant may require a week or all summer for its fertilized eggs to grow through their embryo stages. Each rises vertically as a slender stalk tipped by a knob within which the spores form. As they ripen, the knob completes its growth, hardening into a spore case of exquisite details. Its tip, proportioned like a cap for an elf, dries and drops off. The exposed top of the barrel-shaped spore case then shows a pattern of radiating grooves. They mark the boundaries of long, triangular teeth that point inward, butting closely together and protecting the spores inside from harm. Each tooth is its own hygrometer, curling downward when the humidity is high, upward when it is low. As the weather changes they lift out some of the spores and hold them where the breeze will carry them off. But when a dry wind comes along, they curl back out of the way and let the air current suck out the spores as though they were perfume in an atomizer. In less than a day they may all be gone unless the humidity rises and the protective teeth again unroll.

The magic in mosses lies in their ability to become dormant within a few hours anywhere in their life cycles. Never do their adaptations commit them to reliance upon a continued spell of rainy weather. Yet, in all the long eons since the Coal Ages (or earlier) when mosses first appeared, they have never been able to add extra features permitting them to continue growth during a drought. Or to reach moisture deep in the soil. Or to hold to the ground so firmly that they could grow tall as individuals, resisting the winds. They never developed roots, leaves or conducting tubes. Or freed themselves from the need for a splash of rain drops of just the right size to distribute their sperm cells.

The limitations of mosses confine them to the places where they live today. Better than any fern or clubmoss or any of the myriad kinds of plants with seeds, they can colonize cracks in bare rocks and inhospitable soils. Some remain lowly, like a green lace or a thin velvet. Others raise their branches vertically for half an inch or more and shade themselves until some of the darkened parts die. All mosses trap dust from the air and hold moisture for hours or days longer than any bald rock or bare soil can, giving bacteria a chance to grow. Single-celled animals (protozoans) feed on the bacteria. Roundworms, wheel animalcules (rotifers) and bear animalcules (tardigrades) eat protozoans and one another. In a handful of wet moss, the variety of minute creatures to be found surpasses the imagination. They contribute fertility to the soil by adding humus to it. But all of them, like the bacteria and the moss itself, can dry up and become dormant when the supply of water gives out.

Mosses continue to serve as pioneers, growing and reproducing while making raw land more hospitable for their successors. They have never been able to compete successfully with ferns and clubmosses in wet weather, or with the myriad kinds of seed plants during prolonged periods of low rainfall. These other styles of vegetation crowd the mosses into corners and often replace them completely.

The most common fern in the world is certainly bracken. It is a friend we can count on meeting on every continent. The international name of this cosmopolitan plant, *Pteridium aquilinum,* describes in a classical way the fancied resemblance of its fronds to the wings of a small eagle. These green eagle wings rise over rough pasture lands from horizontal, branching stems which are the thickness of a lead pencil and are hidden below the soil surface. Each spring, furry croziers burst upward and unfurl into twice-divided fronds on slender stalks. When we were small, these three-foot fronds of bracken spread shoulder-high, close under our noses. If we lay down we could look up through the scalloped patterns at the sky. They interlaced like a dull green sea and held a slightly spicy fragrance. Now, as we wade through the bracken, we have to bend to recapture that outdoors smell of a dry summer afternoon, and to recall how easily the fronds bent away from our short, childish legs, never scratching and barely impeding us unless we ran. When autumn comes bracken turns to cinnamon-brown, then crumples and lets the roughness of the field reappear. Pheasants, grouse and cottontail rabbits lose the summer privacy they had under the canopy of bracken fronds, but mice still have their cover.

In Jamaica and New Zealand and Hawaii, we have walked through tree-fern glens, delighting in lacy fronds filtering the warm sunlight overhead, and feeling a nostalgic sense of being back in childhood under the bracken. But now our eyes notice the distinctive spots and streaks of brown below some fronds where spores ripen in tiny spore cases. Like animated slingshots these spore cases hurl their dust-sized cargo into the breeze which wafts away the spores. For most of these particles of life it is a ride to doom. Only a few spores fall on soil that is suitably moist, at a season when gentle rain or nightly dew will provide a film of water when and where it is essential.

Each fern spore that germinates becomes a frail plantlet utterly unlike the familiar fern. Like a green fish scale it lies flat on the surface of the ground, holding itself in place by colorless, threadlike filaments only one cell in diameter. Under these plantlets, sex organs develop and project into whatever film of moisture accumulates there. The water is necessary as a liquid carpet through which sperm cells can swim to reach the ripe eggs and fertilize them. But the supply of moisture must not fail until the embryos grow into tougher plants—miniature ferns with green fronds exposed to the sun and air. By then each will have a stem and roots holding a reserve of water, and a protective cuticle coating all surfaces aboveground.

Those several weeks in the reproductive cycle of every fern, when the offspring cannot survive dry weather, make a big difference in where plants of this kind can live. They are scarce indeed wherever prolonged droughts occur many times each century.

Seed plants generally dodge the drought more easily than ferns because they absorb through roots in the soil all the water necessary for reproduction as well as for growth. All of their sexual stages lie hidden and protected within the parent plant, requiring no dew or rain to furnish a waterway for the sperms. Each fertilized egg develops in the care of an adult plant until it becomes a dormant embryo within a seed—the vegetable equivalent of a butterfly in its chrysalis. The root, the stem and the leaf of the miniature plant in the seed can wait until they have water to absorb, to let them expand, stretch out and establish in suitable ground the independence of the new individual.

To an unpracticed eye many seeds (like human babies) tend to look alike. A skilled botanist, a sharp-eyed farmer, and a world traveler would all find it an impossible task to reach into a tray containing one apiece of several dozen mixed seeds to pick out on request those from a particular continent. To tell the seed of a marsh plant from that of a desert dweller or a prairie weed is equally impossible.

We can hold eight little seeds in the palm of one hand, trying to see why each is distinctive. Each may wrap an embryo with a special in-

herited ability to survive where water is scarce. Scientists or agriculturalists might sort out the grass seeds, perhaps one of buffalo-grass from
a North American prairie and one of beachgrass from a European shore.
They would recognize these as being different from the seeds that mature
and dry in a floral head like that of a sunflower, such as one from a
desert dandelion from the American Southwest and one from a Namaqualand daisy from the South African veldt. They might pick out the
seeds from inside a pod like a bean, possibly a mesquite seed, a palo
verde seed, and an alfalfa seed blown from a field and collected around
a spring somewhere in Arizona. But a seed from a saguaro cactus might
be put in the "bean" category, even though it ripens inside a solid button
protected by an encircling crown of needle-sharp spines. Not one of
these seeds shows in its structure any hint of its amazing heritage.

Soon after it germinates, each seedling reveals how it can be green in
a thirsty land. Quickly the buffalo-grass extends roots horizontally in the
soil, and sends up from them long, slender, green leaves while the prairie
is still moist with the meltwater of winter snow and the rains of spring
and early summer. But when the drying winds of summer blow hotly
across the plains, the grass leaves die and wither. By then the flowers have
been pollinatetd by the wind, and the seeds are ripening in compact
heads. As the soil at the surface bakes in the hot summer sun, the ripe
seeds and the roots both become dormant.

If a prairie fire sweeps across the land, burning the dry leaves and the
seeds of the year, the intense heat is brief. Seldom does it damage the
roots in which plenty of nourishment has been stored. The grass draws
slowly upon these reserves during the late summer, autumn and winter,
and rapidly while it puts forth new leaves the following spring. Without
a fire only a few of the year's seeds would have found a place to grow.
Most of them provide food for ants and other insects, for birds such as
prairie chickens, and for rodents such as mice and prairie dogs. For a
prairie grass, seeds are insurance that any small area killed by fire from
above or the tunnels of prairie dogs from below will quickly be recolo-
nized. Every seedling possesses a slightly different inheritance, some including combinations of adaptive features that improve the suitability
of the plant in matching a land where the growing season each year lasts
only a month or so. A buffalo-grass waits out the annual drought, surviving only through its roots and seeds.

Where buffalo-grass once grew abundantly in the American West, immense herds of bison and pronghorns grazed, getting nourishment alike
from green leaves and dry dead ones that formed a wild hay. Smaller

Tall saguaro cacti and shorter branching chollas that are covered with sharp spines are the most conspicuous plants of the Arizona-Sonoran desert in North America.

numbers of wolves and Indians relied heavily upon the grass-eaters for food, spacing out their meals of bison and pronghorn meat by eating prairie dogs, prairie chickens, and even the grasshoppers that flourished amid the grass. Now alfalfa, a relative of clover that is native to Europe, grows on these same areas, field after field, producing food for domesticated livestock. Alfalfa seedlings are adapted in ways that match a prairie climate, where hot winds dry out the soil ever deeper as the summer progresses. An alfalfa seed that sprouts in early spring continues to extend its roots downward faster than the soil dries. The green tops of the plant get the water they need long after almost every other kind of vegetation has become dormant, because the roots are still reaching moisture thirty, forty or fifty feet below the surface. Even if the farmer harvests the parts of the plant above ground, the alfalfa root can replace them with new stems and leaves, for its supply of water is almost inexhaustible. Once well established, the alfalfa is beyond the drought that shortens the year for native plants.

Green leaves as bright as those on alfalfa grow on mesquite trees in the dry deserts of the American Southwest, where even an alfalfa would suffer from the drought. Seen from a low-flying light airplane, the mesquites are easy to recognize by color amid the gray-green of shrubby sagebrush and the pastel shades of pebbles and rocks upon the bare areas of soil. Generally a mesquite grows beside a temporary stream, where its roots will not be endangered by the raging torrent that passes after a thunderstorm. After a rain the water that drains into the creek bed often disappears completely before it has traveled far, mostly by sinking into the ground. But it continues flowing deep in the soil below the dry stream bed, and there supplies the needs of mesquite trees, helping them grow thirty feet tall with roots reaching downward fifty to sixty feet.

In southern Arizona many of the twisted drainage patterns that are dotted with green mesquite trees descend slopes where giant saguaro cactuses rise like thick fingers pointing at the sky. This tallest of the world's cactuses sometimes achieves a height of forty feet, a diameter of nearly three, a weight of ten tons, and an age of two hundred years. But only rarely does one of its small flat black seeds escape being eaten and sprout where it can grow. Even after it gets roots into the desert soil, its growth seems painfully slow—to a height of four inches in ten years, three feet in thirty years.

During all this time the cactus collects water from each local rainstorm. Virtually all of its roots spread out horizontally through the topmost three or four inches of soil, where they have first chance to absorb the rain while gaining some protection from the heat of the sun. In this position they contribute little support to the upright column of the mature cactus, and it is always in danger of being blown over by a strong wind. The roots show their efficiency only in gathering water. As soon as the air surrounding them is made humid by rain percolating downward through the spaces in the soil, they begin extending delicate root hairs that greatly enlarge the area available for absorption. As fast as the roots receive the water, they transfer it into the thick trunk of the cactus for storage. When no more can be absorbed, the root hairs die and the roots return to dormancy. The next rain to stimulate them may be a month, a year or more in arriving.

Like most cactuses, the saguaro protects its water store behind an armament of sharp spines. They project in little rosettes studding the ridges which number from 18 to 24 up the vertical column of the stem. When a big saguaro has absorbed an extra ton of water from a rain, these ridges are spaced so far apart that the spines cannot overlap. But as the plant uses its moisture (or loses it at a slow rate by evaporation through its thick cuticle), the whole stem shrinks like an accordion, and the spines become more conspicuous as well as closer together. These adaptations confer upon the cactus an almost perfect immunity to the long droughts that produce the desert. Yet today these giants are threatened by extinction because mice and other rodents find and eat practically every saguaro seed. The seed-eaters abound in the desert as never before because man has killed off the predatory animals that once held rodents in check and helped saguaros reproduce—the coyotes, bobcats, hawks and eagles which formerly roamed the American Southwest in reasonable numbers.

The cactuses, which are native to the New World, resemble only certain of the spurges—succulent plants of the Old World that resist and evade chronic drought in much the same ways. They drop all foliage and carry on what photosynthesis they can with their limited supply of water by means of green tissue in the thickened stems. The arrangement promotes efficiency, for the moisture is used close to the centers where it is stored. And a stem without projections offers little surface through which water can be lost into the dry air.

Perhaps we would never have appreciated fully the loss of leaves in these desert plants if friends had not given us some cactus seeds. We sowed them on moist paper in the high humidity of a closed glass dish, and soon began to wonder if by mistake we had been sent radish seeds.

Tree ferns as much as 60 feet tall are weeds in New Zealand and some humid parts of Australia, where these native plants colonize any neglected land.

Each seedling thrust out a thick rootlet, fringed around like a bottle brush with fine root hairs. It raised a short stem bearing a pair of seed leaves and a tiny terminal bud from which more leaves unfurled. Only the slow pace of growth told us that these could not be radish, or any other food crop raised by man. To attain a height of half an inch, the plantlets took six months. By then they had shed every leaf, expanded the green stem, and soaked up the sunshine that passed easily through overlapping rosettes of sharp, stiff spines no ordinary animal would take into its mouth.

Several times in springtime, when the chance of rain on the desert is greatest, we have visited the saguaros in their sunny forests. Only once have we found the tips of the columns and grotesquely branching arms wearing handsome coronets of fresh white flowers. Each three-inch blossom has its own three-inch pedestal, which later turns red as though to advertise the fruit. But the saguaros' flowers have barely faded before attention wavers from the stately giants to diminutive plants whose brighter flowers carpet the desert with red, orange, golden yellow and various shades from sky blue to deep purple.

The scrambled spectrum at our feet scarcely rises more than three inches above the soil. Its profusion attests to the success of an utterly different way in which plants dodge the prolonged droughts of desert lands. These are the blossoms of the ephemeral annuals. Their seeds can survive for many years, apparently unattractive to desert birds and rodents, until a good rain wets them. A brief shower fails to penetrate their heavy seed coats. But a soaking downpour releases the seedling. Pushing down roots, it raises a few leaves and uses the water in photosynthesis. It grows at a frantic pace and comes into flower all within a week or two. By the time the moisture is gone from the soil, another crop of seeds is ripe and drying too. They will spill on the desert and be blown about until the next time conditions for growth are right. Living one generation at a time, they escape the drought.

We again met carpets of ephemeral annuals along the arid western side of South Africa, where deserts and near-deserts extend close to the Atlantic coast northward across the Nama River into Southwest Africa. Namaqualand farmers delight in this prompt response of annual daisies to a spring rain as much as observant naturalists in the Northern Hemisphere do to the first chorusing of frogs. A family of Afrikaners from whom we asked permission to go out into the broad unplowed field to photograph a fenceless landscape of solid colors deliberately prolonged their hospitality indoors until almost ten o'clock, when every bloom would have opened toward the sun and the display would reach its climax for the day. By then, visitors from other parts of South Africa had arrived, driving farther in some instances than patriotic Texans go to see fields of perennial bluebonnets at the matching time of year.

The lovely flowers of Namaqualand daisies can now be enjoyed far from their native lands, for people all over the world have imported the seeds and raised plants in tended gardens. We found beds of them in Kew Gardens near London, their myriad flaring petals fully as colorful and the blooms themselves as close together as in the African fields. Yet no matter how handsomely the imported plants produce, imagination fails to convert an area of a few square yards into a multicolored panorama filling the arid land from horizon to horizon.

For a plant to resist and evade the drought in a desert seems challenge enough. Yet along many of the world's coasts, seeds have taken root where the land itself shifts with every wind, and salt spray falls almost as frequently as fresh rain. On sandy shores and the dunes close by, so little humus accumulates that rain sinks quickly out of reach and the sands are chronically dry. Plants that survive in these places need their roots for anchorage, holding themselves and the sands in place, rather than for absorption of moisture.

Beachgrass (*Ammophila*) thrives along the sandiest and most exposed of coasts because of special adaptations that make the plant less suited to better land in drier air. Its stiff leaves rise up, bend over, and touch again, writing circles around the hidden roots in every gust of wind. By day in fog and rain, when few people walk the beach and fewer explore the coastal dunes, the leaves of beachgrass have flat tops. They exchange gases readily through lower surfaces that bear deep lengthwise grooves, and absorb water vapor from the humid air. But when the fog burns off and the sun beats down, each leaf curls until it is almost a hollow tube. The ridges between the lengthwise grooves come together, shutting out the wind. Into those ridges the plant still reabsorbs moisture that diffuses out, along with oxygen from photosynthesis, through pores along the grooves.

The roots and creeping stems of beachgrass grow quickly but absorb almost nothing—not even when rain falls plentifully and washes deeper into the sand the accumulated salt from sea spray. The plant survives because it can capture from sea air the moisture and dissolved nutrients it needs. In fact, beachgrass that is shielded from actual rain atop a coastal dune grows well, whereas a plant of this kind on good moist soil farther inland dies of desiccation in the drier air.

By comparison with any animal, the green plants take so little from their world to grow and reproduce. They absorb the beneficent light from the sky, the impalpable carbon dioxide from the air, the barest pinch of soluble salts as inorganic nutrients, and moisture however they can. With these simple ingredients they build cellulose walls that shore them up, and a waterproof covering that guards their water. They store sugars and starches, fats and oils, and increase their supply of the proteins that give them character. Yet so long as the sun shines, the breezes blow, the earth holds firm, many of them can become adapted to even less. As though the rattle of raindrops from an occasional shower were the magic tune of a real Pied Piper, the green plants have responded. They have led a parade of living things into the hot sunlight, over the prairies, into the deserts, to the absolute limit of the water supply.

chapter fifteen

Animals That Dodge the Drought

S OON after dawn, the African sun cast a shadow a hundred yards long straight westward from the parked car in which we sat. Directly ahead of the shadow, about a quarter of a mile away, a dozen elephants of assorted ages stood scooping up the dust and throwing it over their backs.

A sprinkle of rain had come from leaden clouds the day before, but now no trace of moisture could be seen. This was normal enough for the arid plains in southwestern Uganda. Here the elephants were fortunate. Every day or two they could walk sedately in single file along a track they had made. About fifteen inches wide and almost as straight as though it were laid out by a surveying team, it led to the historic river Nile where the big animals could drink and bathe and refresh themselves.

Many of the game animals on the Dark Continent have no water so conveniently close. They must travel a circuitous path through grass and edible forage before returning to a favorite water hole or finding another one farther off. Only at intervals of a week or more do they slake their growing thirst. Yet even then their drinking is precautionary—still no matter of life or death. If the water hole is dry they must continue to another, and perhaps another after that. Animals that can manage under these conditions inhabit the high plains. The others became extinct long ago, or have been introduced in human custody during recent centuries.

A truly wonderful assortment of grass-eaters and shrub-browsers have ranged over the high country of central Africa as well as the vast steppes of Eurasia, the prairie heartland of North America, the pampas country of South America, and the less extensive grasslands and scrub of Australia. No one is quite sure how long the feet of grazing kangaroos have thudded against the Down Under continent whenever something frightened these pouched mammals, nor when first the rabbit-sized vizcachas with their clockspring tails began feeding in darkness and abundance on the pampas grasses. But certainly ancestral horses spread from the American prairies about 10 million years ago over a land bridge where Bering Strait lies now. They colonized Asia and Africa all the way to the Cape Province. Camels took the same route, and also found a bridge across Middle America to South, where their descendants today include llamas, alpacas and fleet vicuñas in the high Andes. Perhaps bison spread the other way.

About the same time or a little later, mankind probably emerged from Africa by way of Asia Minor, protecting at the expense of native grass-eaters the newly domesticated cattle, sheep and goats. These favored animals made possible the sudden rise in human numbers and versatility, but they have never become adapted to surviving with as little water as the native creatures they replaced. Today it is hard to realize that until man brought his thirsty livestock and his plows to the American scene, reintroducing horses where they had become extinct, a grasslands community larger than Europe was in balance. Perhaps 50 million bison, in addition to countless pronghorns, prairie dogs and grasshoppers, thrived where water was scarce for most of the year.

For most of these animals of the open range, the secret of surviving without a drink of water is the same as for guinea pigs, which now are the descendants of household pets the Spanish conquerors met in South America. No guinea pig needs drinking water so long as its daily diet includes plenty of raw cabbage, lettuce or other juicy vegetables in place of fresh grass. Its water requirements are modest, and these foods satisfy them generously.

Man too can live indefinitely without liquid water if he follows a guinea pig's routine—staying motionless in some shady place all day and eating large quantities of raw vegetables and fruits every night. Even a few raw grapefruit, oranges and peeled tomatoes daily will take the place of drinking water in a land of questionable sanitation. They fend off thirst before it develops, so long as activity in the heat and sun is studiously avoided. On the range, or wherever water is scarce, only "mad dogs and Englishmen" dash about in the noonday sun. Noel Coward's famous line appeals to what used to be called "common sense." Now the choice of nighttime for activity and fresh greenery for food by animals on a grassland is dignified as a "behavioral adaptation."

The first towns on the arid plains of the world were built by animals with an additional behavioral adaptation: they burrowed underground in colonial interdependence. For many thousands and perhaps millions of years, the grasslands have been home to these town-dwelling rodents. Prairie dogs of North America have their counterparts in the vizcachas of South America, the susliks of the Asian steppes, and the mole-rats of the African plains. By emerging to feed only in darkness, they are abroad during the coolest of the 24 hours. Their needs are minimal for water with which to cool their bodies by evaporation. By day they benefit by staying quiet within deep, cool living quarters where the earth itself serves as an efficient insulator against the dry heat of the sun. And like a bonus, these rodents have a better chance at night to escape from large predators that hunt by sight.

The large grazers, which are chiefly wild horses, antelopes and bovine beasts—the untamed cattle of the world—cannot hide underground. They are too big. But many of them make themselves inconspicuous by eating their fill twice a day: soon after the end of evening twilight and again before dawn begins to brighten the sky. Between times—during the midnight hours and all day—they rest as undistinguished bumps on the landscape, in whatever shade they can find or in none at all. Each appears the acme of indolence. Actually each is a highly efficient machine with few moving parts, digesting its meals without endangering its life.

The little grazers are the insects, particularly the grasshoppers. They stand six-footed on the grasses, body parallel to the stems, and from the edge nip out pieces small enough to swallow. Rapidly the vegetable fragments are liquefied into a brown puree we generally fail to appreciate when a captured grasshopper "spits tobacco juice" on our fingers. The water in this juice came from the grass, tangible evidence that the grasshopper has no need to go elsewhere to drink. And if the insect cannot find much shade from the sun, at least it is armored by a covering more impervious to water than any antelope possesses. It hoards its liquid contents as though in a plastic bag, and is affected much less than most other animals by changes in temperature. The cold-blooded insect adjusts its rate of living over a wide range, conforming to the air around it, spending no energy and sacrificing no water in sweat to maintain a steady temperature.

When the driest season of the year strikes the grasses, withering them to parched hay and killing the exposed leaves, only the big grazers keep on eating. They alone have a way to make most of the water they need from the abundant cellulose in dry grass. The burrowing rodents become dormant. The insects follow an inherited program that matches the season, letting them wait out the waterless months as eggs or pupae hidden underground. On a hot day toward the end of the dry season, only the twisting "dust devils" seem alive on the broad plains.

Insects need few additional tricks to survive in a desert, if their food preferences lead them to get nourishment and water from the special plants that grow there. Chewing their way into succulent cactus stems aboveground or into roots hidden below, these small creatures let the vegetation protect them as well as provide enough to eat. The hazards the insects face under these conditions are hardly unique. Mostly they are the desert lizards and insectivorous birds that are eager to attack as soon as the insect emerges from its feeding site to find a mate and propagate its kind.

As is usual anywhere, not just in a desert, the predators are larger, longer-lived and slower in reproducing than their prey. When food for the predators becomes abundant, as may happen when many insects emerge within a few days or weeks in an arid land, there may be too few predators to benefit from the bonanza. The number of predators is usually limited to those that can find enough to eat—containing enough water for survival—under the worst living conditions, when prey is scarcest. Consequently, the insects benefit from emerging almost synchronously and overwhelming the predators. Then only a few get eaten, and the rest escape.

Certainly this is a major gain for the many plant-eating insects of desert lands when they remain dormant month after month, sometimes year after year, until awakened by a rain. All at once they emerge for dispersal, mating and attack on the vegetation. Another advantage is that their eggs hatch and their young look for food just when the plants are responding to the same rain by putting out new, tender leaves.

After a soaking rain in the desert, animals in miraculous variety make their appearance. In temporary ponds that will not last more than a week or two before the dry wind carries off the last drop, shield-shaped crustaceans hatch from desiccated eggs scarcely larger than sand grains. Spectacularly, they grow in the warm water, eating microscopic algae that flourish under the desert sun in any moisture. Within a week they reach a length of more than an inch, mate and leave eggs to dry. They themselves die, their burst of activity over, their species insured of a hold on the future.

Desert snails creep up out of the soil in which they may have been concealed for years. Around the rim of the drying pool they browse on the algae and grow a little. Some mature enough to reproduce, only to burrow again before the ground dries out and to wait for the next rain to come along.

Frogs and toads sometimes accompany the snails into the ponds, to start tadpoles on a rush of development. To succeed, these creatures must reach a critical size, put out legs and absorb their tails, then gorge themselves on insects before burrowing out of sight to hide for months or years. Like the desert snails, they live on the installment plan. Maturity for those that survive may be decades off.

Desert birds that eat insects, crustaceans, tadpoles and snails are suspected of watching the sky for signs of rain and flying toward any black cloud. We have seen them coming for miles toward a column of dark smoke, and can well believe they overlook no clue to finding food. Perhaps other cues serve them equally well. The fact remains that soon after a local downpour has soaked an area of desert, the birds do arrive —just as the dormant plants begin to grow and the animals to appear. Although they take their toll, the feathered predators can never make serious inroads upon the exploding population of evanescent life. In an area of desert fifty miles across, only a small number of birds can find these types of food somewhere within sight every other day of every year. Yet their special adaptations help them find enough to eat, and make them react in a constructive way to unexpected plenty. Whenever they find a special abundance of food, the birds respond by quick nesting, laying eggs and rearing families before the supply gives out.

The little rodents of the deserts have no way to travel far for water and the extra bounty brought by local rains. They manage, nevertheless, with only a few special features evolved long ago by their ancestors. They wait in their deep burrows until the sunbaked surface of the desert has had time in darkness to radiate away its heat energy to outer space. All this while they inhale air made humid by soil moisture, at a temperature well below that of their own bodies. That these rodents lack sweat glands does not matter, for they never venture into places where evaporation of water would benefit them even temporarily. Under the stars they scurry about, gathering fruits and seeds into cheek pouches lined with dry fur. They store each sundried trophy as desiccated as ever, to be left in an underground chamber for a week or two during which it will absorb water from the humid air. By the end of that time the fruits and seeds add as much as a third to their weight, and increase their water content enough to become acceptable as food. Merely by following this ancient habit, the animal gains moisture from its food without effort or conscious planning.

The jumping jerboas of deserts in the Old World and the kangaroo rats in those of North America never need a drink of water. Indeed, when confronted by a pool or even a few drops of it, they turn away as though thirst were unknown to them. They do have one special safeguard: the most efficient kidneys known. These organs routinely reabsorb so much water from the urine before voiding it that the solution is almost saturated with urea. This is about five times as efficient an operation as that of human kidneys.

These rodents show an extraordinary ability to select among the fruits and seeds they find on the desert. As though shopping for food with a list of dietary values in one hand, they choose those that are richest in starches and sugars, modestly enriched with oily or greasy fats, and with no more than the minimal contribution of protein needed for health. Only recently has the full advantage in this regimen become obvious to science. Yet it has been built into the behavior patterns of desert dwellers for countless generations.

During digestion of organic foods any animal gains additional water. Each pound of carbohydrates contributes nine ounces, each pound of fats eighteen, and a pound of protein barely more than six. To get energy and moisture from a molecule of fat, however, more oxygen is needed than to utilize an equal weight of carbohydrate. The oxygen must come from inhaled air. If the animal must humidify dry air in its nasal passages, a larger quantity of water may be lost—exhaled—than is obtained through oxidation of the fat. Jerboas and kangaroo rats minimize this loss by dining and digesting in the humid seclusion of their burrows, and also by possessing long, efficient noses. Of the small amount of moisture they must add to inhaled air as it passes the nasal membranes, a large part is salvaged again before exhalation by passing the now-humid air over the same membranes, which absorb significant amounts of water.

Those same long noses on desert rodents have an added ability—one we wish we could understand. In some way that is still a mystery to science, they can tell from the odor of a seed or fruit how much protein

The Gila monster of Arizona's deserts, and its near kin the beaded lizard of Mexico, are the only poisonous lizards in the world.

Well adapted to traveling without water for long distances from one oasis to the next, camels match the living conditions on the deserts of North Africa and Arabia.

it contains. And the rodent brain responds accordingly, rejecting any with high protein and accepting only those with low. Our own brains include a comparable feature in that we equate sweet with good and bitter with bad. No one has to be taught this distinction. Yet we cannot be taught to recognize by scent or taste the amount of protein in the food available to us.

Proteins from plants pose special problems to a desert dweller, for a reason that has been appreciated fully only in recent years. Like any proteins, they are digested to units called amino acids, of which about twenty different kinds occur in nature. Substantial amounts of six or seven among the twenty must be gained from food as building blocks for growth, since the animal has no way to make them from anything else. Plant proteins are notoriously poor sources for several of these amino acids that are critical. To get enough of the essential ones, an animal must digest large amounts of plant protein and then dispose of the unnecessary quantities of the other amino acids—the ones it can synthesize for itself. The superfluous amino acids are not wasted. They are converted into usable sugar, which yields energy, and nitrogen-containing wastes such as urea. The richer the diet is in proteins, the more urine that must be discharged to get rid of the urea and the more water needed as a solvent. For any desert dweller, plant proteins in the diet beyond the bare minimum are a mistake. Jerboas and kangaroo rats thrive by choosing well, following their sensitive noses to success.

Camels are even more astonishing than desert rodents, for they are far too large to burrow into the desert to escape the hazards of hot sun and dry air. Yet they plod along from one oasis to the next in the driest parts of the world, carrying a load almost as heavy as their own bodies. Upon arrival after three or four days, a camel can slake its thirst in short order. It drinks without harm water so charged with salts as to sicken a man. No one has discovered how a camel tolerates the ions of magnesium and sulfate in particular, for man uses these only medicinally under the common name of Epsom salts. But scientists have learned other secrets long hidden from men who knew camels best—ways in which these ungainly beasts of North Africa and the Near East fit into their forbidding environment.

Through an adaptation that seems a minor change in its nervous control, a camel actually takes advantage of its large size. By night, when the desert cools off, the camel allows heat loss from its body to lower its temperature into the low 90's Fahrenheit. Even if the following day is a hot one, perhaps with air temperature reaching 120° in the sun at the height of the camel's body from the ground, the animal can absorb thousands of calories before the temperature of its blood rises to that of a man. Thousands of calories more can still be accommodated easily, for the camel does not begin to sweat until its bulky body and blood reach 105°. A person chilled to the temperature of a camel's blood on a cold night would be unconscious, the nervous coordination of essential body functions in danger of fatal failure. A blood temperature matching that at which a camel starts to sweat would be lethal in a man or woman and totally incapacitating in a child. Somehow camels have evolved a tolerance for this variation. They retain most of the advantages of warm-bloodedness while benefiting from thermal inertia in a land of extreme daily temperature change. By saving themselves from sweating, they need much less water to live normally.

For generations, people believed that camels stored water in their stomachs if not in the hump of fat on their backs. Now it is clear that the hump is a reserve of food. To utilize the fat, the camel must expend the same amount of water per pound as a man would. But the camel surpasses man for desert living by having virtually all of its fat in its hump, rather than widely distributed under its skin. Fat under human skin retards the flow of heat from the blood, which is fine in cold weather but often disastrous in hot. Our skin must be at least 5° cooler than our blood for us to get rid of the heat produced by chemical changes in digestion, muscular work and glandular activity. By contrast, a camel can lose heat to its environment so long as the air is a mere 2° cooler than its blood. Since the animal's blood temperature can rise safely to 106°, the camel has no need to sweat until midafternoon when its body has warmed to this amount all the way through. By then, sunset is only a few hours away. Soon the air and the sands and the camel can all begin to cool swiftly.

In any vertebrate animal sweat is mostly water. The sweat glands take what they need for secretion from the blood vessels in the skin. To secrete at the rate needed to cool human skin in hot desert air, these glands withdraw more than than a quart of water from the blood each hour, making the person intensely thirsty. If this water loss exceeds five percent of the body's weight (about a gallon), the mind shows the effect in distorted perception and faulty judgment. By the time two gallons are gone the person is deaf, insensitive to pain and delirious. If water loss continues to make the deficit twelve percent of the body weight, about a third of the volume of the blood plasma has gone and the blood is so viscous that the heart can no longer circulate it in a steady rapid stream. Unable to carry heat from the internal organs to the skin, the body is doomed. Its temperature rises and death is quick. Just before this happens, the life of a person can be saved by giving water in little sips. To replenish the supply more rapidly can be equally fatal.

Not only does a camel save itself from sweating for most of the day, but a peculiar adaptation protects the animal's blood and heat-distribution system from disaster. Its blood retains the normal volume and consistency by absorbing water from the tissue spaces of the body, as rapidly as its sweat glands remove water to use in their secretions or the kidneys discharge the precious liquid along with urea. Without any significant change in its blood, a camel can lose more than thirty gallons of water and decrease its body weight by more than 25 percent. The animal then appears dangerously emaciated, but it is as alert, strong and reluctantly energetic as ever. Moreover, if allowed to drink it can restore its water supply in less than half an hour with no danger. It recovers its customary appearance just as quickly.

When we ride camels in North Africa or observe them for extended periods while keeping up with a herdsman who is tending a small number of these amazing animals, quite different adaptations hold our interest. Their feet fascinate us, spreading like twin sacks of sand to support the camel's weight and then folding together neatly as each foot is lifted. This action, which holds great advantage for walking across a dune, arises from the fact that the sole of each foot is undivided and the hoofs are on the upper surface.

Even more astonishing to us are the mouth and digestive system of these animals for, as herdsmen assure us, "Camels will eat any plant that grows. They are immune to almost everything. That's why they seem to live in a world of their own." We have seen camels nibbling bright green sea lettuce washed ashore by ocean tides along the coast of Morocco, apparently enjoying the white crystals of salt dried on the surface. In Libya and Tunisia they were munching camel's-thorn acacia bushes armed with stiff projections two inches long and so sharp that we could scarcely cut a flowering branch for closer examination. We can't imagine how the camels kept from stabbing their tongues and throats.

Probably a majority of the creatures that live where water is as scarce as in a desert manage in a little world of their own adaptations. How else could fly maggots survive at the bottom of shallow petroleum pools, where they scavenge for water as well as food from the bodies of other insects that fall in and die? The maggots breath through long snorkel-like extensions of their bodies, raised up through the poisonous oil to the air above.

Other flies are equally adapted to pass their preparatory stages scavenging in shallows of salt lakes and alkaline lakes, isolated within their own skins from a solution so toxic that few kinds of life can tolerate it and give them competition. We have seen their empty pupal cases around the shore of Great Salt Lake in Utah in the staggering abundance that impresses any visitor. The fly-fancier J. M. Aldrich estimated that at least 25 flies to the square inch settled on the beach and the surface of the water near the shore, in a strip twenty feet wide. This would total 370 million flies to the mile of shoreline, emerging and mating and laying eggs to repeat the process every year. The number from this narrow zone around the entire lake becomes meaningless to a human mind because the zeros seem to go on forever.

Similar lakes nearer the Equator become bright pink or even red with salt-tolerant algae drifting and absorbing sunlight for photosynthesis. We visit these places to meet the long-legged flamingoes that stalk about, dipping their heads into the water. The birds work their tongues piston-like, to force out the salty liquid through fine strainers that hold in the algae as a paste of food. Salt often cakes the legs of the birds. Yet the skin there and around the beak remains unirritated by the saturated solution. Some of the salt water must occasionally get into the flamingoes' eyes. Apparently their tears quickly flush the sensitive surface and prevent damage. The same solution in human eyes blinds a person for days or weeks until new cells can replace those killed by the concentrated salt. Some salt must accompany the algal paste into the birds' digestive tracts. But again the inherited adaptations save the flamingoes from harm, allowing them to live without losing their precious inner supplies of water.

Each of these animals has become a specialist in its own way of life. Only the scale of their living spaces and the details of their existence distract us from the extraordinary ways in which they fit their water-poor environments. We cannot, nor would we likely choose to, emulate their habits. For us the change would be too great. They did not consciously choose either. Instead, their ancestors were nudged by force of circumstance along evolutionary courses that reduced the competition. One step at a time, their inherited behavior led them away from more generous supplies of water. They moved at a rate paced by their addition of new capabilities. These moves ensured them places in the present. Who can say that for any of them it is the end of the line? No pattern of life is doomed until it becomes too fixed to change still more.

chapter sixteen

Getting Something to Eat

FEW animals that grow to any size eat the same food from the beginning to the end of their life. Everyone can remember a whole series of changes in what food gave the most pleasure, from childhood into maturity. Yet after birth, the nearest we come to a radical transformation in dietary habits occurs when we are weaned.

Ordinarily we think of the metamorphosis of a bullfrog tadpole as far more spectacular. While still swimming in the pond where it hatched from the egg, the tadpole eats small oozy masses of plant food it can suck into its narrow mouth and digest in its long, coiled intestine. Then its body gains a new form. Its intestine shortens to a single loop which suffices for the carnivorous diet of the young bullfrog. The animal begins to capture insects by flipping out a sticky tongue whenever a fly comes within reach.

Actually, there is much more to the dietary habits in a bullfrog's life. The tadpole, which seems so strictly a vegetarian, chooses nourishment by size rather than by taste or color. While only half grown toward the two-inch length at which the tadpole normally transforms, it will eat greedily any small fragments of meat that it finds. Experimenters have discovered that if the meat particles have been cut from the thyroid gland tissue of some larger animal, the tadpole responds to the thyroid hormone as though suddenly its own thyroid had begun to secrete. It transforms

205

into a miniature bullfrog and aims its tongue at small flies that match its size.

By the time a bullfrog grows large enough to interest people who enjoy bullfrog legs on toast, insects are no longer its only choice in food. Collectors have recorded some of the other creatures they find in bullfrog stomachs, partly digested and definitely providing nourishment that helps those legs grow larger. These include smaller frogs, worms, even a young mouse or a bird that has come too close to the pond edge or lily pad where the bullfrog sits. This explains why bullfrogs leap at a bit of red flannel hiding the hooks on the end of a fishing line. Tonguework alone cannot appease their hunger. The big frogs get some of their most satisfying food by gulping it.

A feeling of hunger and going to get something to eat recur so frequently for most animals that it is easy to overlook the exceptions. Sponges and corals and barnacles stay still, depending upon water currents to bring them food. It is seldom that bivalves move, and it is slowly when they do. But "happy as a clam" scarcely describes an animal that must expose itself to attack while getting a meal, or expose itself to any predator sneaking along as silently as possible, to give no warning before it pounces. Most animals seek and find their food as an important and oft-repeated part of life.

More animals are plant eaters than are "red in tooth and claw" from devouring one another. Had Alfred, Lord Tennyson, lived today and kept informed on scientific progress, he might have found comfort in that fact. Would he have realized the inadequacy in so strict a vegetarian diet for his own kind, and withheld his praise for "the grain by which a man may live?"

Probably no healthy, vigorous man has ever been strictly a vegetarian —eating no eggs or milk product—and no animal truly omnivorous— ready and able to use everything organic as food. From the very first time that an animal distinguished itself from a plant by eating something and digesting it, selection must have been fundamental. It depends upon discrimination among several choices, some more suitable than others. Discrimination requires special sense organs in any animal complex enough to have organs of any kind, and a nervous system to interpret the messages the sense organs provide. Even the single-celled creatures possess fine organelles with which they select from among the foods available to them from their environment.

The first animal to benefit from such refinements may have made its choices on the basis of touch and taste, the most immediate of the senses.

Almost certainly the exquisitely refined organs permitting discrimination at a distance—by smell, hearing and sight—came later, in animals whose ancestors had been animals for a very long time. Today few animals can find and take their food without all five of these senses operating at once.

We can feel no certainty that scientists have discovered all the ways in which animals find their food. Some animals have senses that seem more spectacular because we lack a counterpart. Whales and bats scan their worlds with echoed staccato calls they make. Several kinds of fishes explore for food by emitting pulses of electricity and detecting details in the electric field produced. Rattlesnakes and other pit vipers respond to faint differences in heat reaching them from a cool, wet frog on a stone or a warm, sleepy bird in a bush. Honeybees see ultraviolet reflected from the sun as a separate color, and find patterns in it on flowers that seem plain to our ultraviolet-insensitive eyes.

Even among the animals most familiar to people and much like us in their senses, the choice of food differs greatly. Sweets mean nothing to a cat, little to a cow or rabbit, but have great attraction for a dog or horse. The dog would rather have a smelly bone than a piece of fish—but not the cat, although both are meat-eaters. The rabbit prefers a carrot to an apple or a cornstalk, the horse an apple, the cow a cornstalk, although all of these animals are vegetarians. We should not be surprised that their choices are so different, since this allows these animals to live side by side with negligible competition. It would be odd if all of them selected the same food when given a chance to choose.

Most animals make their own choices of food, and live or die by the consequences of swallowing it. The situation is radically different among the many insects that grow by eating ravenously during larval stages, then change in form and habits to those of the adult. Obviously mother knows best. It is always the female butterfly or beetle or botfly or bumblebee that chooses the site for each egg. The young that hatch out will eat what their mother has selected for them. She may choose a very different diet for her own use, but her behavior in egg laying is triggered separately. To match the pattern of sensations called for by her inheritance, her senses must be stimulated in just the right way, as though by a key that is opening a lock. This one pattern, involving touch, taste, smell, sight and perhaps hearing, has brought success to young of her kind in the past. With only slight variations tolerable, it provides for their survival.

A world of difference separates the ways of insects, which learn nothing from associating with their parents, and that of a human mother, who

Called the "paradox frog" because the large tadpole grows much smaller to become the adult frog, this Trinidadian frog lives only in a few remote swamps and marshes.

Monarch butterflies extend their long tongues to probe for nectar deep in the florets of a Zinnia flower head.

searches her childhood memories to recall what was done in corresponding circumstances to care for a youngster. Perhaps it was inevitable that
these two routes toward finding food for growth on land should have
led to direct conflict between small-bodied insects and large-bodied mankind. For insects, virtually all of the direction in behavior is inborn,
inherited, polished only a little by learning through trial and success.
With a multiplicity of patterns, insects avoid competition with each other.
They maintain an immense variety of food relationships and can exploit
each food efficiently. For a person, virtually all of the inborn responses
to the environment are hidden quickly under a wealth of learning. In
building a civilization based on learning how to cultivate certain crops,
the human species must contend with every kind of insect that might use
the same foods. The insects may not win, but a draw seems the best
than can be hoped for.

Our large size as compared to insects and smaller creatures corresponds to longer life and an evolutionary disadvantage. With only three
or four generations in a century, the human species has only these few
chances to change in hereditary emphasis. A fruit fly, by contrast, may
go through a new generation every two weeks. A century gives it five
thousand opportunities to become better adapted to getting food despite
alterations in its environment. These modern understandings place new
meaning on Aristotle's words: "One should not be childishly contemptu-
ous of the most insignificant animals. For there is something marvelous
in all natural objects."

Lacking all knowledge of microscopes and microscopic creatures,
Aristotle could not realize how insignificant some animals are or how
much growth is possible on a diet of microscopic life. Today, with our
microscope and field glasses and bare eyes serving an educated mind,
we can notice similarities that surprise us. A slipper animalcule, just big
enough to see as a white mote in a drop of pond water, can remind us
at one time of a mussel three inches long, and at another of a finback
whale nearly fifty feet in length. Each of them feeds on an appropriate
diet consisting of food particles too small to be sensed individually.

The animalcule, seen through the lenses of a microscope, clings near a
mass of bacteria that are so small as to be barely visible. Continuously
the animalcule beats its short hairlike cilia, creating a current of water
that frees bacteria from the cluster and carries them on a definite path.
They collect close to one spot on the surface of the animalcule where,
at intervals, a special group of cilia slap a whirling mass of these food
particles into the single cell for digestion.

The mussel lies on one of its two dark blue shells in a dish of sea-water, tethered to the bottom with a few threads of secreted plastic material. Cilia create a current of water carrying oxygen and living particles, including bacteria. The current enters the mantle cavity of the bivalve through a small opening where the shell valves gape. We can watch what happens next because we have surgically placed a glass window in one shell. The mollusk's fleshy palps gather masses of living particles caught in sticky mucus and shove them into the bivalve's mouth. How different are these ways of feeding? Surely not as unlike as the sizes of animalcule and mussel, or the specific adaptations that fit the single cell and the bivalved mollusk to eat as they do.

The slipper animalcule lets go, swims along in the drop of water, but continues to gather bacterial food particles as it swims. As we watch it through the microscope, it brings to mind a finback whale that ignored the lobsterman's boat in which we rode. Mile after mile near the Maine coast we kept alongside on parallel courses less than a boat's length distant. The lobsterman and we were equally fascinated to see the whale scull itself at a gentle pace by rhythmically raising and lowering its huge flukes. Each time the flukes approached the surface, the whale bent its back and raised its head. Broad as the top of a railway coach, the head bulged out of the sea while the cavernous mouth below opened and admitted a flood of surface water. Into the mouth, between the downhung vanes of flexible whalebone, swirled inch-long fishes, shrimps of several small kinds, and other creatures that feed among the drifting plankton of the open sea. Every time the whale closed its mouth, it crushed this living food into a pasty mass it could swallow.

Compared to a fifty-foot whale, an inch-long fish is just about the same proportion as a bacterium is to the length of a slipper animalcule. The whale in its ocean and the animalcule in its pond swim where nutriment can be concentrated, using structures and methods evolved and inherited through countless generations.

We see similarities again when a butterfly and a bird take turns in sipping nectar from the same zinnia flower. Yet we know how differently these creatures are constructed, and how unlike are their heritages in behavior. The newly emerged butterfly clings to its empty chrysalis, pumping blood into its expanding wings. It fits together the two long maxillae that suggest slender antennae beside its mouth, until they form a single tube that can be curled up like a watchspring. At the first flower the butterfly visits, it uncurls its tongue and probes the depths for nectar

The calico spider *Nephila clavipes* produces an orb web as much as 9 feet in diameter, strung between trees to catch insects and even small birds and bats.

just as expertly as though it had been doing this for years. To be successful at all, its instinctive actions must be perfect every time.

A young hummingbird has more to learn in life than a butterfly. Until
after it leaves the nest, it gets its food merely by opening its mouth widely
whenever its mother arrives. She thrusts her long beak down its throat
directly into its crop, as though about to pin it to the nest. Then she
regurgitates the nectar and tiny insects she has brought, spilling none
of the nourishment.

We have watched a hummer fledgling take its first flight. Still the
mother brings it food. Then comes the day when the youngster tries to
hover in front of a flower while maneuvering its slender beak into the
nectar concealed there. It sways from side to side, rises and falls irregularly. It needs practice, for this is hard work. But the fledgling has
most of its life ahead of it, whereas the perfect butterfly is the end
product from the long, slow growth of a hungry caterpillar. The two
lines of adaptation meet where the nectar is.

Appropriate to each kind of food is a definite method of eating. But
each kind of animal that uses a particular method must inherit the structures that are necessary. The mosquito that bites us and the aphid that
draws juices from a plant use mouthparts that are highly adapted for
piercing as well as for sucking. When we pause to think about it, we
realize how wonderfully fine these stylets are, and yet they are stiff enough
for the insect to press them through overlying tissues to reach nourishing
liquid underneath. Our own skin or the firm thin bark covering a young
stem or root provide no obstacle. Often we have felt more astonishment
than pain to see a mosquito rest lightly on an arm or leg and probe
straight into the nearest small blood vessel.

We resent the attention of a mosquito beyond the fact that she may
inoculate a disease right into our bloodstream, or that the site may itch.
Actually, she does not need our blood as a transfusion to prolong her
life. She can reproduce moderately well even if she fails in her search
for a red-blooded animal. Her inherited versatility allows her to convert
the iron in the muscle cells that drive her wings into the material she
needs to complete her eggs. But she can lay *more* eggs if she sucks up a
blood meal with red cells full of iron-containing hemoglobin. Otherwise,
she is well nourished by sucking juices from plant stems, just as any male
mosquito is.

Whenever we notice a plant stem studded with aphids, each with its
beak pushed deeply into the green surface on which its six legs stand,

we get the same feeling of disbelief. How could any insect be softer-bodied than an aphid, or more mass-produced by virgin birth, or more preyed upon by birds and ladybeetles and the aphis lions that police the plants? Yet here they rest, concentrating for their own growth the protein they need from a solution that is mostly sugar water. At intervals of a half hour or less, each aphid discharges a droplet of honeydew containing the water and sugar it cannot use.

Immediately after birth, a young aphid manages just as spectacularly as its mother. It guides its stylets through the bark until they penetrate a pressurized cell of the innermost layer. No one knows how the insect hits the slender target so exactly. Yet slices cut through a stem and aphid killed simultaneously show under the microscope how perfect is the aim. Once in position, the aphid need not move or even exert suction. A botanist at Harvard University, Dr. Martin H. Zimmerman, discovered in 1961 that internal pressure from the plant drives the sugary solution out through the insect's stylets right into its mouth. Using fine scissors, he cut away an aphid on a basswood stem, leaving its stylets undisturbed. For days the sap of the plant continued to flow as though through a pipe-line. It dripped to the ground at a rate scarcely different from that at which the whole aphid had previously produced honeydew.

Now we realize why an aphid can be so soft. It needs muscles mostly to slide those stylets to their mark. Even with wings it flies more feebly than anything else we know. Fluttering into the breeze with less control than a balloonist has, the aphid rides in any direction to a crash landing a foot or a mile away. Righting itself slowly and getting a grip with all six feet, the insect begins probing again to get its lancets through to a new supply of food and water. Occasionally aphids settle on human skin and drill there with equal ease. But the taste is wrong, and they soon withdraw to let the wind carry them elsewhere to try again.

Our own experience helps us to better understand the many animals that get their food by biting and munching with jaws that move. Although we cannot take pride in our own coordination when we bob at cherries swinging on a string or apples floating in a tub of water, we laugh at our failures to do so without using our hands. Precise movements of jaws that correspond to ours let a shark or a seal seize a fish, a snake or a stork snatch a frog, a starling or a squirrel pick a scarlet fruit from the dogwood tree outside our study window.

More than the shape of the jaws and the dexterity with which they are used makes these animals successful in getting something suitable to eat.

The sleepy-looking silky anteater of tropical Latin America moves slowly by day, using its sharp claws for climbing, opening ant and termite nests, and self-defense.

This hummingbird, a Nicaraguan hermit, built her nest on the down-hung tip of a palm frond in the rain forest of Panama. Photographed at night by flash, the bird was undisturbed.

Adaptations in the skin that covers the jaws and rims the mouth contribute greatly to efficient operation. The shark and the snake produce a whole succession of teeth and shed them as they wear. Only four teeth in the squirrel continue to grow: the two incisors above and below that meet at the front to give the bite. Growing from persistent roots, these teeth maintain their length and chisel-like cutting edges despite the hard wear they get in a gnawing mammal.

The seal is like the dog and the horse and ourselves in replacing some of its "baby teeth" with a permanent set. But as Aristotle noticed so long ago, "there is no instance of an animal that sheds its molars." * These grinding teeth in the sides of the mouth are actually the last to develop of the first set—the "milk dentition." By the time they are firmly rooted, the jaw bones have taken their mature form and the head is as big as it will ever be.

The fish and the frog have a single set of teeth, a modern bird no teeth at all. Yet however the skin provides hard surfaces to cover the jaws, the underlying pattern remains the same. Only the details differ, matching the type of food and the way in which the animal gets it.

One of the most practical pieces of information about any creature is the answer to the old question "Does it bite?" Nor is language specific about the details. If an animal can seize or pinch or lacerate with jaws of "jawlike organs" (which the dictionary insists include the pincers of a crab), or it can puncture the skin with any sharp-pointed mouthpart, it bites. But when our neighbor's child comes to us for sympathy, showing us a "bee bite," we gently encourage her to beware of the opposite end of the insect and to call it a sting.

From the same origins in Middle English and Anglo-Saxon as the word to bite, comes beetle—a little biter. Some people look closely enough to see that a beetle's jaws meet from side to side, as do those

---

* Aristotle knew that the "elephant has four teeth on either side, by which it munches its food, grinding it like so much barley-meal," but he did not realize that this animal offers an exception to his rule. After shedding the grinding teeth (premolars) of the milk dentition at about three, six and nine years of age, the elephant develops one molar at a time above and below on each side of its jaws. The first erupts at age six and is shed between ages twenty and twenty-five. The second appears at age twenty and is lost at sixty. The third comes into service between ages forty and fifty and lasts for the life of the animal. Each molar is huge. If the elephant is to be well nourished, it must keep these teeth working so many hours each day that the amount of time it can labor for man between meals is strictly limited. The smaller Indian elephant can put in an eight-hour day, but the larger African animal can spare only a few hours at a time.

of any insect, centipede, millipede or crustacean. Indeed, there is practical advantage in knowing whether an insect has biting mouthparts and might swallow a poison along with its food, or is adapted for sucking juices from below the epidermis upon which a poison might be spread. Beetles, grasshoppers and caterpillars are among the biters, whereas true bugs and many of the sucking flies stab deeply for their food.

The bite of a spider is something else again, for the creature has no jaws at all. Instead, it uses a pair of injection tongs that meet near its mouth to introduce into attacker or prey a strong saliva with a dual action. The solution induces immediate pain, then anesthesia in a fly, and follows with a digestive role. If the spider waits an hour or so after injecting its venom into a small victim, the nourishing contents of the prey will turn to liquid and the spider can drink its meal. The shells of flies in a spider's web have all been drained of their contents and offer nothing more.

Most spider webs improve the chance that the spider will have prey to bite. Yet in offering no bait, the spider seems to us a paragon of refinement and good sportsmanship. Its methods commonly match the ways in which fishermen with unbaited nets get their fish, except that it lets a breeze instead of a current of water bring victims that do not arrive carelessly under their own power. The spider appears far more patient than the fishermen on Mexico's Lake Patzcuaro, who use big "butterfly nets" to dip up small fish, or the South Sea lads who stand at favored sites along the shore and from time to time skilfully toss out a circular net. The spider simply sets its snare and lies in wait.

In proportion to the amount of effort expended and the risk taken by the spider that it will be seen and eaten by a bird, the yield from its web is remarkably good. No doubt this is why spiders lie in wait for insects beside one kind of web or another on virtually every bit of habitable land on earth, from sea level to the mountain peaks, from the equator to the poles. They catch the highest insects in the world, on lofty glaciers where little snow fleas subsist on a dust of pollen grains blown upslope by winds.

For us the most amazing nets with which spiders delay prey they can subdue are the orb webs six feet or more across built between trees in warm, moist woodlands and swampy areas. We have blundered into them and felt the restraint of the tough guy lines across our chests and arms. These webs yield before they tear. Small birds and bats sometimes get caught in them and provide the spider with variety in its diet. Generally the

The cottonmouth is all too common in the southern United States, for it can strike with its venomous fangs in complete darkness, aiming by sensitivity to radiant heat.

spider stays near the center of the orb, within easy running distance of a victim. The same pattern is produced by related spiders in the Americas and in parts of Africa, Asia, the East Indies and Australia. All of them seem close kin to the big calico spider (*Nephila clavipes*) which gets food in this way among the palms and bald-cypresses of the Florida Everglades.

In peat bogs we have found unrelated spiders weaving horizontal webs in the throats of the vase-shaped leaves on pitcher plants. They foil the insectivorous leaf by catching the insects that otherwise would fall in, drown and be digested. We have seen literally miles of spiders tending webs spun between the telephone lines along a Mexican highway. Yet surprises remained for us to discover about the ways spiders take advantage of the situations they find to capture insects to eat.

Spiders were farthest from our thoughts when we went to explore some caves in New Zealand to see the strange gnat larvae that are called glowworms there. These slender insect-catching maggots live in horizontal tubes of their own slimy secretion, hung along the ceiling and walls of the caves and sometimes in dark wet ravines outdoors. The maggots slip back and forth while tending a series of homemade snare lines spaced closely at regular intervals along the horizontal tube. Each snare line is a vertical, dangling thread beaded repeatedly by clear jewels of sparkling adhesive.

In darkness, a New Zealand glowworm lights up when hungry, providing a lure for insects that fly in caves or the black of night. The fliers blunder into the adhesive curtains, alerting the glowworm. The maggot extinguishes its light, moves quickly to the snare lines where the victim struggles, and reels them in to get a meal.

Although glowworms of this kind are found only in the islands of New Zealand and in eastern Australia and New Guinea, spiders have taken advantage of their lure lights. To our astonishment we found in the caves dozens of spiders hung on slender silken lines right in front of the sticky curtains made by the glowworms. Clinging by just two of its eight long legs, each spider extended the other six in a symmetrical pattern to grasp any insect that might fly toward the glowworm's light. Somehow these impress us as being the most specialized spiders of all.

Whether on a patient spider or an aggressive insect, sharp mouthparts for feeding and biting seem reasonable so long as no more than two of them meet. That they hinge from side to side scarcely matters. But an

animal with three jaws or more that come together at one point appeals
to us as being more suitable for science fiction. Surely only a monster
would have such a mouth!

Millions of miniature monsters with triangular mouths live in the top
two inches of every square foot of fertile soil. They are slender roundworms which slither through the tiny spaces between particles of soil.
Many of them pursue mites and minute insects, seizing their prey in three
sharp jaws at once. These predatory roundworms could well inspire an
artist to draw fiends more monstrous than any Chinese dragon. Yet such
grotesque creatures in the soil are real.

Leeches, with three jaws each, bite thousands—perhaps millions—of
human beings every year. In many countries that take pride in using
the best of modern medicine, the age-old remedy of applying "medicinal"
leeches is still followed for a variety of complaints. The least of these,
and the one for which the result is most surely successful, is to remove
the bruised blood that gives color to a black eye.

For any bruise a leech can offer quick cosmetic action. The hungry
worm affixes itself to the skin, holding fast by means of the big sucker
that surrounds its mouth, and clinging with the smaller sucker at the
opposite end of its body. Cutting a clean slit with each of its three jaws,
the worm forces saliva into the wounds. The saliva contains a chemical
agent called hirudin, which not only prevents blood from clotting inside
the leech but also dissolves any clot already formed under the skin where
the animal is attached.

Once filled with blood, a leech lets go of its own accord. It settles
down in a pond or aquarium to digest its meal, a process requiring
weeks. Before its capacious crop is filled, a leech can be induced to let
go easily merely by sprinkling some table salt as an irritant upon its
moist back. Among most people, mental relief at being freed from the
painless parasite is so great that no one cares how it reached the blood
it sucked. No one seems to inspect carefully the triple wound through
which the teeth of the leech sliced to reach its meal.

Whenever we visit the seashore we find creatures with more jaws than
a leech has. Gently we free a live sand dollar from the sandy shore, or
lift a sea urchin to see what it is eating. Each of these animals has five
jaws tipped with limy teeth that meet in a central point. It uses them to
dredge up tasty morsels from among the sediments on the sea floor, or
to cut edible fragments from coarse seaweeds. Often, while we hold an

The powerful jaws of the male stag beetle are used chiefly in combat with other males over a female. The larger the beetle, the larger in proportion are his jaws.

Glowworms in New Zealand are slender maggots of small flies. They produce curtains of snare lines studded with adhesive droplets and wait for other insects to fly into the snares and get caught. The longest of these snare lines are found in caves, where there is no wind to blow one line into the next and cause tangling. Six to nine inches is not an unusual length in caves.

urchin out of water and upside down, it continues to nip at a shred of brown alga still protruding between its jaws, like a straw between the teeth of a pensive farmer.

Aristotle examined the mechanism that operates an urchin's jaws and likened it to "a horn lantern with the panes of horn left out." It has been referred to as Aristotle's lantern ever since, intending to call to mind the old-style lanterns set on lamp posts, with a pointed lower end and thin panes through which the light shone from the flame inside. The complex architecture of the limy bars and muscles composing the lantern excites our admiration. No carving made of ivory shows more flowerlike symmetry of design. Yet each piece serves an important role as the urchin extends or retracts its five-toothed mouth, gnawing or biting or managing the pieces of food it has freed.

In seeking to account for a sea urchin's five jaws, which add three more to the minimum number for pinching action, we have only to notice that radial pattern of the creature's shell. Five petal-shaped areas bear rows of perforations through which its slender flexible tubefeet extend. Between the petals are five double rows of rounded knobs which are the balls of ball-and-socket joints where the stiff movable spines fit, each under firm muscular control. This symmetry probably arose as ancestral sea urchins sought to travel in any direction without rotating, whether to exploit food or to avoid a hungry fish.

There is nothing particularly subtle about an animal that regularly bites to get its food. Its adaptations match the direct attack, the harsh seizure, the firm nip, the hard munch, the quick snatch. They offer no surer way to the future than the soft approach. The same seas where the urchins live support symmetrical animals so sedentary and pliable that for centuries they were believed to belong to the plant kingdom. Yielding to each current as though it were an underwater wind, the sea whips flex, the sea fans wave, the sea plumes flutter, the sea anemones sway to and fro. Often an anemone might be mistaken for a glorious dahlia of white, black, red, orange or even bright green due to its algal partners inside. Corals are similarly colorful, their lax tentacles swinging as though flabby. Below each big jellyfish or Portuguese man-of-war, fishing lines trail like elongated sensitive fingers, reaching as much as forty feet into the sea. All of these graceful animals manage nevertheless to get living, active prey to eat. They catch and subdue their food by means of microscopic nettling cells, explosive tools that can be felt but not seen.

We know better than to be completely complacent about such nettling cells, for those of some coelenterate animals contain an especially virulent venom. The pinkish jellyfish known as the "hairy stinger" or the "lion's mane" is one to avoid, as readers of the Sherlock Holmes story *The Adventure of the Lion's Mane* will remember, since the famous detective discovered the cause of death to be a fatal encounter with this animal.

Accidents involving the Portuguese man-of-war are more common. A friend ignored the signs put up by lifeguards along the Florida coast: "BEACH CLOSED TO SWIMMING. PORTUGUESE MAN-OF-WAR." Since he saw none of the purple floats drifting with the onshore wind, he went in for a dip. Soon he brushed against some of the outstretched tentacles from a small man-of-war. His arm burned immediately where they wrapped against his skin, and he decided to leave the water. But he had barely reached the shore when the poison spread through his blood. Gasping for breath, he collapsed on the beach. "If I had stayed in the water another minute, I'm sure I would have drowned," he told us. "As it was, I wondered for a while if I could pull through. I certainly could not have kept swimming after the poison hit me."

Small compact jellyfishes known as sea wasps strike special fear into fishermen around the Philippine Islands, where the most deadly species of all swims with a characteristic elegance. Pulsating slowly, it expels water from below its four-cornered bell, causing its long hairlike tentacles to swirl as they stream out where food may be. The fishermen claim that many men have died in as little as eight hours after running afoul of one or two of these creatures. We wonder how long a fish lasts after colliding with a sea wasp's tentacle—how long before it is inert, hauled up and enveloped by the soft body, to be liquefied and absorbed.

Each cluster of stinging cells acts on its own. Whether used in gathering food or fending off attack, the cells discharge only a single time before they are discarded. New cells within the tentacles move into surface positions and transform into the needed armament. Neither the number of nettling cells nor of tentacles appears to be as important as the chemistry of the poison. By producing a more potent venom, a small coelenterate can capture prey and repel attackers as easily as its larger kin. All of these creatures survive in the same way, subsisting on vulnerable neighbors that carelessly come into contact with nettling cells.

A small fish or crab need only approach to become the prey of a squid or an octopus in the same coastal waters. These predators have excellent eyes and are ready to attack the food they need. Their tentacles or arms,

Porpoises are small whales with teeth used to hold fishes, squids and other sea creatures caught as food. Their apparent intelligence holds great interest for man.

Marine Studios, Marineland, Florida

A sea lion becomes an expert diver and swimmer at an early age, able to pursue and catch fishes to eat in their own medium. After a meal, it basks in the sun.

ten on a squid and eight on an octopus, hold each victim with hard-rimmed suction cups in rows along the inner surfaces. Each cup has a piston operated by strong muscles. Perhaps this is why we automatically withdraw quickly when we meet a squid or octopus at too close range.

On any of these animals we are likely to encounter, the suction cups are too small to do us any real harm. They produce no poison and leave no lasting mark. But a squid or an octopus, when threatened, may pull itself forward by its tentacles and bring its soft mouth to bear. The mouth conceals not only a flexible filing organ, the radula, with which the animal can cut a hole through a conch shell, but also a horny beak like that of a parrot, except that the upper part is noticeably shorter and closes inside the lower. So hard is the beak that a squid or octopus can clip the legs off a crab one after another and then bite through the crab's shell. On a thirty-inch squid, the beak is capable of cutting a deep gash in a fisherman's leg or even amputating a toe. What surprises us is that men who have been bitten severely by a squid continue to be so wary of the tentacles on the next one they meet. Often they appear to ignore completely the mouth within which the powerful beak remains concealed.

Near the surface, squid are preyed upon by sea birds. Far below, the toothed whales use their peglike teeth to catch larger squids. Bottlenose whales eat almost nothing else, and have been known to have undigested in their stomachs as many as ten thousand beaks of squids. Irritation from these hard parts is suspected as the actual cause that leads a sperm whale to secrete a gelatinous mass of precious ambergris from its stomach wall. Yet hungry sperm whales cruise submerged for periods of half an hour or more to find giant squids that live at depths exceeding 1,500 feet. Occasionally they get caught in transoceanic telephone cables laid along the bottom, as far as 3,240 feet below sea level where the pressure exceeds 1,500 pounds per square inch.

The most gargantuan chase in the world goes unnoticed when one of these huge sperm whales, sixty feet long and weighing sixty tons, charges along at twelve knots after a giant squid in the dark depths of the sea. No one knows how big the squids get, although one of the largest ever found was washed ashore along the east coast of Newfoundland and measured more than fifty feet in length. Yet sperm whales must find larger ones, for captured whales often bear circular scars as much as six inches in diameter around the mouth, produced by the suction cups on the arms of giant squids that resisted being swallowed. The undigested jaws of giant squids found in sperm whale stomachs far exceed these hard parts on any squid yet examined. Probably the famed sea serpents are creatures of this kind that expose themselves momentarily at the ocean surface.

On land the fastest race of an animal chasing something to eat is a frequent event on the high plains of equatorial Africa. There the cheetah, speediest of the great cats, runs down its prey in broad daylight. Just once we were fortunate enough to be present for the finish. Over the short grass between the thorn bushes an antelope came springing along with a full-grown cheetah bounding after it, catching up at better than a mile a minute. Just as the racing pair passed our hiding place, the long-legged cat overtook its prey and swung one powerful foreleg sidewise, parallel to the ground. The cheetah's blow knocked the feet right out from under the antelope, and the victim skidded to earth on its side with the predator's jaws already at its throat. Ever since, we have had more respect for what one outstretched leg can do to catch a dinner. We think of the cheetah again whenever we see a kitten striking playfully at a ball, one paw at a time, practicing the stroke that can become so successful during a hunt.

Slow-motion movie records of a cheetah running at top speed show that the racing cat makes use of all the flexibility in its body. It shifts its shoulder blades forward and back at each stride, and twists its hip girdle to throw an advancing leg farther ahead while thrusting the opposite leg farther behind. Scientists have calculated that a cheetah with no legs at all—just pads on its body in place of appendages—could still take advantage of adaptations within its torso to run at better than five miles an hour.

No antelope can outrun a cheetah. Yet these big cats make the chase easier for themselves by watching a herd of grazing animals for as much as an hour before attacking. The cheetah picks out as a victim an animal with a limp or some other physical defect. So often does a predator cull from the herd the individuals that show signs of deterioration that the survivors tend to be the healthiest and no more numerous than the land can support in good health.

We wonder how much selection a bear shows in deciding whether to use its claws to rip open a bee's nest and feast on the contents. A mother black bear that brought her half-grown cub along night after night while she raided the apiary of a neighbor showed her taste for honey by knocking over and raking open whichever was the next bee hive in the row. Under more natural conditions the separate colonies might have dif-

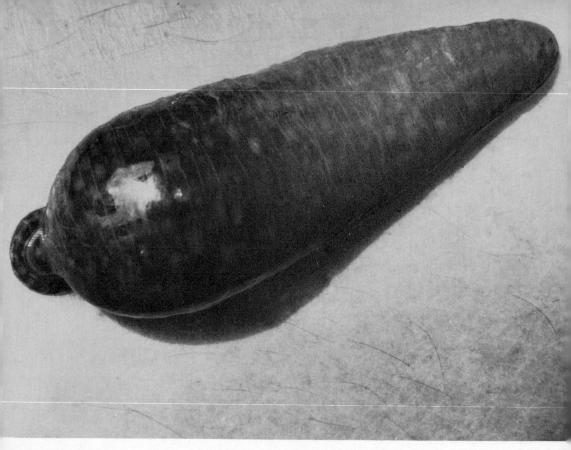

Although leeches are chiefly predators in ponds and stream edges, they welcome an opportunity to suck blood from a vertebrate animal, even a human leg.

The mouth of a sea urchin, located at the center of the body next to the support, has five teeth that meet at one central point—used chiefly to cut food from seaweeds.

fered enough in accessibility to reward some with survival while the bears broke into the rest. The unpredictability of raiding bears and the readiness of the aroused bees to sting kept us from observing at close range. Instead, we helped our neighbor bang on tins and shout to drive the bears away, back to the woodlands where bees nest in hollow trees and might benefit from their choice of site.

In the tropics the mammals that dine on ants and termites seem less dangerous and sometimes easier to approach under the tall trees. In the New World we have crept close to the big anteaters of the treetops, called tamanduas, and also the small silky anteaters, to watch them use their knife-sharp claws to slit through the tough covering of a termite nest. In eastern and southern Africa, the unrelated scaly anteaters—the pangolins in their overlapping armor—perform almost identical movements to cut their way through earthen termite mounds so hard we could make no more than a dent on the surface with a shovel. Each of these insectivorous mammals is a specialist at opening the galleries of termites and ants, then catching a meal of bewildered insects by slithering out a long sticky slender tongue. Any passageway large enough to allow two streams of insects to move through simultaneously in opposite directions is big enough for an anteater's tongue. The animal works with its clawed forelegs and tongue with all deliberate speed to wreck the edifice of the insect society and to reach every termite or ant that remains among the wreckage.

Fascinating as we find the clawwork and tonguework of an anteater, and magnificent as their adaptations are for getting their favorite food, we cannot help feeling some pity for the insects. Any anteater's tactics are the brutal ones of pillage and plunder, destroying the young and the old. One successful anteater swallows in five minutes more termites or ants that a dozen spiders could catch in a year. Yet virtually all of the individuals in each nest are sterile workers, and every one is an offspring of the same mated queen. The anteater is liquidating a large family with one pattern of inheritance. We cannot be sure that these are not the ones with the weakest nests.

As we look about the animal kingdom, we realize how limited is the variety of ways in which animals can extend a part of themselves and pick up something to eat. We can identify most readily with mammals that use their paws to handle things. It may be a squirrel rotating a nut in its forefeet, or a raccoon "washing" a grasshopper or a crayfish by rolling the edible body between opposed paws just below the water surface close to shore.

Perhaps a nearer approach to our use of hands is shown by a sea otter lying on its back amid the kelp beds floating off the coast of California or Alaska or the Russian peninsula of Kamchatka. The animal dives for sea urchins and other shellfish, but brings them to the surface to eat. It may hook one arm around a strand of kelp to keep the waves from shifting its body farther than it wants to go while it cracks its food and eats the contents. The sea otter uses its paws individually in dexterous movements and seldom drops a morsel. According to Miss Edna M. Fisher, who has spent hundreds of hours observing sea otters through a powerful telescope, when one of these animals brings up a bivalve to open, it also clutches against its undersurface a flat stone six or eight inches across as an anvil. Rolling over onto its back, the sea otter balances the stone on its middle and pounds the bivalve repeatedly against the anvil until the shell breaks and the soft flesh can be eaten. At the end of the meal the otter even licks its fingers.

We see our near kin, the apes and monkeys, grasping things with their feet as well as their hands. Yet for some reason they went no farther than the use of the simplest tools. Miss Jane Goodall has photographed in Tanganyika a wild chimpanzee with a slender twig probing a termite nest. It withdrew its tool loaded with termite soldiers as tasty morsels, each gripping the twig with its hard jaws. In captivity, chimps improvise with sticks that can be fitted together to reach food hung beyond reach. But none of these animals seems to include talismans and treasures among things to carry.

It seems easy to imagine the sequence of objects our own ancestors carried as they progressed along the road to the present. Food in hand let them traverse inhospitable territory, eating enough to save their lives until they could reach new sources of supply. Tools in hand improved their use of their environment, and encouraged versatility. Talismans in hand gave them a boost to courage, and sometimes provided hope despite the impersonal operation of the laws of chance. Treasures in hand reminded mankind of past and future dreams. We cannot think of human progress without a special tribute to adaptations that gave us a grasp on the world and helped so much to make it ours.

How an animal or a person gets something to eat is only one side of the coin. The other face is equally vital: what foods are found, and will they bring health and success. To be an animal is to sense repeated hunger for organic compounds of considerable variety. Each pattern of inheritance spells out what must be eaten, as a specific combination of carbohydrates, proteins, fats and vitamins to provide energy and building blocks for growth. More than 600 million years ago our remote ancestors committed us to this hunger that distinguishes animals from green plants. Those ancestors gave up the ability to synthesize from simple substances many of the compounds that are essential for life, at the same time that they traded reliance upon sunlight for greater freedom to move around. Our grasp of the present and chance at the future is one outcome of that exchange.

chapter seventeen

How to Avoid Being Eaten

EVERY summer, by way of showing a few outdoorsmen the importance of a wide familiarity with animals, we point to a golden-brown insect hovering over a flower or busily seeking nectar within the blossom, and ask: "What is it?"

Our friends look at us with amazement. How can we be so ignorant? "A bee!" they almost shout.

We prod it gently with a finger, and it buzzes but keeps on feeding. "Don't do that. You'll get stung!" someone is sure to warn us.

By way of answer, we swoop down on the insect with open palm and snatch it from the flower into a clenched fist. Instantly the buzz rises to an angry whine. While our friends watch apprehensively, we reach in with thumb and forefinger and casually pluck out the struggler by its wings. The insect's abdomen prods around toward us as though ready to drive home a vicious sting. But nothing happens. The "bee" is a fly—the drone fly—an impostor that has fooled many people, as well as millions of hungry birds. It is completely defenseless but so like a honeybee in shape, size, color and antics that a practiced eye is needed to detect the difference.

The great naturalist Alfred Russel Wallace once remarked that with so many kinds of insects in the world, it was only natural that some of them should look alike. But when any creature gains security by resembling an animal that is dangerous or by blending inconspicuously among its surroundings, the masquerade becomes meaningful. The resemblance may have arisen by chance. It is perpetuated because it improves the chances of survival.

Wallace left England in 1848 on a collecting expedition to Brazil, accompanied by another self-taught scientist, Henry Walter Bates. Bates remained there for eleven years, studying the wealth of animal life in the rain forests along the Amazon. His most important discovery was the phenomenon of protective resemblance among insects, which are a major source of food for larger animals and have been driven by natural selection to evolve highly efficient means for surviving. Bates marveled at "the mimetic analogies of which many species are subject . . . Some show a minute and palpably intentional likeness which is perfectly staggering. When a Moth wears the appearance of a Wasp, we infer that the imitation is intended to deceive insectivorous animals, which persecute the Moth, but avoid the Wasp."

Any badge of immunity may be counterfeited. The drone fly demonstrates how freedom from attack may be achieved by a lamb that wears wolf's clothing. The closer the resemblance to honeybees, the fewer times the drone flies are eaten by birds. Yet honeybees are subject to attack by predatory robber flies, and these mistake the drone flies for their customary prey. Each robber fly sucks out the contents of its prey, using a technique that protects it from being stung. It follows the same procedure with the drone flies, which could not sting if they wanted to. The carcasses of both insects, mimic mixed with model, accumulate as a cemetery of empty shells under the favorite perch of the hairy robber fly.

The drone fly belongs to a celebrated group of aerial acrobats with perfect wing control—the hover flies. They are members of the family Syrphidae. Many of this great group of interesting insects mimic the bees and wasps in body form, pattern and habits. Some are slender like hornets, others robust like bumblebees. A few of them use their disguise to enter undetected into the nesting areas of the more industrious bees in order to rob them of their food stores or lay eggs that will hatch to maggots and fatten at the bees' expense.

Almost anywhere, beetles can be found mimicking bees, particularly bumblebees, and frequenting the same flowers. In the northern United States, the bumblebee flower beetle (*Euphoria*) often visits us in spring, flying a few inches above the ground in nicely controlled flight. It enters

So long as a tame flying squirrel has enough light to see, it never bites. But in red light, to which it is blind, it does not recognize its friends.

Disruptive coloration in a tropical bird (Cuvier's toucan from South America) distracts the eye from the outline by which a predator could recognize it as a bird and as food.

among raspberry canes and other low-growing vegetation, humming very much as does a home-hunting bumblebee. In southern regions, the fig-eater beetle (*Cotinus*) is easily mistaken for a bumblebee as it visits flowers and ripe fruits. Neither of these scarab beetles makes any known use of its resemblance to a bee, except as this frees it from attack by birds. The curled, white, grublike young of these beetles feed upon roots underground.

A few moths that are active by day are readily mistaken for stinging insects. The bumblebee hawk moths emerge from their pupal shelters in the earth with a full covering of overlapping scales on their wings, just like those worn by others of the sphinx group. But most of the scales fall off as soon as the wings are used, and before long the insect is as clear-winged as a bee. Even the antennae are shorter, blacker and more clubbed, as though in imitation of the prominent elbowed antennae of the armed insect. Active on the same flowers at the same time of day are clearwing moths of the more slender aegeriids, which have a closer resemblance to wasps. Presumably they enjoy freedom from molestation by virtue of the "pointed arguments" the stinging models carry.

Ants that sting and bite have their mimics too. Some longicorn beetles and several true bugs resemble ants in markings, body dimensions and manner of walking. But the strangest assortment of insects, representing various groups, not only imitate ants in these ways but associate with the ants. They acquire the odor of the anthill and roam about freely within it. They feed on the stores of food that the ants accumulate, and even beg drops of regurgitated nourishment from their passing models. These "guests" form a most interesting addition to the anthill population. There can be no question but that their similarities benefit the mimics.

Most of the time, when we look carefully, we can tell the mimic from its model. But we take no chances when the model is the venomous little coral snake whose shiny body is completely encircled by bands of bright red, yellow and black. In southeastern states from Cape Hatteras to the Florida Keys and westward to the Mississippi River, the pine woods and open fields are equally the home of the coral snake and the unrelated and harmless scarlet kingsnake, which bears the identical colors in a different sequence. The coral snake grows slightly larger and has a black snout followed by a yellow band, whereas the scarlet kingsnake has a red head. Over and over we've been told to think of a traffic signal: red means STOP, yellow merely CAUTION. On the dangerous coral snake these colors touch, whereas a black band always separates red from yellow on the mimic.

It is far easier to remember that unless we are sure, the laws of chance are against us. The gain in imitation would be lost if many harmless mimics could be molested before a predator learned its lesson by meeting the dangerous or unpalatable model. Henry W. Bates reported "seeing the excessive abundance of the one species [the model] and the fewness of individuals of the other." Models must always outnumber the mimics if Batesian mimicry is to succeed.

Two decades after Bates returned to England, the German zoologist Fritz Müller went exploring through the jungles of Brazil. Gradually he became aware of another kind of mimicry, in which mimic as well as model are able to teach a bird or monkey to stay away. The bold coloration of animals that are unpalatable, malodorous, poisonous, stinging or able to bite comes in less variety than might be expected from the number of different kinds of creatures protected in these ways. The bees and wasps resemble one another more in color and pattern than could be explained from their kinship alone. Müller suggested that each bird could learn from one or two experiences with stinging insects banded in black and gold to leave unmolested all that wear this marking. The predator would disable far fewer individuals this way than if the wasps and bees came in many different patterns. Survival would thus reward well-armed insects that evolved superficial similarities. The larger the number of species and of individuals wearing a similar warning, the more each would benefit by being left alone.

Predators do learn quickly to rely upon many different senses. They come to expect one situation, and often overlook anything closely resembling it. This provides opportunities for countless pretenders, animals that can be preyed upon, for which it is almost as important to avoid being eaten as it is to find something to eat. The world is full of startling physical attributes that protect these creatures from attack. At one time or another, most species are liable to be looked upon as a possible source of food. Their survival requires some way to disappear among inedible objects. The arts of concealment match every clue by which a predator might recognize its prey.

A number of animals evade notice because they resemble parts of plants that offer little value as food. One of the most spectacular of these is the tripletail fish (*Lobotes surinamensis*) which lays its eggs among the roots of black and of red mangroves along shores of the tropical Atlantic Ocean and the Indo-Pacific. By autumn, when the mangrove trees begin to shed their old foliage, the young tripletails are just the size of a dead mangrove leaf and the same yellowish-tan marked

So long as the gray underwing moth *Catocala* rests on gray bark and hides its colorful underwings, its camouflage is highly effective. On brown bark it is conspicuous.

with brownish-black spots. When the leaves drop into the water and float along, the young tripletails rush to the surface and literally "school" with the dead leaves. Each fish acts as dead as a leaf. It drifts along with one flat side uppermost, its body curved downward in a slight arc, often with its head slightly lower than its tail. Lazily moving through the water by waving its transparent pectoral fins, it gives no appearance of muscular activity. Concealed in this way, the fish remain with the leaves until the tide carries them over deep water. Into it they disappear, darken in color, and complete their growth.

Many other creatures hide in plain sight. We sought in vain recently for the famous leaf butterfly while visiting in Southeast Asia. More than any other insect known, it resembles a dead leaf that has turned tan and brown, with dark markings to suggest a midrib and branch veins. The butterfly stands on slender stems in such a way that a pointed projection from each hind wing appears to continue the midrib all the way to the stem and provide the connection by which the leaf is attached. With its wings held together above its back and only these drab surfaces exposed, the insect conceals from every eye the handsome pattern of orange and brilliant blue that flashes from the upper surfaces of its wings in flight. Because of these hues the butterfly is named *Kallima,* the Greek word for beautiful.

As though emerging from a conjurer's bag of tricks, many of the large butterflies and moths of the world can flash their colors and then hide them just as quickly. At rest they expose only surfaces that blend with the customary background, whereas in flight the same wings exhibit the hues and markings that conspicuously separate the various species. These features have real importance in helping one potential mate find another of the opposite sex but identical kind.

Most brilliant of these insects that can disappear are the magnificent *Morpho* butterflies of tropical Latin America, whose wings are flat, large and coated above with iridescent green-blue scales. From an airplane above the green canopy of the rain forest they can be seen as twinkling specks of intense blue reflecting the sunlight almost like signaling mirrors. Far less of this hue shows when a *Morpho* comes lower, progressing erratically along a jungle trail in characteristically flopping flight. There the insect performs its magic, settling on an outstretched bare branch, folding its great wings together smartly and disappearing in a split second. It becomes just another dark brown shadow among the myriad other shadows of the forest.

We need not go out of the North Temperate Zone to find butterflies that suggest leaves. Our kinds are anglewings, with an outline so irregular as to imitate foliage tattered and lacerated by wind and winter. Several of these ragged-wing butterflies follow a seasonal cycle that gives their resemblance more than coincidental value. They are active chiefly in late autumn and early spring when green leaves are rare. They have only to cling to a branch and close their wings to disappear. In winter they conceal themselves as adults under bark or in crevices. Judging by the number that flit around on a warm day in March or April, they succeed quite well in avoiding being eaten.

A bare stick may attract even less attention than a ragged leaf. Resting among twigs, our native stick insects are almost perfectly concealed, and their movements when undisturbed are so slow that the illusion is seldom destroyed. Nor do most of them descend to the ground to lay their eggs. Instead they drop them, like so many radish seeds, to bounce from leaf to leaf. They patter like rain when the insects themselves are numerous, to lie among the fallen foliage through the winter. In the spring each pale-green stick insect emerges by a private trapdoor in its seedlike egg.

Tropical stick insects grow to larger sizes, and many of them are winged. Some have leaflike extensions on legs and body that look like the remains of foliage after an army of caterpillars has hurried through. Their kin, the katydids and other long-horned grasshoppers, seem equally bizarre when removed from their leafy homes, yet blend inconspicuously among the vegetation. Some of them bear the most fanciful projections, as though each had become a caricature of an insect. They seem as unnecessarily decorated as a billboard embellished by small boys with crayons. These are no useless impediments, but features that aid in concealment by matching the streaks and spots of fungus growing on the leaves where these animals ordinarily stand or feed.

Protective resemblance attains far greater extremes in the Tropics, where competition for space and predatory activity are especially keen. Except for the largest ants, the animals stay hidden so well that the forests and jungles seem empty groves and tangles of vegetation. The only sounds come from high overhead, where monkeys and birds move freely in search of fruits and insects among the topmost branches of the dense green canopy. To see the elusive creatures of the jungle, a naturalist must wait a while until they move on errands of their own and disclose themselves.

Glasswing butterflies (*Hetaera*) in Guatemala are easier to see on flowers than when they flit through the woodland on transparent wings.

The sand-colored grasshopper on a sea beach may be less obvious than the shadow cast on the sand where the insect made a depression.

We'll long recall one midday in Panama when we tired of treading carefully along a slippery, root-entangled trail through the rain forest. We found a place to rest on the huge trunk of a tree that had recently fallen. So that we would not make the mistake of sitting on a scorpion, a snake or any of the stinging insects, we brushed off a place to seat ourselves. Enjoying just a comfortable amount of shade, we gazed out across a sunny area where light of high intensity reached ground level, coming through the hole in the forest canopy left vacant by the tree on which we sat. Perhaps five minutes passed before we noticed that two of the short bare twigs on the nearest shrub were more flexible than the rest. They bent over, in fact, under their own power, to touch the edges of adjacent leaves. Those edges grew rougher as well as farther away, for the flexible "twigs" were caterpillars akin to inchworms. Reaching out to the leaves, they nibbled off little bits as food.

Suddenly a tattered object that we had scarcely noticed on the same branch of the shrub did something no dead leaf would do. It swiveled around from being in line with the branch to being crosswise of it, opened butterfly wings that were brilliant orange marked with black and blue, extended a pair of sensitive antennae that had been held close to the front edge of the wings while they were together, and probably prepared to fly.

The flight stopped before it started. A ragged bit of greenery higher on the shrub leaped upon the butterfly, and snatched it up in spiny forelegs, crumpling its wings and ending its life. The sharp teeth on the inner surfaces of those forelegs provided a grip as inescapable as the spikes that lined the Iron Maiden of medieval torture chambers. The newcomer was a praying mantis that had stood motionless or swaying gently from side to side as though yielding to a slight breeze. Leaflike expansions of its body (thorax) and wings bore irregular dark spots resembling patches of mold. Once again it stood motionless, waiting perhaps to be sure its leap had gone unnoticed by a bird. A minute passed, and another. The mantis bent its triangular green head and began, almost caressingly, to nibble at the butterfly it held so tightly. Little green horns on the mantis' head tilted back and forth—spiny projections we could imagine only to be decorations since now they emphasized the insect's feeding movements.

We still do not know whether the trogon perched on the tree branch above saw the mantis turning its head. The bird may merely have taken time to follow the mantis after that one sudden leap. But the trogon darted downward, picked off mantis and butterfly together in one snap of its beak, and flew back to its observation post on the jungle tree. It was from there that we saw the butterfly's wings drift down like petals.

So many creatures go unnoticed. They make no odor, no sound and no move that would help a keen-eyed predator distinguish them from the surrounding scenery. Instinctive inaction and protective appearance go hand in hand if survival is to be achieved.

Sometimes we forget that the birds tend to be less critical than we as they search the shrubbery for insects to eat. They overlook true bugs called tree hoppers (or more imaginatively, "insect brownies") that bear extraordinary projections from their armored backs, causing each insect to look like a thorn or bur. Often the tree hopper comes to rest with its thorn pointing in the wrong way, or it settles on a plant that has no burs at all. Few birds are good enough botanists to spot the careless mimic.

In evaluating protective resemblances, we must remember that man's vivid imagination can suggest similarities that have no significance in survival. The habits of the animal must always be taken into full account. We see that long-horned grasshoppers escape from being eaten all day by resembling green leaves, and realize that the insect remains silent and motionless in the light as though taking full advantage of the illusion. It becomes active only after the sun has set, when most insect-hunting birds are asleep. But when the longhorns go flying through the night air, as they often do, their protective resemblance is of no avail. Barn owls catch them in remarkable numbers.

Colors are so much a part of our everyday life that it is difficult to think of the world without them. Yet as far as can be learned, we and the other primates (monkeys, apes and their kin) are the only mammals that can distinguish the various regions of the spectrum except through differences in brightness. Birds, fishes and insects may have good color vision, though different from ours. But among our familiar four-footed friends—the horse and cow, dog and cat, rabbit and guinea pig—we find no recognition of color. For them scenery, neighbors and mates exist only in shades of gray. How then do their eyes evaluate what we call camouflage? What is coloration that matches the inanimate environment to an animal that is truly color-blind?

For us the landscape and its inhabitants consist of a kaleidoscope of multicolored patches—some light, some dark, most in-between. We depend upon matching patterns in this patchwork against patterns we have identified before. Outlines, we conclude, must mark off separate parts.

The common stick insect of North America is generally overlooked as it stands still among bare twigs or while eating, standing on a twig to reach an appealing leaf.

Sudden changes in color or brightness are portions of the outline. Gradual transitions suggest continued planes, while roundness and shadow-casting go hand in hand.

We base each judgment on combined appreciation of difference in color and variations in brightness. Yet where this color sense is lacking, the same scene need not mean monotony. Only photographers dream up the extreme examples and claim that a white cat sleeping on an ermine coat under a noonday snowstorm (a "high key" picture) is as devoid of details as a black cat eating licorice in an unlit coal cellar at midnight (a "low key" picture). Both situations are extremes rarely met. Neither involves color.

A green katydid imperceptibly quivering its green wings to scrape out its familiar calls on a dark night is no more contrasty on a green leaf when illuminated by a floodlight. To us it has color. But so successfully does it match the surrounding foliage that its vociferous presence may escape our diligent search. It avoids being discovered (and being eaten) by lacking contrast in tone, texture and color. It blends so perfectly with its background as to be indistinguishable.

Despite our ability to see colors and the excellence with which our eyes identify delicate differences in tone and detailed pattern, our initial reactions to most objects are in terms of the most pronounced feature. Frequently this is the overall silhouette. Everyone knows how easy it is to confuse new acquaintances when their silhouettes change from street attire to bathing suit or evening gown. Even among our companions, it is often the combination of silhouette and movement that allows recognition. Shakespeare recognized this: " 'Tis Cinna,—I do know him by his gait; He is a friend."

A silhouette must be destroyed for an animal to disappear. The various means employed all gain this end. Distraction provides one effective means of concealment. On its body an animal may wear an irregular pattern of spots, stripes or other markings that catch the eye and hold it, drawing attention to meaningless details and away from the creature's outline. We call this trick "disruptive coloration." It separates a single body into a series of seemingly disconnected, unimportant parts. A fawn in the spotty shade of an open woodland becomes a series of sunlit patches on a brown lump devoid of distinctive contour. A badger crouching in a field turns toward you a face sharply marked in alternating vertical bands of cream and blackish-brown, and you tend to overlook the outline of the head itself. The coarse camouflage painted on military installations and jungle suits achieves its purpose in the same way. The marks may simulate a number of different objects—none of them clearly visible—and distract the eye from the true boundaries. The scaly, mottled color pattern of a water snake, the contrasty feathers of a killdeer, the wing markings of numerous moths and butterflies have this uncanny ability to confuse the eye.

Disruptive bands and mottlings extend across the folded back legs of many familiar frogs as they sit at rest. Our eyes see the markings but our brains fail to notice the legs, and without the legs the frog remains a blur. Among the most spectacular of these patterns are those that conceal the eyes. Any neat circle attracts attention. The eye of a wood frog or a painted turtle would have an obvious pupil and iris if not for a black stripe of pigment through it, continuing the dark disruptive band along the creature's head.

A few animals blend with their surroundings despite movements because their bodies are so transparent that the eye sees through them as through cellophane. The glass-wing butterfly (*Haetera*) of the American tropics is one of the few on land. We have marveled at them in Guatemala, as they suddenly materialized on a flower in front of our noses and then vanished again abruptly—almost like the Cheshire Cat in *Alice in Wonderland*.

Animals that frequent upper levels of the sea are often diaphanous, like jellyfishes. Several different kinds of prawns and many young fishes appear to be disembodied eyes, because these alone bear conspicuous pigment. Early stages of the eel achieve this clear quality in all but a few vital organs, yet they have firm bodies, good sense organs and active habits. Whether at rest or in motion, these creatures are difficult to discover.

Transparency is difficult to achieve. Adaptations that help animals avoid being eaten allow them more easily to match a customary background composed of blended shades of gray, buff and green. To remain safe, the animal must then inherit habits that keep it in these settings. A gray underwing moth (*Catocala*) that vanishes on the bark of beech and gray birch becomes a conspicuous target if it settles on a black cherry trunk. A green katydid on a scarlet poinsettia would be almost as conspicuous as a crow on a snowbank.

The pale tiger beetles, the grayish-white spiders, the ghost crabs that scamper over a sea beach, vanish as soon they stand still. The late William Beebe referred to them as "autochthones . . . that . . . drifted about like sand-grain wraiths . . . And when they did move, recognition usually came too late to some fly, which had trespassed on this littoral hunting ground." He did not mention the sea birds that flew past, noticing nothing edible on the beach below.

Generally we underestimate the rate at which a change in coloration can spread through the inheritance of a species of animal. If the background alters rapidly, as it can with air pollution, the only survivors may be individuals at one extreme in the range of normal hue. Moth-fanciers in Britain noticed a change of this kind during the latter half of the nineteenth century, as soot from combustion of soft coal began to kill the gray lichens and coat the trees near industrial communities. Until soft coal took the place of clean-burning wood for fuel, the peppered moth (*Biston betularia*) had matched the lichens well enough to escape the attention of insect-eating birds. A few individual moths varied from the average. Some had been raised from caterpillars in captivity and been preserved in collections as curiosities. In the wild, however, any moth paler than the average (with "too much salt"), or significantly darker ("too much pepper"), was gobbled up. On sooty bark, the dark moths gained a new advantage. Birds eliminated moths in the normal range of speckled gray, as well as all of the abnormally pale ones. Within less than fifty years in forests tracts near industrial towns, this pressure from hungry birds changed the genetic constitution of the surviving peppered moths to one producing mostly dark-colored wings and bodies. Beyond the range of soot, the old pattern holds, pruned at each end of its normal variability by birds attacking the moths they see.

We explored a similar situation within a few miles of the site of the first atomic bomb test, the White Sands National Monument near Alamogordo, New Mexico. On this strange series of glistening gypsum dunes grow a few yucca plants and a scattering of other herbs. But types of lizards and even insects that are dark in color on land immediately surrounding the Monument are represented on the gypsum by white individuals. They scamper from clump to clump of yucca or alight on the dunes and disappear by camouflage.

Even the New Mexican pocket mouse (*Perognathus intermedius*) displays this extraordinary coloration. Individuals on the sand are almost pure white, though they are not albinos since their eyes are black. Those on surrounding rocky soil, which is the normal habitat for this little rodent, are brown. And close by, on black beds of lava deposited in the fairly recent past, a third color phase of this same pocket mouse is uniformly blackish except for its pale paws. Other than in their color, no differences have been detected between these populations of the same species.

Like the distinctive grasshoppers that click in the air over each of these three types of terrain, the mice have achieved an almost perfect match for the very different types of background. Yet these dunes and lava beds have been in existence only a few thousands of years. Inherited coloration has changed rapidly to save these animals from being seen and eaten. The same hawks and foxes seek them in all three environments.

Difficulties still confront the animal that duplicates its environmental background. Sunlight brightens its back and casts shadows below its body. To compensate for this inequality, many animals have developed countershading as a feature of their pigmentation. Their backs are darker than the surrounding landscape, and the shine of sunlight there provides no warning clue. Their bellies and flanks are pale, but because these parts receive less illumination they reflect a matching tone. When we look down upon the black or brownish back of a fish in sunlight over deep water, we barely see it. Its silvered belly shows a minimum of difference to eyes looking skyward from below. The sides are gradually counter-shaded, thereby reducing visibility from the side. Only when such a fish swims over a sand bar does it become obvious. Then it stands out sharply from the bottom for any kingfisher to see, while the added light reflected from the sand brightens its undersurfaces until they, too, no longer match when viewed from any angle.

Countershading protects an animal in its customary surroundings and in ordinary illumination. Conventional positions for the body are required also. And animals that regularly spend their lives inverted, as sloths do in tropic trees, are usually pale along their backs and dark over the surfaces they hold toward the sun. The same arrangement of colors gives protection to certain bugs, as for example the back swimmers (*Notonecta*) and the small crustaceans (*Scapholeberis*) that swim inverted in the same fresh ponds.

Often an upside-down habit can be predicted simply from examining such a creature. The caterpillars of the luna moth and of several different kinds of sphinx moths are dark green along legs and undersides and pale greenish-white along the back. When discovered among the foliage, they are clinging below the leafy twigs on which they customarily browse.

An animal that matches its background perfectly may still be obvious on a smooth stretch of sand or a clean tree trunk or leaf, because its

With the reputation of being the only insect able to look over its shoulder, the praying mantis uses its special forelegs to snatch insects as prey.

shadow traces a telltale black outline around one side. Ghost crabs on a beach would often be almost invisible as they rear high on eight bowed legs, except for the conspicuous black shadow they cast. Artists often employ shadow lettering in advertising copy, and we read the word that isn't there. The shadows alone enable us to imagine the letters to be raised. To eliminate its shadow becomes part of an animal's problem in self-concealment.

Perhaps the simplest way that animals hide their shadows is by squatting or lying at full length on the smooth surface—spreading their bodies and pressing flattened edges against the terrain. Horned toads bury their fringes under the sand so that shadow and underparts disappear together. The badger's broad, flattened body helps it vanish in a field. Moths on bark employ the same procedure. Ghost crabs quickly twitch their legs and sink their bodies and appendages into the beach until only upright brown eyestalks remain exposed to watch pursuers pass them by. A few lizards and fishes even have extra frills along the sides of the body and tail, which spread out on any supporting surface and eliminate shadows.

Perfect countershading and shadow suppression are not enough. The change of seasons can upset camouflage. A snowshoe rabbit must be white in winter and brown in summer. The weasel that follows the rabbit fears the hawk, and except for a jet-black tip to the tail, it turns to ermine white when snow begins to fall, then to an earthy brown when the spring sun melts through to the ground again. The transition periods may be dangerous ones.

The grouselike ptarmigans of high altitudes and high latitudes have an adaptation that saves them from being eaten by making their feathers match almost perfectly throughout the year. In winter every feather is pure white, but as rocks and moss begin to project through the snow, little patches of brown feathers appear in the bird's plumage. The last few white feathers are shed as the snow vanishes. The reverse sequence protects the ptarmigan in the fall.

Such drastic changes are needed only where seasons are so different. In Florida and other snow-free states, rabbits and weasels replace their summer fur with winter pelage of the same neutral brown color.

The advantages of matching a background in tone are evident even after dusk when day vision ends. Details are no longer visible, and color ceases to be important. As John Heywood, the famous epigrammatist of sixteenth-century England, observed: "When all candles be out, all cats be gray."

Owls and other night hunters still recognize their prey by sight as well as by sound. A contrasty target scampering across a starlit field is far easier for them to catch than the same sized object camouflaged to match the terrain. Dr. Lee R. Dice at the University of Michigan tested this in the laboratory, and found that white mice on dark loam or black mice on pale sand lost their lives to a hungry owl sooner than others that suited their background.

An animal need not match its background so closely if it can keep a good distance between it and any predator. This is true because the ability to see contrast depends upon the proportion of the total scene that the object occupies in the observer's eye. We experienced this effect of distance one hot day when we drove across the flat Serengeti Plain of East Africa. Scanning ahead we could see only grass and the distant mountains, the details blurred by the turbulence of heated air. We were almost upon a herd of quietly grazing Grant's gazelles before we saw them. Their fawn backs and white underparts stood out against the grass at close range. They flashed their white tails and turned away, displaying their white rump patches as they ran off. A few hundred yards away they stopped and began to feed again. Through our field glasses they remained perfectly distinct. But to the unaided eye, they once more blended so well that we could scarcely make them out.

Only a few kinds of animals can actually change their color to match their surroundings, as chameleons are supposed to do. Chameleons do change, and so do tree frogs and some other creatures, but more in relation to temperature and emotional condition than according to their backgrounds. Nervous excitement from detecting a snake or large bird nearby, or from being handled, is enough to cause a rapid shift in color. Perhaps this sometimes saves a life, when a predator drops its victim and searches for it again by color.

A better demonstration can be seen by trapping a few individuals of the common little catfish known as a bullhead or mudpout. In the surface layers of their skin are star-shaped cells containing pigment, most of it black. The pigment is under nervous control and can either be collected together in the middle of each cell or spread out into the many branches. If concentrated, the tiny black dots can be seen only with a microscope, peppered at intervals over the fish's body. The pinkish-whiteness of the skin shows clearly, and the overall effect is white. But if the pigment is dispersed, it renders the whole exposed area of the cell a deep black. The overlapping extensions of the many cells effectively cover the body surface so that the overall effect is black. The change from concentrated pigment to dispersed pigment may require less than a day.

The exact shade depends chiefly upon what the fish sees. If a mudpout is placed in a black tank, it too soon becomes black. If another mudpout is in a white tank, it becomes white. If both are now transferred to a gray tank, both adjust themselves to match their new environment.

Perhaps the ultimate in this direction is the ability shown by flounders and their flatfish relatives, the turbot and halibut. These fishes lie on the bottom, on what originally was one side of their bodies. The young fish has a more normal shape, but as the fish grows one eye migrates to the upper surface. This, together with a strange twisting of the mouth, allows the fish to operate in a seemingly lazy position. But again the eyes and pigment cells on the upper surface are intimately related.

Unlike a mudpout, a flounder has white, yellow and brown pigment in addition to black pigment. Not only are the different colors under individual control, but even the areas of that uppermost surface are regulated separately. If a flounder is on a sandy bottom, the overall tone of the pattern matches the brightness and yellowness of the sand. It changes if the fish is moved from white coral bottom to a muddy gray sand or black volcanic particles. The pattern of the pigment corresponds also to the coarseness of the sand by being speckled. If the flounder is on a gravel bottom, the speckling on its back is much coarser.

The ability of flounders to match their background was investigated by the late Professor Francis B. Sumner at the Scripps Oceanographic Institute in La Jolla, California. He placed the fishes in special tanks with linoleum patterns for background, and recorded photographically the accuracy with which the creatures matched the sequence and coarseness of the squares of black and white on which they lay, quietly waiting for food to swim within capturing distance. If the fish moved, its pattern soon adjusted to the new locality on the linoleum. If transferred to a tank with a different bottom design, the body pigment cells performed again.

Professor Sumner glued plastic goggles on his flounders. Each transparent eye-cover had the form of a little dome painted black around the rim, to prevent the fish from seeing the surrounding bottom. It could still look upward at the sky and any gull that might be ready to attack. Within a few hours, every fish with goggles turned a uniform dark color, regardless of the bottom on which it lay. It could not match its background unless able to see the pattern.

As we look about us at all the ways in which animals avoid being eaten, we realize how rarely any conscious weighing of alternatives enters their actions. Their versatility arises more from inheritance than experience. To a lesser extent, we as human beings rely upon our inner natures. This impressed the Greek philosopher Menander in the third century B.C., who observed that "We live, not as we wish to, but as we can." Mankind escapes from being eaten by keeping escape routes open. Menander commented on this too, in philosophy that was rephrased in the sixteenth century A.D.:

> That same man that runnith awaie
> Maie again fight an other daie.

We see our own reactions more in the monkey that climbs a tree, the antelope that speeds off at the first sign of trouble, and even the bird or the insect that takes to its wings when danger appears. We pride ourselves on being farsighted and reacting in time.

The chattering of the monkeys, the signaling of the antelope, and the cries of the frightened birds are all forms of communication we understand. They help animals survive. Actual language is but a refinement upon the private messages that pass between animals of the same kind, between mated pairs, between parents and young, between members of the same social group. Our contribution is to include ideas about the past and future along with comments on the present among the information that can be imparted.

It is part of our pattern to look around and ahead, expanding our own versatility by understanding what makes weak creatures stronger. Our way is to decide when the survival of our kind becomes more likely through concealment or through aggressive activity. As much as any creature does, we need every means we can develop to protect us from attack. No doubt the difference is a narrow one, between good enough, and not quite. The "not-quite-good-enough" lines of life die out. The others survive.

chapter eighteen

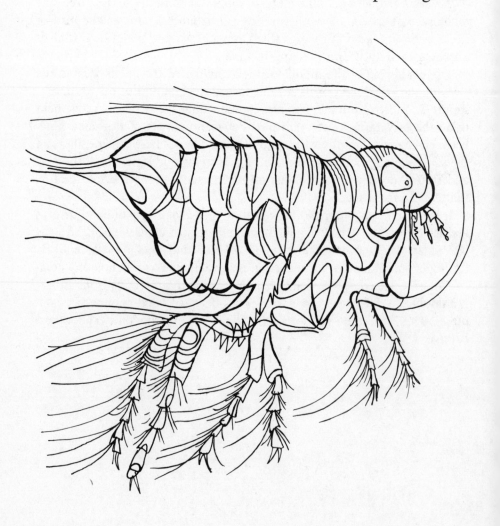

Eating by Proxy

I N selecting topics for inclusion in his book *On the Origin of Species by Means of Natural Selection,* Charles Darwin limited himself to well-known examples that needed no documentary support and to his own observations, where these could be told simply. From among the array of parasites known to him, he selected two. Neither would be a likely candidate for mention by a modern parasitologist, yet they served Darwin's purpose well.

He considered the European cuckoo, which regularly lays her eggs in the nests of other birds, as having inherited this instinctive habit because it proved advantageous. "I could give several instances of various birds which have been known occasionally to lay their eggs in other birds' nests. . . . And analogy would lead me to believe, that the young thus reared would be apt to follow by inheritance the occasional and aberrant habit of their mother, and in their turn would be apt to lay their eggs in other birds' nests, and thus be successful in rearing their young."

Darwin carried this view one more step, to the insects now known as cuckoo-wasps, noting that "these . . . have not only their instincts but their structure modified in accordance with their parasitic habits; for they do not possess the pollen-collecting apparatus which would be necessary if they had to store food for their own young."

Ever since Darwin's day, parasites have provided some of the greatest

253

challenges to science in accounting for the origins of their extreme adaptations. One broad answer fits all queries of this kind: The animals had to become adapted in order to survive. Temporarily, at least, their adaptations reduced competition for them. The marvel is that this process of adjustment, repeated over and over, led to the complex dependence of parasite on host that is so evident today.

With so many different types of parasitic animals to study, professional parasitologists turn their backs on parasitic birds, fishes, wasps, fleas, mosquitoes, mites and ticks, as well as some crustaceans so extraordinarily degenerate that it is hard to credit kinship to lobsters and crabs. Single-celled parasites, such as those that cause malaria and sleeping sickness, interest about half the parasitologists in the world. The other half concern themselves with parasitic worms, and often call themselves helminthologists.

No gourmet is likely to understand animals that seek no variety in foods and, instead, let others do their eating for them. Yet this way of life has led to so many special adaptations to aid these animals in eating by proxy that parasitologists act like detectives to learn how the parasites succeed.

Sometimes the transition required to turn a free-living animal into a parasite seems as minor as Darwin suggested for the cuckoo. Few special adaptations, other than in habits, seem needed in an adult lamprey. These creatures spend their immature stages filtering microscopic food particles from the water around them, competing with clams and mussels for plankton drifting near the bottom. Juvenile lampreys live almost buried in the silty sediments, exposing their round jawless mouths while inhaling water, straining it, and discharging the liquid through a number of gill openings on each side of the head. Rapidly or slowly, depending on the amount of food available and the temperature of the water, the lampreys grow.

Most kinds of lampreys attain adulthood and eat no more. While fasting they emerge from the silt, find mates, and use their sucker mouths to hold to one another or to rocks while placing their eggs in suitable locations. Instinctively they choose an area of shallow water where the hatchlings will be able to dig in and start feeding as their parents did.

While a lamprey is using its round mouth to hold to a stone or other solid support, it is blocked off from its former mode of ventilating its gills. No longer able to produce a current of water bringing oxygen in through its mouth, it makes use of special muscles near the gill openings. Uniquely among fishes, it is a "pouch-gill"—a marsipobranch—able to inhale and exhale water by alternately dilating and contracting each gill chamber separately. Among lampreys that become parasites, this feature is the key to success. Yet it could not become important to them until suitable hosts appeared for lampreys to attack.

Opportunities multiplied when big fishes with jaws evolved during Devonian times, about 400 million years ago. When dead or so close to death as to be unable to defend themselves, these meaty creatures offered a new food resource to any taker. Even a jawless lamprey, with a straight digestive tube and no paired appendages of any kind to help it in vigorous swimming or in grasping at a meal, could use its sucking mouth to hold to a fish carcass in the water. Apparently the ancestors of parasitic lampreys increased their efficiency in this kind of feeding by evolving a more potent saliva, charged with digestive enzymes. It softened and liquefied the tissues to which the scavenging animal held, freeing particles suitable for further digestion in the alimentary canal. Lampreys still produce a saliva so potent that it liquefies flesh in a few minutes.

What could be simpler than for a few additional adaptations to develop in the mouth of such a creature? A few dozen horny spots, sharp-pointed like teeth, gave a nonskid grip over liquefying flesh. A few more horny projections on a muscular tongue could be worked against the food, loosening faster the small particles that would be swallowed. How easily these hard parts could be used to let a lamprey cling to and rasp flesh from a fish that was still vigorously alive.

No evidence remains in the fossil record to show that lampreys attacked sea-going dinosaurs, when these reptiles joined the jaw-bearing fishes in the seas of Mesozoic times. Or that the first turtles attracted attention, as their descendants do today. The oceans still hide from human eyes the full story of what adult lampreys eat after these creatures transform from filter-feeders in fresh water and let themselves down to the salty estuaries and the vast reaches of the marine world. Perhaps lampreys attack sick whales—or did until whalers brought these huge sea-going mammals to the edge of extinction.

During the sweeping transformation that converts an eyeless denizen of the silty bottom into a free-ranging fish of adult form, the lamprey develops a pair of eyes and a heightened awareness of objects in its vicinity. Often its eyes seem so inconsequential by comparison with those of other fishes that they are referred to as degenerate. The lamprey seems condemned to partial blindness as a consequence of its parasitic ways. But it is impossible to prove this correlation. The degeneracy is slight, no greater than that in free-living bats. Both types of animals depend to a great degree upon other senses.

In darkness and turbid water, lampreys show a masterful ability to locate victims and mates by smell and electricity. Each individual swims with creditable directness to the source of an attractive chemical substance diffusing through the water or spread there by currents. At close range, it zeroes in on any object whose electrical conductivity differs from that of plain water. Emitting weak pulses of electricity from special generators in its head, the lamprey orients its movements according to the electrical "feel" of its charged environment. This is a common enough ability among fishes, but in lampreys electrical sensitivity is so great that vision becomes less important.

The distinctive features in the inherited pattern that sustains the survival of parasitic lampreys might have gone undiscovered for many decades if engineers had not built canals to help navigation bypass the rapids and falls between the lower St. Lawrence River and the Great Lakes that the Ice Ages left along the boundary between Canada and the United States. Parasitic lampreys spread into Lake Ontario, lowest of the chain, as soon as men of the nineteenth century built a seaway past the formidable rapids. The lampreys laid their eggs in suitable parts of cool streams entering the lake, and died. But their offspring, upon metamorphosis, had no need to journey all the way to the sea to find big fish to parasitize. Instead, they could stay in fresh water and feast on whitefish and other lake denizens. Soon this resource, upon which many commercial fishermen depended, diminished and virtually disappeared.

Niagara Falls remained an obstacle until the twentieth century when the Welland Canal went into operation. Still, lampreys from Lake Ontario found a barrier in the warm waters of shallow Lake Erie. Not until the 1930's, in fact, did they spread westward far enough to swim up the rivers into Lake Huron. Then their numbers burgeoned in the upper Great Lakes, and the fisheries industry there collapsed for want of something saleable to catch. Lamprey numbers sagged too, but the parasites turned for survival to perch and smaller fishes of no economic significance.

By ruining an international fishery of local importance, lampreys came into conflict with a more persistent competitor: man. Skilled scientists turned to studying the lamprey's way of life, seeking a vulnerable point in hope of exterminating the invader. Suddenly the past, present and future of lampreys became important. In a few years—a few generations of the parasites—man may discover whether his adaptability in providing artificial hazards for the lamprey or the lamprey's versatility in adapting a way around each barrier will win the battle. The fisheries men hope that time is on their side.

Whenever control of a troublesome parasite is sought, this same search begins. How can the succession of generations be halted most economically? To learn the answer, the private details of the parasite's pattern of survival must be discovered. Where do its adaptations depend most upon a chance combination of fortuitous circumstances, which can be made less likely to combine?

Sometimes a parasite loses out so quietly that its absence is overlooked, its former abundance largely forgotten. We think of this when we read the urgent pleas from amusement-supply companies: PLEASE HELP US FIND A SUPPLY OF LIVE HUMAN FLEAS! The "trained flea" act in the sideshows of the world is dying out for lack of these insects, which were so common until the present century. Even the charity cases in public hospitals are too well washed today, their clothes too frequently laundered and dry-cleaned (or discarded), their quarters too often swept out, for *Pulex irritans*—the flea that adopted man—to survive in numbers.

Like the dog flea, the cat flea, the rat flea and about 1,200 other specialists in this little order of wingless parasitic insects, the human flea seems ideally adapted to its way of life. Its body is so flat in the vertical plane that it can walk between the hairs on a human head as though between the columns of a colonnade. Its jaws are lancets with which it can pierce the skin. Its stomach (proventriculus) is armed with hard sharp internal points that pierce individual red blood cells for a meal, making their red contents available more quickly to the flea.

Only about a tenth of an inch tall, a human flea can leap seven inches vertically and more than a foot along the floor at a single bound. Confined within a cleverly-fitted harness, it will pull a little cart several times its own weight. Concealed under a little cone like a flaring skirt, it will dance about while hunting with its tiny compound eyes for an avenue of escape. This was the insect Robert Hooke examined with special delight under his homemade microscope. He drew it for all to see in a double-page illustration, 16⅝ inches wide, in his book for the coffee tables of London in 1665, entitled *Micrographia: or Some Physiological Descriptions of Minute Bodies Made by Magnifying Glasses. With Observations and Inquiries Thereupon.*

Like lampreys, fleas of every kind go through a larval life, eating a diet wholly unsuited to the adult. Like larval lampreys, flea larvae need particles of food far smaller than their own bodies. These insects find suitable morsels while scavenging among the matted hairs and other debris where the host animal lives: a dirty human house, a dog's kennel and blanket, a cat's basket and bedding, a rat's nest. There, when fully grown, the flea larva transforms into a fasting pupa and continues to reconstruct its body within the pupal skin. If undisturbed, the flea emerges in its distinctively different adult form, as an active parasite with its own peculiar patterns of behavior. They lead it to blood, to mates and, if a female, to depositing about five hundred eggs where the hatchling larvae will find their own type of food.

We can only marvel that a creature so versatile in its feeding as a larva and so strikingly adapted as an adult, should have decreased so drastically in population during the past century. Few of the changes made in human ways of life were aimed specifically at flea control. Even the old custom of beating the rugs weekly and spanking the pillows and mattresses every day appealed to people because it got rid of dust or "freshened the bedding," rather than because it killed all the flea pupae concealed there. Virtually no one was aware how delicate a flea pupa is, how quickly it dies if jarred a few times. Yet the new fashions that spread through civilized countries altered the environment for human fleas faster than their adaptations could accommodate.

Where modern methods have scarcely penetrated, human fleas survive and plague the poor. Military men met them during World War II in southern Europe, northern Africa and the Far East. Quick remedies were applied, requiring no education or change in habits. Flea powders containing poison deadly to adult fleas were puffed into the dirty clothing and dirty homes where the parasites were numerous. But poison proved to be just a new kind of dirt. It killed only 99 percent of the fleas, or slightly more. A few of the parasites were resistant, and so were their offspring. In just a few years the fleas became as numerous as ever and virtually immune to the poison in concentrations that previously had seemed effective. So long as the creature survives, it still has a chance to evolve a little more and make a comeback everywhere.

Going from person to person, a human flea causes no lasting damage, although it drives its piercing mouthparts deep into the bloodstream and leaves irritating substances from its saliva that cause swelling and intense itching that may last for many days. Related fleas are highly dangerous to the hosts they attack. The rabbit flea is most efficient in carrying the deadly virus of myxomatosis from rabbit to rabbit. The rat flea serves equally well in transferring the bacterium of bubonic plague and the rickettsia of typhus fever from rat to rat. Unfortunately, these parasitic insects will vary their diet of blood rather than go hungry. If a human flea bites a rat that is infected with bubonic plague, it can subsequently carry this disease to man. Rat fleas that bite people can set off a disastrous epidemic.

Thoughts of the diseases we might contract if bitten by a flea that made a mistake crossed our minds almost nightly in Trinidad, where we camped out rather luxuriously in a run-down mansion formerly owned by a famous family of chocolate makers. The Department of Fisheries had taken over the building and grounds, and the School of Tropical Agriculture had loaned us some heavy blankets against the nightly chill. But no one had kept out the rats, which played games in the attic and walls.

Through the gaping, glassless, screenless windows of the same mansion, bats flew in pursuit of winged insects while we slept with heads exposed. Trinidad bats include vampires, which are the blood-letting, blood-lapping parasites of batdom. A hungry vampire shows no clear preference for locating a tethered cow if it can "smell the blood of an English man" or any other breed. Vampires often carry rabies, as do other bats as well. We took our chance that a rabid vampire would visit us in the darkness, satisfying its own inner drives, even though the parasite was itself doomed by the disease it carried.

In the rain forest of Panama we slept behind screens with the door closed to shut out vampires, tapirs and all other creatures that might disturb our dreams. But we worried about the mosquitoes we saw clinging to the inside walls—insects that entered by day when we had the door open for ventilation. We concerned ourselves needlessly, for those mosquitoes were all specialists that made no mistakes. They fed only on bats or birds, tapirs or sloths, or other hosts far different from ourselves.

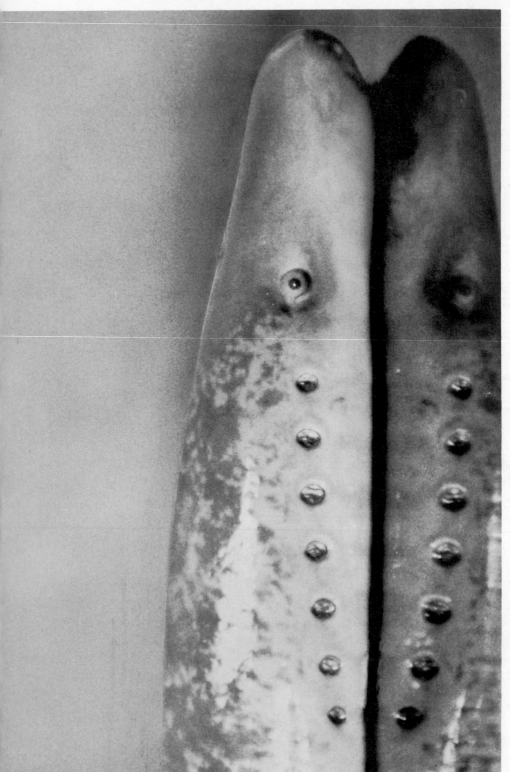

The sea lamprey has a round, jawless sucker mouth and several pairs of gill openings behind its eyes. Through these it can breathe even while sucking blood.

They never bit us, or even flew close. In fact, no mosquito bit us, although we felt sure that the carriers of malaria, of yellow fever, and of diseases less known to us were all about. Looking apprehensively toward those insects indoors with us, it was hard to think of their ancestors. Yet we knew that, until birds and mammals appeared on earth, mosquitoes were suckers of plant juices, just as male mosquitoes are today. Then hosts and parasites evolved together, into the unseen warm-blooded denizens of the rain forest around us and into the visible insects on the walls just below the high ceiling. Should we annihilate them on principle, or let them continue evolving their distinctive patterns of survival? We let them live.

What we feared, of course, was a parasite carried by a parasite. Only a transfusion of blood from a person with malaria could give us the disease more surely than the saliva of an infected malaria mosquito (*Anopheles*) pushing through our skin to reach a meal of blood. To save ourselves from malaria we could only rely upon our heritage from civilization: Our knowledge of how the parasite could reach us, and of the drugs we might take to make our blood unsuitable as an environment for its reproduction.

The malaria parasite itself is so perfectly adjusted to the *Anopheles* mosquitoes that, when sucked up along with a blood meal, it is unharmed by the digestive juices of the insect. Instead, it seems stimulated by them to attain sexual maturity. From the many matings inside the insect come malarial cells that penetrate the mosquito's intestinal wall and swim through the blood to the salivary glands. There the malaria parasites transform into an infective form, ready to go along with saliva into the wound the insect makes. Until these changes have been completed, the mosquito cannot inject the parasites it carries.

So essential is the mosquito to the dispersal of malaria parasites that any interference with the activities of the insect would diminish the chance of success in reaching a new host. Yet to be carried by so slender and fragile a creature without changing its own delicate adaptations to blood-finding requires in the malaria organisms the utmost in inherited matching adjustments. As the disease agents slip down the salivary ducts while the mosquito is probing for blood, they must interfere in no way with the flow of saliva. That flow does more than carry the parasites deep into the wound, as individual passive cells ready to invade the new host. The saliva acts as a lubricant for the mosquito's sharp lancets and as an anesthetic. Locally it dulls the victim's sense of pain at being stabbed, and reduces the chance of a quick slap or a scratching movement that might crush the mosquito before its action as a living hypodermic needle is complete.

Even the synchronized reproduction in the blood, that brings fever and chills to the person with malaria, serves the parasite. The fevered skin radiates heat that attracts mosquitoes, and the repeated cycling of the disease releases into the blood fresh supplies of the infective stage a mosquito can suck up.

We have often asked ourselves how long a time—a day, a decade, a million years—the ancestors of malaria parasites required to adopt their present mode of transport from host to host. The dual compatibility seems too complete to have arisen overnight. Yet the life cycle could scarcely develop a piece at a time. No matter how well the parasite fitted the structural details and chemical conditions inside an *Anopheles* mosquito as a site for mating, some reproduction, and readying for injection, there would be no way to infect one mosquito from another without the vertebrate host and its blood vessels full of red blood cells. Without the mosquito the parasite has no natural way to travel from one malarious mammal or bird to a fresh one. Its adaptations to the larger host selected by the mosquito have no significance until the right mosquito comes along. All essential adaptations must have arisen simultaneously, like the winning line of symbols in a slot machine.

Even the origins of malaria in mankind remain obscure. Its name perpetuates the observation made in the early days of the Roman Empire, that the disease came when people exposed themselves to the "bad air" (*mal aria*) from damp places such as the marshes between the seven hills of ancient Rome. But where was malaria before that? What did the parasites attack before people began spreading over the earth? Today no other animals are known to harbor the particular species to which man is so susceptible, providing a reservoir of infection from which mosquitoes can pick up the disease.

Perhaps malaria is as old as mankind and came originally from Africa. Only on that continent has the human body evolved countering adaptations. One of these first gained recognition just prior to World War II, when a Royal Commission from the Netherlands went to Dutch Guiana to investigate whether displaced people from Europe might be accommodated in the sparsely populated interior of the little South American colony. The Commissioners discovered that the only healthy people inhabiting the area without constant medication were the Bush Negroes, whose ancestors had escaped from slavery soon after being brought to the New World from West Africa. Most babies of Bush Negroes are born with an inherited condition known as splenomegaly, in which the spleen is enormously enlarged. Babies born without this abnormality in the malarious interior of Dutch Guiana sicken and die of malaria in a few weeks, whereas those with a bulging spleen hold back the parasites in this organ until the body as a whole builds an immunity to the disease. As the immune baby grows, its bulge disappears but its adaptive advantage continues. Reluctantly the Commissioners concluded that only European families with hereditary splenomegaly could safely join the Bush Negroes as colonists in the Guianian hinterland.

To most parasites to which we are susceptible, infection of a person is a mistake—a move that blocks effective reproduction and dispersal for the parasite as soon as the disease is diagnosed. A man who contracts yellow fever is put in quarantine. He gets the disease from the bite of a mosquito that normally transfers this infection at treetop level from monkey to monkey as a mild malaise. Behind screens the human sufferer is treated toward recovery where no mosquito has a chance to pick up the disease and pass it along to more men. Similarly, the person who eats pork products that have not been sterilized sufficiently by cooking may suffer intense pain or even die from being invaded by hundreds of trichina worms. Yet each victim is closed away from rats, which normally participate in an endless shuttling of the parasite between rat and pig.

On every habitable continent man has established domesticated animals and cultivated plants in artificial communities. Here they are close to land on which the native kinds of life survive, if they can. Constantly the door is open for a two-way traffic in parasites: from tame to wild, and wild to tame. Infections go rarely in the tame-to-wild direction because competent agriculturalists and public-health officers try to maintain domestic animals and people so free of parasites that they have none to share. They watch for arrival of new disease agents from wild reservoirs and attempt to block the spread of every one.

We remember the day we drove southward through Swaziland into Natal, South Africa. Near the border, guards stopped us for tsetse fly control. The officer in charge apologized for the delay that would be necessary. "But would you please open all windows and unlock the luggage? My men will push the car into the shed, fumigate it thoroughly, and push it out at the opposite end." We walked around outside as directed, carrying our cameras after demonstrating that no tsetse flies were hiding in them. Guards scrutinized us carefully to be sure none of these insects would get past them. Then we were off again, wondering why a tsetse fly could not wing its way past the control station without entering the fumigation chamber to be killed.

Like *Anopheles* mosquitos, the tsetse fly need be feared only where its bite may infect a person or a domestic animal with dangerous parasites. The single-celled trypanosomes, which are the disease agents tsetses carry, cause sleeping sickness among mankind and the deadly illness known as nagana to cattle and horses. Together, these diseases and the flies that spread them have made difficult man's efforts to utilize vast areas from South Africa north to the great deserts, and from the Indian Ocean to the Atlantic.

Almost any bush gives the kind of shade in which a tsetse fly can wait between one blood meal and the next. Warthogs and the larger game animals provide most of the blood. But the presence of the trypanosomes in many other kinds of mammals, as well as birds and reptiles, shows that tsetse flies will bite cold-blooded creatures as well as warm. Although few of these animals show any symptoms of disease that can be attributed to trypanosomes, all of them serve as reservoirs for infection.

No doubt the trypanosomes of sleeping sickness and nagana have been introduced into other continents on many occasions. Slave traders were cautious only to reject men in whose necks they could feel the swollen glands that are an early symptom of this infection. Slaves who developed the disease in Europe or America could not spread it, since all of the tsetse flies had been left behind in Africa. Efforts to save some of the big game animals by raising them on the Mecom Game Ranch in Laredo, Texas, pose no special danger from the trypanosomes they contain, unless some suitable blood-sucking carrier arises on American soil.

We never cease to marvel at the intricacies of habits shown by parasites. Surely here evolution has attained the utmost in complexity! It seems almost incredible that the inherited features of an animal can include a whole sequence of behavior changes just as easily as they include the color of eyes or skin. Yet somehow the spiral molecules of DNA (deoxyribonucleic acid) that constitute the genes must spell out the enzymes and their timing that control what an animal does, as well as how it grows. No other avenue seems open for instinctive behavior to be passed on from generation to generation.

In the jungles of Dutch Guiana we found a tree snail with one eye-stalk grotesquely enlarged by a cylindrical worm banded in bright colors. As though unaware, the snail continued to feed from the surface of a green leaf while the worm in the eyestalk twitched this way and that, like a caterpillar held at one end. Insectivorous birds could scarcely help being attracted by the bright bands on the twitching worm, or refrain from flying over to snatch it away from the snail and swallow it. The worm, however, consisted of two parts. One, in the body of the snail, remained hidden while absorbing nourishment. The other bore the bands, produced the twitching, and contained dozens of reproductive individuals. Swallowed by a bird, these individuals could take up residence in its intestine and there mature, mate and produce eggs that a snail might eat in a film of contamination where the bird emptied its wastes upon a leaf.

Unless the bird swallowed the whole snail, the hidden part of the worm remained unharmed. Once the snail regenerated its damaged eye-stalk, complete with a new eye, the worm could extend a new, banded, twitchable, reproductive growth into the hollow eyestalk and attract another bird. Over and over the jungle drama could be silently repeated. Over and over we ask ourselves: How can such a way of life evolve, complete in its final details to the last twitch before a bird snaps at the imitation caterpillar?

On another day we spent an hour on a cultivated part of the savanna country north of Nairobi, Kenya, watching at close range a grayish-brown bird the size of a starling. From its bright pink beak, white under-parts and white sides to the tail we could have learned its name from a book. But its actions alone identified it as the greater honey-guide. It chattered continuously while sitting on a tree limb close to a knothole through which a constant stream of honeybees flew in and out. We waited to see if a ratel or other mammal with a taste for honey had followed the bird, to raid the hive deep in the tree. The honey-guide would stay to feast on the leftover beeswax and bee larvae, for both of which it has the correct digestive secretions. While we watched, we talked quietly and fitted together the remembered details in the life of a honey-guide. It starts out as a parasite, hatched and tended by foster parents in whose nest the mother honey-guide surreptitiously deposits her egg—as though she had learned this easy way to motherhood from a European cuckoo or an American cowbird. Until each fledgling honey-guide goes off on its own, its food includes only items of diet chosen by the involuntary foster parents, which are of quite unlike kind.

No honey-guide youngster has a chance to learn anything from its own parents. Yet when free to choose, it follows an inherited pattern of guidance that unfolds as the young bird grows up. At first it eats only fruits and seeds of various types. Then, as its digestive tract begins to secrete the rare enzymes capable of splitting the molecules of beeswax into nutritious substances, the honey-guide commences to seek out bee trees. Having found a tree, the bird circles in search of a honey-loving mammal—sometimes a man. Excitedly chattering "ke, ke, ke, ke . . . ," the bird moves toward the bee tree as rapidly as the honey-lover will follow. Often the honey-guide shows this strange behavior even when its craving for beeswax has been satisfied.

Someone, and we wish we could recall who it was, once assured us that in an animal's DNA molecules is recorded a perfect description of its environment and how to live there. So far as scientists can discover, each individual—be it parasite or host—climbs its own way along its inherited DNA molecules in the nucleus of every cell. It grows and acts out its drama of life according to a pattern that previously has spelled success. Yet while watching a live honey-guide we can scarcely credit the sequence of runglike links in molecules shaped like spiral ladders with calling forth so perfect an interaction in structure, function and the unpredictable environment.

Only a small change in a molecule and only a thin line drawn in the human mind separate the parasite that eats by proxy, getting its nourishment from an animal of some other species, from offspring that depend completely upon parental care. It is a distinction as simple as whether an American cuckoo lays her eggs in a nest of her own and tends the hatchlings, or a European cuckoo puts them in the nests of other parent birds and lets them do the work.

Most tapeworms are better adapted for clinging to the inside of a host's intestine than an unborn human infant is for holding to the nourishing wall of its mother's womb. Many a parasite can survive and reproduce in an unfamiliar host, whereas one human infant in two hundred is such a stranger to its own mother that it withers and dies before having a chance to go off on its own.

One small difference in a DNA molecule determines whether a mother can become inhospitable to her own child growing within her, making her blood Rh-negative and that of her baby Rh-positive. So small a difference must alter the world for parasites, too, letting them take a new host or lose access to an old one. For every kind of creature, life depends upon having the right messages in the heritage that bridges time—right for the moment when survival is at stake.

chapter nineteen

The Gains in Coexistence

A
S quietly as we could, and slowly so as not to raise dust, we drove
along the narrow trail through the elephant grass of northwestern
Uganda, looking for an elephant. It was hazardous hunting, for there was
no place to turn around if an elephant blocked the road. Nor could the
little car go in reverse fast enough to get away from an elephant in pursuit, or give us much protection if the behemoth caught up.

All at once we saw our elephant, close to the road on our left, facing
away and apparently unaware of our arrival. Smoothly we switched off
the engine and brought the car to a stop. Still the great beast paid no
attention. But three red-billed oxpeckers on its back shied away from
the parked automobile by running along the elephant's tough hide, over
its forequarters and down out of sight beside its neck. There they clung
with their sharp claws, as though protected from us by a big dusty
boulder.

Ordinarily an oxpecker can go about its business—eating ticks from
the body of any large animal—without disturbing the creature on which
the ticks are feeding. We have seen one of these starling-sized birds reach
right into the ear of an antelope, while the antelope held steady, its ear
turned toward the oxpecker as though inviting this attention. Yet when
three oxpeckers run to one side of an elephant, the significance of their
action is not lost.

Immediately the elephant raised its trunk and fanned with its big ears, testing the air for scent and sound. Then slowly it turned about, while the oxpeckers scrambled around the far side to keep out of sight. By the time they were clinging to its haunches the elephant began walking straight toward us. We started the car and took off, frightening the oxpeckers into quick flight. As we drove down the trail, we saw them circle and return to the elephant's back.

This was tit for tat, ticks to feed an oxpecker and sharp eyes to warn an elephant. The world is full of ways in which one kind of life benefits from associating with another of quite different type, or where both gain from their close coexistence.

Oxpeckers go about their tick-hunting wherever ticks and large blood-sucking flies are numerous. We have watched them working over a rhinoceros, creeping close to all the thin joints in its heavy armor, snapping up the parasites in their strong, thick beaks. Often the dull brown color of the birds and the dust on the rhino's body match almost perfectly. Rarely, however, do oxpeckers visit the hippo pools, where they might get leeches by policing the exposed backs of the hippopotamuses. Instead, the buff-backed herons (known in America as cattle egrets) fill this role. The white birds stand for hours on the huge half-submerged animals, as though each hippo was a smoothly rounded boulder and a fish might swim nearby. The herons snatch any leech that is exposed, and serve as sentinels while the hippos socialize, snooze and soak their tender skins.

On the African plains and savannas, both oxpeckers and buff-backed herons attend the big mammals. But the oxpeckers are clearly professionals, specializing on parasites freshly gorged with blood. This dietary restriction, called for by their inheritance, limits these birds to areas where large mammals graze and forage in great numbers. They have never spread beyond this territory in Africa, whereas the buff-backs within the present century have flown from the equatorial highlands into South Africa, southern Europe, and by way of eastern South America into North America and the West Indies.

Any buff-backed heron standing on the back of a grazing animal in a field is always ready to dash down into the nearest grass to pursue a grasshopper or other insect small enough to swallow. It is expert at running among the hoofs of the herbivore without being stepped on. To the buff-back it makes no difference whether its oversized companion is an elephant, a rhinoceros, a buffalo or a domestic cow. As we have seen in

Puerto Rico and the Philippines, these birds are equally expert in following a tractor being driven at moderate speed, pulling a disc cultivator or other implement that stirs up the insects and exposes the worms. No flock of chickens ever did so well.

The sea has its counterparts to oxpeckers and buff-backed herons. We have delighted in meeting them and observing them at work in the tepid waters of the Tropics over coral reefs of many types.

The grazers of the sea include many fishes, large and small. They too accumulate parasitic hangers-on and need a way to get clean again. We have watched the cleaners at work amid the corals of the Caribbean, where the fishes seek out the services of small gaily-banded shrimp that step audaciously over the corals and wharf pilings, in plain sight and with nowhere to hide. Parrotfish, jewfish, groupers, one after another they arrive as though queued up. Moving slowly, the fishes present their heads and sides, doing nothing to frighten the shrimp that nibble away the projecting parasites. Stepping lightly all over the fish—and from fish to fish—the two-inch crustaceans wave constantly their extraordinarily long white antennae in all directions. These gestures and the conspicuous red bands that mark the body and legs of each white shrimp are well known to the fishes. They signal the location of a cooperative cleaner and not the location of a meal. To a skin diver they are the mark of *Stichopus*—the banded one—popularly known as the "barber pole shrimp." Every warm ocean has them, and everywhere the large fishes enjoy the same casual partnership.

In the Indo-Pacific waters that lap against the Great Barrier Reef, a far stranger and closer cooperation provides food and cleaning for both members of an odd twosome. The obvious partner is a little fish two to three inches long, banded crosswise with three stripes of brilliant white on a body that is uniformly apricot-brown. Called the clown damselfish, it earns its name by flipping about as though on a limited stage not more than three feet across. Repeatedly these movements caught our attention as we explored the tide pools on the great Reef. We completely overlooked at first the other partner—a giant sea anemone whose hundreds of soft dark purple tentacles waved slightly and passively with each little current of water produced by the sportive fish.

Through much of the day the clown damselfish continues its display. Occasionally a larger fish of another kind notices the clown and lunges at it, only to miss and to avoid collision with the "stage" by brushing broadside against the anemone. Instantly the microscopic stinging cells in the tentacles stab into the large fish, holding it and anesthetizing it, capturing it as prey. The clown damselfish can return in safety to bite out pieces and, days later, to clean away any debris left over from the anemone's meal.

Neither of the partners thrives if transferred alone to an aquarium. Without a clown fish brushing against its tentacles and disturbing them repeatedly with swirling water, the sea anemone contracts slowly and goes into a decline, seemingly unable by itself to capture anything to eat. The fish, in a separate tank, has no chance to feed in the way its ancestors have been doing for countless generations—by being a decoy for an anemone.

Using the superb aquaria at Marineland of the Pacific, Drs. Demorest Davenport and Kenneth Norris kept vigil on a clown damselfish and its anemone under conditions that seemed ideal for both the sea animals and their human observers. Over and over, they noticed, the fish turned on its side and brushed against the soft tentacles that would catch and kill fishes of other kinds. Experiments convinced them that some substance in the thin film of mucus covering the damselfish soothed the anemone and prevented it from discharging its stinging cells. But the more they watched, the more they suspected the anemone to be cleaning the fish that slid against it. Its stinging cells might be killing the minute parasites that projected through the mucus from between the scales, or actually catching and pulling them off much as an oxpecker might do with the ticks on an elephant. We tried to decide this for ourselves as we gazed, fascinated, at the same kinds of partners undisturbed at low tide on the reef along the opposite side of the Pacific Ocean. But so quick is the action and so small are the parasites on a two-inch damselfish that the sea hid the answer as it does so many others.

When we stop to think about it, we realize that the clown damselfish is as limited a specialist as the oxpeckers, restricted to the warm oceans in which cooperative sea anemones of the appropriate size and kind abound. The barber pole shrimp are closer parallels for buff-backed herons, since almost any large fish is in need of frequent cleaning.

Most partnerships between living things of unlike kind operate in a different dimension. One partner, at least, is invisibly small. To discover its existence we need to hunt through a microscope. We overlook it completely while snorkeling or diving in the sea. Yet its effect is tremendous.

Only with microscopic partners can the largest clams in the world grow to as much as four feet across, their heavy paired shells weighing

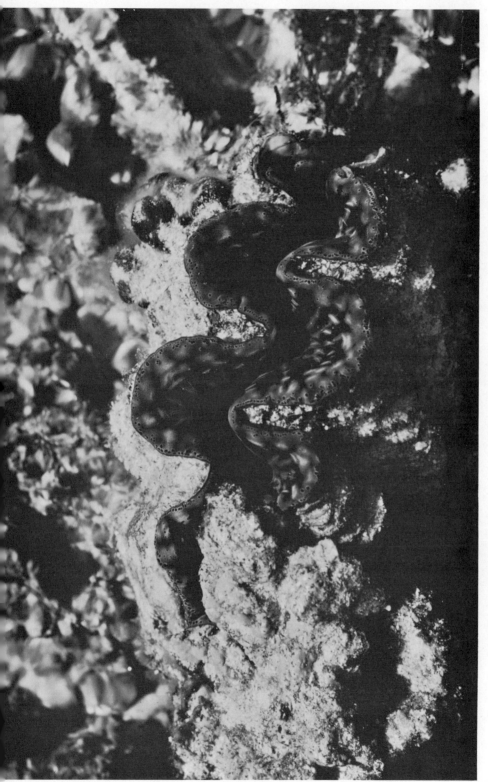

In coral reefs of the South Pacific, bear's-paw clams (*Tridacna*) rest hinge downward, gaping to display a thick, colorful mantle in which algae are grown as food.

five hundred pounds or more. Individuals of this size are fairly common around New Caledonia and adjacent islands in the South Pacific. We found smaller ones of the same kind (*Tridacna gigas*) everywhere in the Great Barrier Reef as far south as the Tropic of Capricorn. Individuals six to ten inches across lay embedded among the corals where only the lowest tides of the month would expose them to air. All of them lie hinge downward in sunny shallows where every day they gape their valves and spread out the colorful edges of the fleshy mantle. No two were exactly alike in color and pattern of dark spots. In all hues of green and tan and purple, from bright to blackish in shade, their soft tissues marked the reef with wavy lines conforming to the sinuous gape of the shell.

We could not blame the scientists who first saw *Tridacna* for believing each clam wore dot-sized eyes along its mantle edges. The dots are there, and the clam responds quickly to the approach of a hand or the shadow of a passing gull. Its mantle edges pull back or push out again like expressive lips. We could make them vanish altogether and the clam clamp its valves together tightly, spouting water, merely by reaching too close to the living animal.

Professor C. M. Yonge of Oxford University sleuthed out the true story, a discovery so astonishing as to rate a place in volume one of the Great Barrier Reef Expedition report from the British Museum. The bright spots in the clam's mantle are not eyes, but illuminators. They suggest the glass blocks built into city sidewalks to let daylight penetrate to basement rooms below. While the clam displays its mantle, sunshine penetrates into small chambers that are true greenhouses, full of microscopic algal plants which grow and reproduce there. Surplus plants are harvested by the clam's white blood cells and digested for the clam's benefit. *Tridacna* is an agriculturalist; the algae are its crop. It has no need to filter food from the surrounding water, as other clams do. On its hidden, inner partners it can grow large. At the same time, it protects the algae from being washed ashore to die in the sun, or being browsed upon by all the small animals in the sea. The algae thrive in their artificial environment.

We can feel a kinship with *Tridacna* in our own way of life. We too depend upon our captive rice and wheat, corn and potatoes, cattle and sheep, goats and domestic fowl. They are our generators of culture, our "cultigens," upon which civilization continues and expands. Without them, men would once more become inefficient hunters of edible roots and wild meat, with no time to develop the vast potential we know is there.

Man has carefully selected for continuation those useful plants and animals that evolved adaptations benefiting him. To increase production of the grain, the root tubers or the meat, he has permanently altered their inherited nature, until now they are unable to survive in the wild. Their existence depends upon a continuation of human protection and cultivation.

How would some unbiased visitor from another world react upon observing a productive farm today? Which would seem the regal forms of terrestrial life—the ones given most space, most light and air, most water, most food or fertilizer? Which would the visitor notice scurrying about, attending to the needs of cow and corn, then huddling for the night in manhouses or in crowded cities? In our coexistence with the pampered plants and animals, perhaps we are the captives and they the enslavers of mankind.

Throughout nature, the test of a new combination is simple: Does it work? The world is full of patterns that succeeded. The misfits have no chance.

The use to which a giant clam puts microscopic green algae corresponds to the plans of space engineers as they seek to move mankind toward colonizing planets around distant stars. They plan to equip any long-distance space ship with green algae in special greenhouses in which the plants will grow, exchanging oxygen for carbon dioxide from human respiration and producing foods man might make palatable. Never is there serious thought for hauling along boxes of seeds and a Noah's ark of domesticated livestock. Living things too small to see individually with the unaided eye are the logical choice. Similar kinds of life have served this pioneering role before—long, long ago. In partnerships they made possible the spread of life out of the seas during the Age of Fishes, onto a bare, bald land—the continents. No soil awaited them because no living things had been there before to produce a soil.

Today single-celled algae and threadlike fungus plants cooperate in forming lichens, which slowly grow under the most adverse weather in the world. They salvage everything they need in life from rain, sun and particles of dust which the wind brings. They encrust rocks that would otherwise be bare, close to the perpetual snows on the highest mountains. Recently we found them growing in the same way on boulders only a few yards from the Dead Sea, almost 1,300 feet below the level of the open oceans. We saw them like red paint on the rocks where the mists drift through a deep valley in New Zealand, and like Spanish moss in the rain forests of tropical Honduras.

Lichens tolerate the splash of salt waves from storms along almost every rocky coast. They spread unplanned patterns on tombstones, stone walls and tree bark. In the Arctic, "reindeer moss" is a slow-growing lichen, its algae and fungi cooperating so effectively that once these lichens supported vast herds of nomadic caribou, and indirectly the wolves and Eskimos that preyed on the antlered animals. No life on land can outpioneer a lichen.

The fungal partner in a lichen takes the brunt of adverse weather. It faces the wind and sun. It fits tightly into the supporting rock or bark. It sponges up the rain and meltwater and doles out the moisture to the algal cells it surrounds. It shields them from desiccation and dispersal, and collects from them a share of the foods they make by photosynthesis. Yet lichens fall into water and get covered by sediments so rarely that fossils cannot help us make an educated guess as to the time when this partnership began. Probably the date was in Devonian times, more than 400 million years ago.

We cannot prove it from the fossil record, but we have every reason to believe that in the Devonian came the beginning of a different venture in which a green plant and a fungus cooperated with outstanding success. Today the fungal partner is easy to meet almost anywhere in the world merely by pulling a healthy pine seedling from the crumbly soil of the forest. Around each of its root tips are fine strands of fungus, tangled so intimately that they give the impression of being part of the root itself. While in the ground these strands extend outward from the roots among the mineral particles, into the films of moisture that coat each grain of sand and bit of clay. There the fungus acts as a vital go-between. It absorbs the nitrates and phosphates and ammonium salts that are dissolved in the moisture, as well as the water itself. It passes on these nutrient materials to the roots of the pine in return for sugar and other products of the larger plant. Both partners benefit from their close association.

We have reasons to credit the first shrubby plants on land, far back in Devonian times, with taking similar partners into their novel enterprise. This strange vegetation consisted only of green stems which forked repeatedly after rising from the sandy ground. No leaf or root of any kind had yet evolved. But the stems did show one new adaptation that helped them solve the pressing need for water all the way to the topmost tips—conducting tubes to carry watery solutions lengthwise. To keep these tubes full by absorbing water from the ground, the plant needed help. We believe this came by taking fungal threads into partnership. From such a frail beginning all of the terrestrial vegetation with stems evolved. This vegetation now includes more than seventy percent of the known kinds of plants in the modern world.

The pines and their kin among the cone-bearing trees are not alone today in relying upon fungal strands around their roots. Some of the fern allies—the clubmosses and horsetails and whisk ferns—live in the same way. So do the heaths and the orchids among flowering plants. Hundreds of different kinds of both find places to grow from the polar tundras to the lofty limbs of tropical forest trees. They cling to the old ways although their flowers are of complexities that show them to be on the forefront of diversification among land plants.

Flowers are cooperative adaptations which promote a loose partnership between a plant and its pollinators. Such partnerships became worthwhile during the later millennia in the Age of Reptiles, when the first beetles and bees on earth began chewing on the reproductive parts of seed plants. But no one could then have guessed how differently the descendants would fare according to whether their ancestors evolved resinous woody cones or evolved showy parts an insect could recognize. One pattern of survival shut out the animals and hid the developing seeds deep inside a close spiral of reproductive leaves. It led to the cone-bearing trees and a limited future, which seems steadily to be shrinking. The other adaptation rewarded any animal that would come gently. It made possible the flowering plants which today constitute the great majority among terrestrial vegetation.

From his careful studies of flowers and their helpful visitors, Dr. Verne Grant of the Rancho Santa Anna Botanic Garden in California has tried to reconstruct the steps that led to this doubly beneficial arrangement. He thinks of a little beetle, perhaps half an inch in length, crawling out of the close quarters between reproductive organs on a primitive seed plant. The beetle has been feeding there and still bears telltale pollen grains upon its sides and back. Still hungry, it spreads its wings and buzzes off, looking and smelling for another similar source of nourishment. Clumsily, after the bumbling manner of beetles, it alights on a whorl of pale-colored leaves which flare out from the tip of a stem, providing a generous landing platform. Jerkily it walks toward the center of the whorl where the scent is strongest. There it finds more pollen, in paired bags with thin walls that are easy to bite through. While feeding on this golden powder, the beetle brushes against sticky surfaces of the plant which pick off some of the dusty pollen from its body. Hidden be-

From a bud resembling an artichoke, the flower of a night-blooming cereus cactus opens at sundown and summons insects with a powerful fragrance, to waiting nectar.

low those sticky surfaces, within a closed fold of the reproductive leaf, are eggs waiting to be fertilized by sperms from those pollen grains. So long as the beetle travels from one plant to another of the same kind, the chance is good that cross-pollination, then cross-fertilization, will take place. The plant gains from the mobility of the insect and from its co-ordinated sense organs and nervous system, which confer upon the animal its power to discriminate. Flowers benefit from that discrimination in beetles, in many other kinds of insects, in birds and bats, even in people who have learned to serve the plant by pollinating it for a share in the fruits that follow.

The partnership of flowers and their pollinators is so mutually benefi-cial that we need often to remind ourselves how long it took to develop, through separate processes of matching adaptations. A blossom could attract a bee or butterfly only by reflecting the part of the solar spectrum a bee or butterfly can see. These flowers range from orange into ultra-violet, often with distinctive patterns and guide marks in contrasting hues within this range. For many day-flying insects, red is just a colorless dark shadow. Reds, instead, attract birds that come to flowers. They may be hummingbirds in the New World, or sunbirds in Africa, or the many honeyeaters with brush-tipped tongues in the Old World, even far out among the islands of the Pacific. For a night-flying moth, a blossom should be powerfully odorous and visible as a large pale target. To be identifiable by a fruit bat in the tropics of either hemisphere, it should reflect a distinctive echo and offer a landing stage where the winged mammal can rest while exchanging pollen and gathering a reward in nourishment. All of these combinations of floral pattern and attending pollinator have proved eminently successful. They have passed the test of time.

While the flowering plants were evolving their interlocking adaptations with the animals that visited them, an offshoot from the lily family—the grasses—dispensed with this aid and spread into the world's windy, semi-arid highlands, to carpet the first prairies. Grasshoppers went along. So did a number of different rodents, most of them small and able to vanish underground. But a new type of large mammal followed, superbly fitted through cooperation with bacteria to exploit the grasses despite the long periods of drought that so often came between one rainy season and the next. The bacterial partners in this venture have the rare ability to digest the cellulose in cell walls of dead grass leaves and stems. They make this food available to the grazing animals that carry the bacteria.

Together these big mammals and their minute cooperators conquered the broad steppes of Asia, the great plains of Africa and North America, the lowland llanos and high altiplanos of South America. A few of them —chiefly donkeys, goats and camels—became adept at "following the green" as the nomadic Bedouins do, from oasis to oasis in the desert. They take advantage wherever the fleeting rains bring dormant grasses above ground.

Recently, while skirting the northern fringes of the great deserts across Africa and the Middle East, we became aware how life depends upon grass and water to make it grow. We chatted with a family of Arabs who were traveling along one of the well-worn camel trails. "We have to move on every few days," they told us. "No place has enough grass to let us settle. But we are used to moving. Our ancestors have been living this way all through history."

The Arabs are well aware that their camels and donkeys thrive on grass, as they themselves cannot because of inner differences. A man has no four-part stomach like that of a camel, or intestinal pouch like that of a donkey. The secret of success in eating grass lies concealed in these special organs.

All the cud-chewers of the world have a four-part stomach. Yet the details of its action are still being discovered. Its advantages are more obvious. A bison in the Northern Hemisphere, an Andean vicuña or an African antelope can graze for a few hours after sunset and several more before dawn, filling with grass its spacious paunch—the rumen that makes the animal a ruminant. For the rest of the night and day the cud-chewer can lie down in as inconspicuous a place as possible, no longer silhouetted against the sky, while continuing to digest its meals.

Almost like a machine, the rumen advances small quantities of the unchewed grass into the second part of the stomach, where it is mixed with digestive secretions rich in living bacteria, then wadded into a mass the size of a human fist. Each wad is a cud, to be brought back to the mouth of the ruminant for patient chewing—a process which breaks up the fibers and intimately works through them the liquid containing the bacterial partners. Swallowed once more, the grass in the cud goes straight to the third part of the stomach, where the bacteria complete their work and reproduce. From time to time some of them spill back into the second part of the stomach, to be incorporated into the next cud. More of them go along with the digested food into the final part of the stomach and into the absorptive regions beyond.

No calf is born with the bacterial partners it will need when weaned. It acquires them, as a beneficial infection, along with its mother's milk. Ever since this fact came to light, scientists have wondered what diet they could substitute for milk to keep healthy and growing normally a calf that lacked cellulose-digesting bacteria of any kind. Only by succeeding in this effort could they know what the bacteria really provide that is important to a ruminant. Finding ways to keep a calf free of all kinds of germs proved far easier than discovering what to feed the animal in place of sterilized milk.

Searching for the answers took so long that the research itself broadened out. Every animal large enough to see proved to require microbes as partners while living on its usual diet. So do people. Harmless microbes also help us fend off the attacks of harmful bacteria. Often, when a person is treated with a powerful antibiotic medicine to cure a dangerous infection, the bacterial partners are killed too. Physicians are now recognizing the cause of new difficulties that arise after treatment, and are deliberately replacing the helpful microbes that can restore health.

At several centers around the world, scientists are studying animals under "germ-free" conditions. By comparing the special diet that is required with what the same kind of animal gets to eat in the wild, they learn what substances are ordinarily contributed by the bacterial partners. Dairy cattle get fatty acids and certain vitamins from the bacteria in their stomachs. Our own bacterial partners supply us with several of the B vitamins and vitamin K, in return for a share of the food we eat.

Each species of animal shows its own peculiarities. Its bacterial partners unlock a supply of essential ingredients which could not be obtained otherwise from the foods that are available.

These discoveries, showing the interdependence of living things, require additions on the checklist of items to be taken along when men go for extended visits to distant planets. That astronauts may encounter microbes for which they have no resistance could be a bad dream. But that people and other earthlings sent on missions away from our planet will need their customary inner partners is no fantasy; it has become an established fact.

chapter twenty

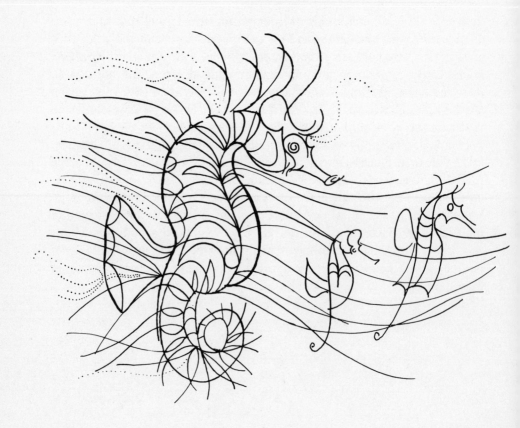

All in the Family

IN the welcome shade of a big bo-tree, we sat on the lawn in the botanic garden of Singapore, enjoying our picnic lunch and the antics of a troupe of about forty monkeys. They were long-tailed macaques. Some scrambled among the spreading branches of the bo-tree, eating the rusty-red figs that ripened on short stems and dropping their mistakes—the occasional immature fruits they plucked. Others sat and played on the ground.

From somewhere behind us a big male crossed the grass. He eyed us as he walked unhurriedly, his tail arched like a furry rainbow with the tip almost brushing the top of his head. Every monkey in his path stepped aside, recognizing that arched tail as the mark of dominance.

We tossed a small piece of sweet biscuit in his direction. He ignored it, and continued on his way. A mother with a baby clinging below her body ran lightly over and picked up the food. She stood watching us, to see if another would come her way. Her baby freed itself and scampered in our direction. She caught it by the tail and hauled it to her.

These are Old World monkeys, unable to hang by their tails as those in the Americas do. But this long appendage still serves in other ways important to everyday life. So do the grimaces, the threat movements, and the cries that take the place of actual fighting and keep the troupe together.

283

Under a bo-tree, sacred to the memory of Lord Buddha, seemed an ideal place in which to think about the gregarious habits of monkeys, people and other animals. Alive, all around us, were the facial and vocal forms of communication described by Charles Darwin in his book *The Expression of the Emotions in Man and Animals*. Here was the smacking of lips over a particularly tasty fig, and the motherly cuddling of a baby that seemed to need reassurance. Here two monkeys disputed the right to a cluster of fruit, and each drew back its lips to expose its shining eye-teeth, letting the other make an instantaneous decision as to which could give a sharper bite.

Every action we could see seemed to arise through mutual awareness of monkey to monkey. Usually the conclusion settled "This close you can stay, but no closer!" Sometimes, the converse seemed more significant: "This far I can go, and no farther." But all of the variations in timing and relative position entered into the judgment. A mother with a baby brooked no interference and no close approach. Yet as soon as her youngster grew enough to venture safely a short distance on his own, she could relax with others of her sex and age, to engage in mutual grooming. The monkey that failed to move smartly and far enough when the dominant male strode by got cuffed (or worse) to teach respect. The one that lagged behind the troupe and suddenly noticed his isolation came racing back as though pursued.

All of these monkey rules seem to us worthy of a human society. They relate to a common need for parents to protect helpless babies for a year or more. For a monkey or a child, it takes a long while to grow and to learn how to take care of self within the confines of the group. True independence is never achieved, just as Henry Thoreau never outgrew his need to walk from Walden Pond to Concord to enjoy a home-cooked meal with other people.

We can see no sharp distinction between the complex interplay of sociable monkeys and that of gregarious people. Both promote survival in the young. Nor do clear boundaries separate these relationships from simpler ones in other animals. Every gradation in parental care, in awareness of the next generation or in instinctive provision for offspring, is in regular use by some kind of creature as a pattern that earns it a place in the future.

Some form of communication lies at the heart of each pattern. It may be only a willingness in the mother to stay with her eggs, using her body as a shield for the little ones that hatch out. But those eggs and young

The female tree cricket has no ears and cannot hear the male as other males can. But she comes to the luring scent he produces while he makes his call.

must communicate with her through her senses, by scent or touch or sight or some combination. We discovered a new facet of this behavior recently in a dark brown wolf spider, whose legs would span an area larger than a silver dollar. She stood atop a little birch tree that we had planted close to a pond, contrasting conspicuously with dense webbing that tied all of its foliage together. We assumed that caterpillars of fall webworm moths were in that silken tent, eating the birch leaves, and we wanted to get rid of them. But the spider seemed surprisingly reluctant to move off.

Only after we had pulled all of the webbing together into a ball and freed it from the birch did we realize that it was spider web, spun around an egg mass that had already hatched. Hastily we dropped the silken swaddling on the ground, perhaps a foot from the mother spider. Already the dozens—possibly hundreds—of spiderlets were swarming out of their torn covering and running off in all directions.

We stayed to watch, to ward off any hungry toad or any spider-hunting wasp that might seek to capture the spiderlets to stock a nest. In a minute or two each little spider seemed to sense that danger had ended. It returned to the ruined nest on the ground along a fine thread spun automatically as it escaped. Soon the mother spider began to hunt. She found her brood huddled together and brushed against them. Immediately the spiderlets climbed atop her back—every one of them. Without hesitation the mother spider strode over to the birch tree and climbed to its top. Still burdened with her young, she began pulling leaves together and spraying them with silk. Part way through the operation, she stopped and every spiderlet crept off her body, down into their new nursery. Did she communicate to them by sound or by some subtle vibration meaningful only among spiders? As soon as all had left her, she continued building her silken tent.

For nearly two weeks we visited her daily as she stood on guard. Below the tent we could see the spiderlets all clustered together. She could not feed them or get anything for herself to eat either. But she had already provided enough food in every egg to nourish a spiderlet to a stage at which it would go off on its own. Only when all had departed and the nursery stood empty for several days did she leave, her instinctive duty done.

To see a creature with eight legs, eight eyes and a miniature nervous system manage so well despite adversity, getting her offspring launched in the normal way on schedule, gave us confidence in evolution. The spider mother came from a long line of similar ancestors whose reactions had been right for each occasion. They were the successful ones, passing to their spiderlets at every generation the pattern of inherited guidance we had seen succeed. Our hasty interference, like the drenching rainstorm that wet the spider (but not her young) a few days later, fell within the range of situations she could handle almost automatically.

In the slow changes that make living things suit so well their conditions of life, time is no dice box from which a purely random cluster emerges at each throw. Instead, the living dice are loaded for success because most of the losing combinations have been removed. The changes allowed by inheritance are just variations on a winning streak—enough to let most of the offspring match the old way of living and a few be ready for whatever change may come in the environment. To the mother spider we could have been a windstorm, even on a calm day.

For the female alone to receive the inherited guidance that led her to guard her eggs and young did not surprise us. In this pattern she matched a host of other animals. The mother octopus in her rocky cavern fasts in a similar way for almost a month while she strokes her strings of eggs with sensitive tentacles, polishing away any algal slime or syringing out any particles of silt with a well-directed jet of seawater from her mantle cavity. The female python and the mother crocodile are the only members of the family to guard the nest. The female hummingbird drives her mate away before she completes the lichen-covered cup in which she lays the two eggs he fathered; she attends to incubation and feeding with no help. Only the female marsupial, such as a kangaroo or koala bear, has a pouch for her baby. Only the female of any mammal has milk to offer, although there is nothing wrong with the mammary glands of the male; his inheritance simply does not call forth the hormones that would cause milk to form.

When not tending her nest, the large wolf spider would pounce on any carpenter ant she found. Yet these ants follow genetic instructions at least as complex as those of the spider, despite their smaller size. The queen ant is the largest member of her family, with the largest responsibilities. It is she alone that scurries into some place of seclusion following her mating flight. Twisting and turning, she breaks off the shining wings she will never need again. She prepares a small chamber, and in it lays a few pale eggs—a dozen or so—before settling down to tend them.

When her eggs hatch into small hungry grubs, the queen ant feeds them in a special way. She lays a new egg, an expendable one, chews it

In northern Australia, the mound-building termites orient their cement-hard nests as though with a compass, edge-on to the hot sun at noon, flat-on to early and late sun.

The black scarab beetle, rolling its ball of camel dung to a suitable burial site where it can serve as food for her young, became a sacred symbol in early Egypt.

up thoroughly in her hard jaws, and presents the mashed material to each grub in turn. When she needs more food for them, she gets it from her own body in the same way. For weeks the grubs grow on this strange diet, with their queen mother in constant attendance. Finally she can relax, for they spin little cocoons for themselves and slowly transform into worker ants.

From this point on, the queen's inherited guidance calls for her to do almost nothing except lay eggs. The worker ants are the most dutiful of children. They forage for food and feed their mother. They care for the eggs she lays to expand the colony, and tend the grubs that hatch. They find a new and larger home when it is needed, and help the queen to reach it. They even communicate with their queen when they are ready to care for another egg.

The ties of motherhood are most familiar to us among the birds and mammals. They appear also among the lesser animals in which the mother remains guarding her eggs until she sees her offspring. According to the charming Arab proverb, "In the eyes of a mother dung beetle, her young are as the gazelle." Perhaps the Arabs also noticed what scientists know today: that if the mother gives her mate some attention, he may stay around to help. Scientists call it reinforcing the pair bond. Even a male dung beetle is ready to work, but the length of his stay depends on his own inherited guidance and on frequent communications from his mate.

The big black dung beetle that the ancient Egyptians venerated as their sacred scarab may roll a big sphere of dung from morning until night. A female will attempt this by herself. But her chances of getting it to suitable soil in which to bury it, and raising a family, are improved greatly if she keeps her mate interestetd. To do so she needs only to go around the ball from time to time and touch feelers with him, as though to prove that she knows he is there. Given such simple encouragement, he will push the ball while she pulls, or pull while she pushes. He will help her dig earth from under the ball, sinking it below ground where it will be safe from the dry heat of the sun. Two beetles can cooperate also in enlarging a brood chamber, like a private cave beside the buried ball. They will wait there, touching one another frequently, until their eggs hatch and it is time to feed the grubs. Somehow the hatchlings make their hunger known in the darkness of the chamber. Each adult beetle responds by eating at the dung ball and transforming the nourishment into a milklike liquid the grubs take greedily. The young cannot feed themselves. They depend upon this strange food until they have grown to full size and burrowed away, to transform into beetles with the same inherited instructions.

When we find a dung beetle working alone with her precious ball we wonder if her enterprise is doomed. Did her failure to maintain the pair bond end her chance to raise a family, or will another mate join her and give her a second opportunity? She still has the ball like a bank account. She still has her unlaid eggs. If she harkens to the inner messages we assume she inherited, and chance (or some communication from her) brings a fresh male in her direction, surely her life can roll on again.

The little wren who nests in an empty gourd outside our study window is not always so ready for a new partner. If she neglects her mate while spurning the other sites he chooses in favor of the gourd, or while hauling in twigs and feathers, or while incubating her ten to fifteen eggs, her work is lost. She must keep him interested and show him the hatchlings, because one wren cannot bring enough insects to feed all those youngsters to flying age. If tragedy takes the male the female soon abandons her little family. With luck she will find a new mate and try again when next the breeding season comes around.

On three separate occasions at the edge of our pond we have lowered a finger and saved a life. Each time, a female damselfly has gained another chance. We have lifted her out of the water and set her down to dry her wings and try again. We can't be sure whether she or the male who deserted her brought on the crisis. Ideally the male damselfly fulfils his role. As the mated pair fly in tandem, he leads. His claspers hold firmly around her slender neck, linking the two and providing an avenue for communication between them. She signals to him when her eggs are ready, and he changes course. No longer does he fly as though at random, low above the water or to resting places on rocks and overhanging leaves. Instead he seeks out a soft stem of a waterweed or other plant that rises out of the pond. Alighting expertly, he places his mate where she can cling farther down to the same slender stalk. Still in tandem, the two back down the plant until the female is completely immersed and the water film rises halfway up his long slender abdomen. Now she can lay her eggs two inches below the surface of the pond. No change in water level should expose them to dry air during the few days before they hatch.

Again the female signals. Her work is done. She relies upon her mate to hold firmly and pull her up the stem, through the water film. He walks and fans with his wings to provide the power, as though aware that his

A mother wolf spider running over the pebbles of a beach, carrying with her several dozen spiderlings that are not ready to become independent.

mate has held her breath quite long enough and is too frail—or perhaps exhausted—to clamber out of the pond by her own efforts. Until she is free in air and her wings are dry, he usually hangs on and responds to her communications.

But what happens if she takes too long laying her eggs, or if another attractive female damselfly alights on the waterweed, tantalizingly close? The male may let go with his claspers, walk up the stalk, let his abdomen dry in the sun, and go winging off to chase a new mate, leaving the old one to drown. When we see this happen, we give her the benefit of any doubt and gently lift her out. Until she is rescued and dry again, the damselfly is willing to cling to any finger.

Around the ponds and swamp edges of northern South America, the male of the famous Surinam toad has an equally important responsibility written into his inheritance. After he has fertilized the eggs his mate lays, he must smear them in their jelly over her rounded back. He finds place there for about sixty of them. Slowly her skin crinkles up around the eggs and cups each one in a private crypt. The mates can part company, for she has become a living perambulator. Able to move about as freely as ever, she feeds herself while the embryos develop, hidden in the skin of her back. Under cover they attain the form of tiny toadlets. Then each creeps out of its crypt and goes off on its own.

The tables are reversed by a one-inch water bug. The female seizes her mate before he can get away and cements upon his back a whole raft of cigar-shaped eggs. She departs, presumably to find another mate, while the loaded male appears to sulk among the weeds at the bottom of the pond. Until the eggs hatch in a week or two, the cement remains waterproof. No scraping on his part can free him of his burden.

It is unusual for the male to take over by himself so many of the duties of motherhood. Yet among some fishes and birds, paternal care seems to be given quite willingly. We often see one of the small sunfishes patrolling back and forth above a sandy area in the pond, so intent upon his fatherhood that he seems unaware how conspicuous he is in the bright sunshine. Even the little spot of iridescent blue tipping his gill cover shows on each side as he turns this way and that. Alertly he drives away any other fish that approaches the nest he prepared in the sandy bottom. He has already enticed a mate to lay her eggs in it. He fertilized them and chased her away. Until those eggs hatch he will do nothing else but protect them in every way he can.

A male stickleback seems equally devoted, but with a difference. He has built a nest of plant materials with a front door and a back, shaped almost like a doughnut. Facing the pond from either door, he watches for a female fish of his own kind to come within sight. He darts out to investigate any females that approach, and does his best to nudge and cajole each into his sanctuary. Occasionally one comes willingly and takes the hint: she lays a few eggs and departs while he sprays them with milt. He will be the father of all the young that hatch, but any willing female of his species can be a mother. He keeps no harem. He simply tends the nursery, and continues to do so until the offspring swim away —in so many directions that he cannot possibly herd them back to the nest.

These successful patterns of behavior seem repeated in some of the world's most amazing birds. The mound-builders of Australasia correspond in this way to the sticklebacks, for the male tends the nest for a single mate. Yet he manages to incubate her eggs without supplying the heat himself. In the hot tropics he may use the warmth of sand baked in the sun. Where steam vents and other signs of volcanic activity are present, he relies on heat from the ground. Otherwise he and his mate work hard for weeks in scratching together vegetation and earth into a huge mound—the largest nest in the world—as much as ten feet high and fifty in diameter. Then the male takes over while his mate looks for food, part of which she will transform into the yolk of the eggs she soon will lay.

The male mound-builder rearranges the earth to cover the vegetation in the mound, and repeatedly probes with his beak as though it were a thermometer to ascertain the temperature below the surface. If the hot sand he has buried, or the earth's volcanic heat, or the warmth from the fermenting vegetation raises the temperature above 92° F., he pulls off some of the covering. If the temperature is lower, he piles on more— like a blanket. When the temperature is just right, he calls his mate and digs a deep hole into which she lays one egg. Day after day he repeats this probing and adjusting and calling until the mound is a great incubator, full of little birds developing in their shells. As each one hatches, it scrambles to the surface and runs off. It is almost ready to fly, and fully equipped to feed itself. The male pays no attention. He is too busy tending the nest.

Among the largest of living birds—the rheas, emus, cassowaries and ostriches—the male guards the eggs for a number of mates in a single nest. Only among the ostriches of Africa does a female relieve him for a few hours, when the sun is too clouded and the day too cool to keep the eggs warm while he gets up to stretch his long legs. Then back he comes, sending her away. Carefully he places his feet among the twelve to twenty eggs, and sits down over them. Craning his neck, he looks to see if any of his smooth charges remain exposed. By rising slightly, he can crook his neck like an old-fashioned buttonhook around any egg and pull it into the cluster below his body.

In seeing a similarity between the behavior of the male ostrich and the male stickleback, we notice also how many more successful patterns are evident among fishes than among birds. Perhaps the explanation lies in the fact that fishes have had three times as many millions of years to diversify, and at least three times as much space in oceans and fresh waters to seek nesting sites. The world today has roughly three times as many different kinds of fishes as it has birds. Each kind has its own successful pattern.

Many of our friends are fish-fanciers. Those among our neighbors who raise tropical fishes often call us over to see some special activity. One evening we hurried to watch a male sea horse following his mate around, displaying his empty pouch. At intervals the female was ready. Acting as though just to oblige him, she laid an egg into his pouch, giving him something to guard. A few weeks later, our friend called us back to the lighted aquarium to watch the male sea horse "giving birth" every few minutes to miniature fishes. They popped out of his pouch, launched by a jet of water on their individual careers.

It is far easier to go to a neighbor's home to watch these unusual antics than to see fishes behaving in the same way in some far-off place. One of our neighbors has a fish that particularly delights us. It comes from Lake Tanganyika. At breeding time the male identifies himself by digging a depression in the gravel bottom of the aquarium. His mate looks identical to us—just a small black cichlid with white spots. But she responds by laying eggs in the nest he makes, and gets out of the way while he fertilizes them with milt. Then he picks up the eggs into his capacious mouth, one or two at a time until he holds them all. For nearly two weeks he guards them in this curious way, keeping his mouth slightly ajar. We can see the eggs inside, rolling about in the water current that aerates them. When they hatch, the tiny fish swim out. But still he eats nothing—just stands by, literally gaping toward his young. At the slightest tap on the glass of the aquarium, every one of those little fish darts back inside his mouth to safety. Our neighbor assures us the father never makes the mistake of swallowing one.

Another pair of fishes puts on a more spectacular display. They are pompadours from South America, shaped like angelfishes although members of the same big cichlid family. Both parents tend the eggs, taking turns in guarding, mouthing and fanning them. When the little fishes hatch the parents seem to compete for the privilege of picking them up and depositing them carefully near the edge of a leaf somewhere in the tank. There, for three or four days, each youngster dangles at the end of a short thread, still being nuzzled and tended by the two adults.

When the little pompadours use up all of the yolk from the egg, they wriggle free and swim to the nearer parent. They cluster on a broad flank, nibbling hungrily at a secretion from special mucus cells that protrude from the skin. Every once in a while the adult fish with the nursing young swims by the mate. With an abrupt flip, every little fish is transferred to the other parent. "Now it's your turn to feed the babies!" seems a fair translation of the wordless message that must pass between them.

All adult pompadours have the special mucus cells. We see no reason why any mature fish could not offer equal protection and nourishment to a brood of young. But in these creatures, as in so many others, the timing of parental care is part of the instinctive pattern. Only for a month or two after the eggs are laid will a mated pair of pompadours tolerate their hatchlings and defend a territory around the nesting site. Once the young seem independent, the family ties dissolve and all boundaries lose their meaning.

Most animals are like these fishes, or the toads and spiders, in going off on their own as soon as they are old enough. Thereafter, except during the breeding seasons scheduled by their heredity, they may ignore so far as possible all other members of their species.

We notice any massing of animals of the same kind, possibly because it is less usual. But just because many are close to one another does not necessarily mean that they are cooperating to form a society. Some cluster together while feeding or drinking, or hibernate in large aggregations as some ladybeetles do. Others assemble into large groups to migrate, as is characteristic of swallows and hawks and some insects. In Europe, cabbage butterflies travel southward in autumn in such large white clouds that they can be seen for miles. But as soon as the migrants reach their destination, their pattern breaks up. They form no lasting liaisons.

Parental care is shown in some horned lizards of the American Southwest, whose new-hatched young ride pick-a-back for a few days on the patient mother.

There is one very good reason why most creatures free to move do not show the tolerance and interdependence needed to travel in groups. Very few eat the kind of food that can be obtained under crowded conditions. The herrings that swim in schools filter microscopic plants from the sea as they travel. Grazing animals in herds walk almost daily to reach untouched pastures. Fiddler crabs on warm seabeaches can swarm like armies on parade to pick from the wet sand and mud the small particles they eat; they can do this only because the tide recedes twice a day and spreads a fresh supply of food on the same area. Yet in none of these aggregations does one individual do anything for another of the same sex and age. Mature adults give no special care to younger members of their kind unless they are the parents.

To be sociable is to give, generally with gifts of food and frequent communications going in every direction within the group. Yet being sociable is not enough to produce a society.

Sometimes the beavers in a pond appear to cooperate as a society. Any one of them, if strong enough, will help repair the dam. Whether male or female, a beaver can fell a tree, providing bark and young branches for all to eat. But each pond is home to a single family—a male in his prime, his mate, their kits of the year, and sometimes the members of the previous litter if they have not yet reached sexual maturity and been driven off. They are sociable enough, but show no division of labor, no castes or classes such as we find in a colony of ants or a hive of bees.

On the golf course at Entebbe, Uganda, we once made the mistake of stepping too close to a column of driver ants, underestimating their organization. Scouts found our feet and signaled to their fellows, perhaps by a stridulated call inaudible to us. Immediately the marching column split. Nearly a hundred half-inch workers and larger soldiers swerved aside and began to climb our legs. Each ant bit at one end and stung at the other before we could jump clear and brush away the attackers. Within a few minutes they rejoined their comrades, who were rushing along forty or fifty abreast on a winding path at least five inches wide.

The driver ants of Africa live by hunting, as do their counterparts, the army ants of tropical America and the bulldog ants of Australia. Arriving by the thousands, they kill and cut into pieces any other insect, snail, spider, scorpion, reptile or warmblooded vertebrate animal they can overpower. A part of the booty serves immediately as food for the adult ants and for the young they carry with them. Small amounts of meat may be held high in powerful jaws and saved as a snack before dark when the columns cease their foraging and cluster together in large bivouacs for the night.

So much sharing of food goes on among the marching ants, and so many of them manage to present a morsel to a maggot—licking the maggot while it eats—that the nomadic colony gains a chemical coordination. Indeed, when the maggots reach full size and spin cocoons about themselves, the loss of maggot flavor seems to provide a signal to which all the ants respond. They find a suitable place in which to settle down while the maggots go through the pupal changes until they emerge as tender adults. This is the time when the queen ant can lay another batch of several thousand eggs and wait for them to hatch. As soon as there are new grubs to carry and young adults to march on their own, the whole colony breaks camp and sets out on a fresh safari.

We realize, of course, that the only fundamental differences in organization between an ant colony with many thousands of individuals and a pondful of beavers with a dozen or less lie in the size of the population and the division of labor among castes within it. Except for one or two parents present, every member of either colony is the offspring of one mother—the female beaver or the queen ant. The same relationships hold in colonies of social bees and wasps, and among termites in their galleries. These are all enormous families, not societies comparable to a herd of elephants, a troupe of monkeys or a community of people. Rare indeed among other animals is the tolerant cooperation we experience among unrelated parents of both sexes and young of all ages.

Social behavior, we feel sure, enhances the likelihood of survival for individual offspring. With it comes a pressing need to control reproduction to prevent a disastrous explosion in population beyond the limits of the food supply. Social insects solved this difficulty by evolving sterile castes of workers and soldiers—individuals who labor for the good of the colony but take no part in its reproduction—and by systematically eating or abandoning any surplus eggs and larvae. With less success, people have sought to regulate human populations by evolving marriage customs that reduce promiscuity, by contraception, abortion and infanticide. A more effective method for matching the number of people to the supply of food, water and living space remains our greatest challenge.

We see a parallel in the enlargement of human communities based upon successful agriculture and the evolution of large colonies among ants that have given up nomadic hunting to exploit plant foods. The famous ants of the Near East, mentioned by King Solomon in his proverbs, bear the appropriate name *Messor*—the reaper. They harvest seeds according to an inherited pattern of instinctive action, needing "no guide, overseer, or ruler." Some of the harvester ants on the American prairies include special castes of individuals with oversize heads and tremendously powerful jaws, which seem to serve in crushing hard grains into a paste that can be eaten by all members of the colony.

In the deep tropics of Central and South America, we have met agricultural ants that are as highly specialized as any human farmer. They are the leaf-cutters or parasol ants, whose larger workers (the "majors") rove widely through forest and garden, using sharp jaws to scissor out leaf fragments a half-inch across. Holding one fragment firmly overhead like a sail, they run back to the underground nest, which may be hundreds of yards away and the home of up to 600,000 individuals. Usually, at the entrance to the dark passageways, each major passes the leaf fragment to a smaller sister—a "minor" who takes the material below and chews it into a pulp to be added to one of the special compost heaps known as "fungus gardens." Leaf-cutter ants eat only the small nourishing knobs of fungus that grow on these compost heaps, growing only when tended by the ants and manured with their feces. (Part of the pattern of adaptations that makes this way of life so successful is reminiscent of the way human brides used to once take along a "starting" of live yeast for breadmaking in the new home.) Each virgin queen ant before she leaves the nest for her marriage flight instinctively stuffs some of the living fungus into a peculiar pocket below her mouth. After mating, she prepares a small nest burrow, collects into it a few fragments of leaves or petals, and smears them with the fungus from her pocket. By the time her first batch of eggs hatch, she has a good crop of fungus knobs to feed her grubs. Until these young emerge as workers and relieve her of her agricultural chores, she alternates between tending her grubs and her fungus garden.

Among the most successful ants are those that have adopted aphids (plant lice) and other insects that excrete honeydew. Often described as "ants' cows," the aphids actually produce more of the sweet liquid when ants stroke them gently and drink the honeydew than they produce when untended and merely sucking juices from the plant. Just as man moves his cattle from a depleted pasture to a better one, so too the ants carry their aphids from plant to plant. They protect their "cows" from parasites, and often provide shelter from the elements as well.

The abundant dark red ants *Lasius americanus,* which probably are the most common insects in North America, pasture their aphids all too often on the roots of man's corn and cotton crops. They may dig a complete system of underground tunnels connecting every plant in the field to every other. In the American Tropics, a far smaller black ant installs its aphids on tree branches and then builds over this captive source of nourishment an elaborate nest of chewed plant fibers. By constructing these bulky "carton nests" with several stories, the ants need to carry their liquid food only a short distance from the dark basement full of aphids to the nurseries on upper floors where their own grubs are growing. Many a time we have smarted from the burning stings of these ants, which rush out of their tree nest when the branch is jostled.

Wherever ants accumulate food in storehouses they become capitalists, preparing for the future rather than living only in the present. Whether their store is of seeds or of honeydew, they are in constant danger of being robbed—usually by mice and men. On every continent we have found areas of soil several yards across where rodents have ripped into chambers that the ants had filled with dry seeds. Moisture, too, may reach these storehouses, causing the seeds to swell and sprout. To this extent the harvester ants sow as well as reap. But in the American Southwest and in Australia, a more surprising pattern of behavior allows for the storage of honeydew. Unlike bees, which build a honeycomb of secreted wax to hold their dehydrated nectar, the ants rely upon living casks. Callow adults accept regurgitated honeydew until their abdomens bulge to the dimensions of small cherries. Known as repletes, these individuals cling inverted to the roof of storage chambers, always ready to share their inner hoard with any sister ant that provides the correct stimulus. Aboriginal children in Australia's dry heartland like nothing better than to discover a nestful of honey-sweet repletes, which they catch and pop into their mouths whole, like candy. Latin Americans are often more commercial in their use of comparable ants in Mexico. We have seen for sale in Mexican markets trays full of live repletes to be bought as delicacies. Our own preference seems fastidious by local standards. We prefer to bite off the distended abdomen and savor its delicious contents, while discarding the rest of the distorted ant.

In accumulating grain stores, fungus gardens, honeydew cellars and carton nests of papier-mâché to protect herds of ants' cows, the sociable insects have progressed a long way in paralleling the efforts of the most social of mammals. Building upon a body with six legs and a pair of jaws meeting from side to side, they added more refinements in inherited behavior than in structural specializations, until each giant family attained high efficiency.

To a degree that has surprised layman and scientist alike, the insects maintain a large measure of the plasticity that gives living things a sporting chance when environmental changes come in quick succession. Ants and other insects take man's insecticides in stride, changing their susceptibility and attaining relative immunity to chemical agents just about as rapidly as engineers can invent and test new ones. They have ridden along with man to distant continents, thereby jumping the barriers posed by mountains, oceans and deserts, and adjusted to strange conditions upon arrival.

Only mankind among the social mammals has shown a comparable versatility. Without appreciable change in the structure or function of the human body, the cooperating families have fitted into almost every conceivable environment. They have communicated with one another and learned how to cope with the most challenging situations. By changing the environment locally to make it tolerable, and by discovering ways to pass along to coming generations the gains made in each century, our species has made itself almost independent of any inherited patterns of behavior.

Perhaps our civilization will flourish or fail according to whether we can care, as a mother instinctively cares for her child, about the welfare of people to whom we are not related. This may make the difference, the strength or the weakness in human societies.

chapter twenty-one

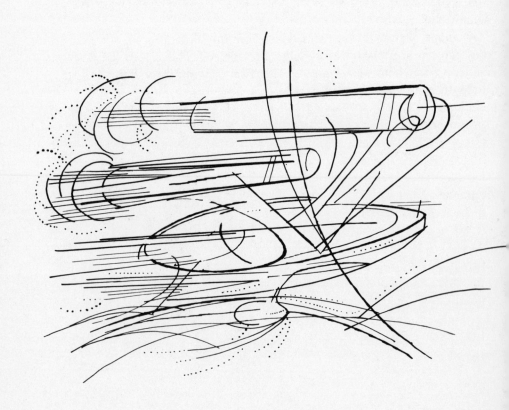

What Will the Weather Be
a Thousand Years from Now?

"A NEW era has begun," said Dr. Archie Kahan, chief of the Office of Atmospheric Water Resources in the Bureau of Reclamation. "Since early in 1966, the scientific world has admitted what could only be rumored before: that modification of the weather is both feasible and worth trying." And he took us to the top of a hill near Denver, Colorado, to show us a special camera used for recording the movement of storm clouds.

We asked Dr. Kahan about long-term trends in weather and what might be causing them. He mentioned the slow warming that has been noticed during the past century in the North Temperate Zone. Most of its glaciers are in retreat—melting each summer more than they accumulate from snows in winter. "The burning of coal, fuel oil and other materials that free carbon dioxide into the atmosphere could have a large effect," he said. "Although invisible, the carbon dioxide acts like a blanket in the atmosphere. It traps much of the radiant heat that is produced when sunlight strikes the earth." He thought it unlikely that this blanket caused the prolonged drought in so many parts of both hemispheres, beginning about 1962.

Coming by swift aircraft, as we had just done from desert lands where the air temperature plummets every day toward sundown due to loss of radiant heat through the cloudless sky, we wondered about the trails left

303

by jet airplanes. "Every pound of jet fuel used," said Dr. Kahan, "adds a pound of ice crystals to the upper atmosphere, in the form of long cirrus clouds. With so many civilian and military aircraft of this type flying all the time, there is a measurable increase in cloud cover. This must help make the world warmer, but no one yet knows how much." Commercial jet travel began late in 1958 and is steadily increasing. The higher the airplanes fly, the longer their condensation trails persist.

Knowing whether the whole world is getting warmer and how fast could be one of the most important topics for scientific study. Geologists have already predicted that a rise of only three degrees Fahrenheit would be enough to melt all of the ice on Antarctica and Greenland and many mountain tops. Running to the oceans, the extra water would raise sea level by about two hundred feet—not all at once, but perhaps within a century. Nuclear warfare could hardly do more widespread damage to man's civilization.

A rise in sea level of this magnitude would cover Tokyo, New York, London, Shanghai, Bombay and thousands of other cities. Waters from the Indian Ocean would flow over the site of the Suez Canal into the Mediterranean. Cairo would be flooded, and also vast areas of desert and the valley of the Nile. Tel Aviv and Istanbul, Athens and Naples, Nice and Tunis would all vanish under water. Seas 115 feet higher than the surface of Gatun Lake would flow across Panama from the Pacific Ocean to the Atlantic. The Isthmus of Tuhuantepec in Mexico would be flooded, as it was a few million years ago, isolating Central America as a big island between South America and North—both continents far smaller than they are today. Most of Florida would vanish under water, along with vast areas of food-producing land around the globe. No longer would the Gulf of Mexico send a warm Gulf Stream obliquely across the North Atlantic, making the climate as liveable as it is in the British Isles, Scandinavia and Iceland. The whole pattern of oceanic currents would change radically, and with them the weather over most of the world.

We cannot pretend that this is preposterous. In two hundred years the temperature of the North Atlantic Ocean has risen along the coasts of New England and the British Isles. Codfish and many other forms of life have withdrawn northward to escape the warm water, although doing so has cost them their best spawning grounds and much of their nourishment. Now amphibious airplanes belonging to the U. S. Coast Guard are carrying special equipment to measure sea temperatures from Cape Hatteras to Cape Cod in order to find out what is happening offshore.

In less than two thousand years the weather has become so much warmer and drier in North Africa that desert wasteland now spreads in Libya and Tunisia where once immense grainfields produced food for the Roman Empire.

Geologists go back a few thousand years farther to find clear proof that the level of the oceans has risen more than four hundred feet along most coasts. They attribute it to unwarping of continental margins deformed by the weight of thick glaciers during the Ice Ages, and to more water from melted ice as the glaciation ended about fifteen thousand years ago. Some of this change occurred while mankind was busy domesticating plants and animals, inventing the wheel and the alphabet, and building port cities that now are under water. It may have happened as slowly as a twenty-fifth of an inch per year—four inches in a century. The last big ice fields in the world could melt faster than that.

When we consider the flooding that would be caused by so slight a warming of the weather, we think of the brave measures taken recently above the dams at Kariba and Aswan. The world treasured the colossi and temples farther up the Nile, enough to pay for cutting them free and raising them beyond the reach of Aswan's backwaters. Behind Kariba, the wildlife conservationists risked their lives trying to rescue the antelopes, monkeys, snakes and other animals flooded from their homes by the rising lake. But we remember too that the animals had no place to go. Other members of their own kinds already occupied every suitable bit of territory within hundreds of miles, and twice as many could not live there—could not find enough to eat and places to raise more young. Where would the inhabitants of Tokyo, New York, London, Shanghai, Bombay and all the other coastal cities find a welcome and a living, if the sea flooded them out at the same time? People would be far harder to move than treasures of art.

Perhaps those forecasters are right who predict the economic end of fossil fuels of all kinds within eighty years, with some substitute such as nuclear energy or hydroelectric power taking over and releasing no more carbon dioxide. Efforts to protect the atmosphere from pollution may hasten the changeover, even require suppression of the cirrus clouds from jet aircraft. We may have reached the peak in world temperature and be headed for cooler weather. How much cooler?

During 1966, the weekly journal *Science* carried two reports of careful comparisons between changes that geologists have recognized in the seas with those known for the extension of continental glaciers during

Pleistocene times. They sought to explain the cyclic swings between warm and cool by using new techniques, which might also help guess what the future is likely to bring. Dr. Cesare Emiliani of the University of Miami interprets the new information to mean that we are now midway between glaciations and that a new Ice Age "will begin within a few thousand years and reach its peak about 15,000 years from now." He anticipates that glacial and interglacial ages will continue to alternate for millions of years, until the mountains erode down and great inland extensions of the seas reduce the reflection of energy from the sun by our planet. Dr. W. S. Broecker of Columbia University believes the timing of these mighty changes can be predicted from the amount of sunlight reaching high latitudes. This varies regularly according to the tilt of the earth's axis and to the distance between the earth and sun on the longest day of each year. We seem closer to knowing what climate the future holds than ever before in man's past.

We have a special reason for being so concerned about temperature. The effect of heating or chilling is practically instantaneous in any animal, and becomes evident only more slowly in a plant. Far more than just the chemical reactions of growth are affected, or the speed at which an animal moves around. Quite a number of creatures react in a way that is evident in the little water flea known as *Daphnia,* which jigs around in ponds by lashing with its long antennae. Through the transparent sides of the quarter-inch amber-colored body, the heart of this crustacean can be seen beating. The rate of beat doubles for each 18° F. the temperature rises, between the freezing point of water and about 70°. *Daphnia* acts as though its life span were measured by those beats. It lives twice as long if its heart beats half as fast. Yet longevity is a poor measure of success. Like so many other animals, the water flea can survive at temperatures too cool and too warm for reproduction. Beyond a narrow range of temperature, it simply beats out its life without leaving any progeny.

On land, the walking rate of ants, the chirping of crickets and the flashing of fireflies all show this same dependence upon temperature. Scientists sometimes delight in drawing a graph to see how well the animals fit the predictions of an empiric equation worked out by the Swedish chemist Svante A. Arrhenius, who thereby earned a Nobel prize. Others rely upon a more amusing formula to tell their friends the temperature on a summer evening. They count the number of chirps a cricket makes in fifteen seconds, and add forty. Over the range from 55° to 100° F., a cricket is a fairly good thermometer.

Just as a premature summer day in springtime seems far warmer than a fall day with identical temperature, relative humidity and wind, so too animals and plants become acclimated if given time. Within limits, they can survive weather just a little worse than they have grown used to, and do so much more reliably than if the adverse conditions arrive suddenly. A flowering dogwood tree transplanted to New England from Pennsylvania has a better chance of living through the icy months in its new home than one brought all the way from the Carolinas. Yet a hard frost that comes early may kill either tree—at a temperature they could both tolerate in midwinter.

Many of the most significant steps toward survival have been adaptations that freed living things from a rigid dependence upon some particular range of temperatures. These are the gains that provide meaningful patterns in the unpredictable future. Whether the weather is warmer or cooler a thousand years from now, the living things that face it will be descendants of those we can see today. They will depend upon the same adjustments, probably with a few innovations.

From the experience of mankind we can see that behavior changes faster than the body dies. A thousand years suffice for the adoption of new ways to do things. But a million is too short a time for the introduction of many fundamental differences, let alone the spread of successful patterns among a large variety of survivors. It is fully 150 million years since our ancestors and those of other mammals and of birds evolved the necessary small changes in the nervous system to make them warm-blooded instead of cold. Today, about 8,600 kinds of birds and 4,400 kinds of mammals profit in this way through comparative independence of the weather. That averages out as one fresh pattern for success in each 11,500 years.

Not so very long ago the eminent British biologist Joseph Bancroft of Cambridge University set down his thoughts on what he called *Features in the Architecture of Physiological Function*. He was impressed by the number of ways in which living things have escaped "from the tyranny" of the chemical rule shown by the equation of Arrhenius. He saw how far-reaching was the change when, instead of just slowing down as the weather chilled, the ancestors of mammals and birds began to shiver inside their coats of fur and feathers. Here was "the cold-blooded animal successfully adopting ingenious mechanisms, first biochemical, then physiological, in order to adapt its heart to the variations of its environment; the warm-blooded animal discarding what its cold-blooded predecessor has laboriously beaten out, invoking the nervous system to reverse the normal biochemical relationship and gaining a new freedom by adapting, not itself to the internal environment, but the internal environment to itself." Birds and mammals keep their living cells warmed to the temperature that is best by heating or cooling the blood that circulates as their "internal environment." Cold-blooded creatures mostly adapt their cells to be unnaturally active as needed when their blood is cooler or warmer than the ideal temperature. Only a few kinds have added through inherited behavior some way to stay active despite numbing cold or hazardous heat.

Sometimes we look enviously at the flocks of birds assembling in autumn, ready to fly south where the sun will be warm. Theirs seems such a logical way to escape the rigors in the months ahead. We overlook the hazards in their path, and marvel chiefly at their ability to hold their course in the right direction. Their ancestors, of course, were the individuals who made the proper turns, held to the correct pattern of skymarks and landmarks, who got to both destinations on time.

But then we ask ourselves: How did the migrant birds and bats, butterflies and dragonflies ever begin this annual shuttling back and forth? What change in one twisted molecule of DNA could so affect the chemistry inside a young crow that when autumn days grow shorter it will fly off on its own from Canada to Oklahoma? Marked birds that were raised in solitude and not released until every other crow had long since flown, took this course successfully all by themselves. The eggs from which they they hatched contained the directions, and also those for the return trip in the lengthening days of springtime.

We think of the early morning in mid-September when we accompanied our friend Dr. Fred Urquhart and his wife and son through the predawn chill to oak trees along the north shore of Lake Ontario. With a huge net about a yard in each direction, Fred reached high into the oak branches to gather monarch butterflies clinging there by the dozen. Until the day warmed them they were too chilled to flutter. But if left alone, they would have been flying before noon—streaking along in tandem, south southwest across the open water, bound for the Gulf States and Mexico.

Fred put all he caught in a big carton and closed it to keep out the light and warmth. We spent the whole morning affixing numbered paper tags to those butterflies, flight-testing them in the screened porch, then taking them into the open and freeing them carefully by the handful

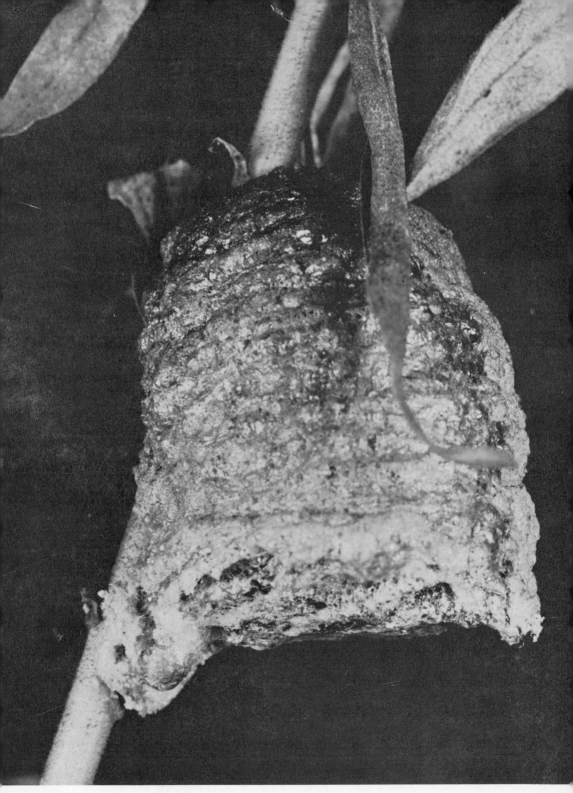

A plastic froth, like hard meringue, shields more than 100 developing embryos of praying mantises over winter from weather, birds and mechanical damage.

in the sun. As if shot from catapults they rose steeply into the sky, fell into the formation specified in their inheritance, and headed south southwest as though the leader had a compass. How many, we wondered, of the banded females would return the following spring, loaded with fertilized eggs to be laid on milkweed leaves? We could not tell which ones would succeed in the round trip of four to five thousand miles. Yet we knew that enough would to keep monarchs flying in eastern Canada, summer after summer.

These migratory patterns must have attained their present form far fewer than thirty thousand years ago, for then the breeding grounds of the Alberta crows and Ontario butterflies were locked up under hundreds of feet of ice. Geologists tell us that the glacier was a mile thick where we live in New England. Butterflies flit silently, crows caw their way across the sky, and huge jet aircraft from the nearby base roar through the air above our house where only ice was during the Pleistocene. Did the crows and butterflies inherit their directions for avoiding winter weather so few millennia before man began traveling the same skies?

The great German experimenter August Weismann, who continued to ponder and to publish his ideas long after his eyes gave out, called attention to the limited areas in Eurasia and North America where birds could live during the Ice Ages. Perhaps, he suggested, they grew used to short migrations—away from the ice front in winter and back toward its well-watered margins in spring. As the ice retreated altogether, they just went farther. When we see Canada geese depart northbound as soon as the late winter weather warms to 35° F., we recall his idea. The geese continue at whatever pace the springtime does, staying with the isotherm of 35° all the way from the marshes along the Gulf of Mexico to northern Canada or Alaska. Only when they reach their individual breeding grounds do they settle down and let the weather around them go through spring and summer.

Off the Australian east coast, on an island athwart the Tropic of Capricorn, we remembered Weismann's glacier theory of bird migration. In our hands we held a muttonbird—a young wedge-tailed shearwater—caught and detained for a few minutes as it ran with wings half spread from the nest toward the open ocean. Once airborne, it would not return to its native island for four years. For all that time it could roam the vast reaches of the Pacific, north and south, east and west, and still remember the way to a coral cay half a mile in longest dimension. No glaciers gave its ancestors practice for travels of this kind. The shearwater had to rely upon its inherited guidance, hidden deep inside every one of its cells as a code in a twisted molecule.

No adaptation surpasses wings for traveling to places in search of food. A thousand miles mean little. To a swimmer in the sea this is a greater distance, requiring a bigger effort, whether by sculling with a powerful tail as whales do, paddling in the manner of sea turtles and penguins, or swishing a tailfin as most fishes can. But on land a thousand miles is just too far to walk, run, hop, slide and crawl. Terrestrial animals may migrate with the seasons up and down a mountainside, after the fashion of elk and mountain sheep. Or they may flee from the bitter winds along the arctic coast and take shelter among the spruce forests, as caribou do, only to head northward again as soon as spring softens the tundra.

Shorter travels seldom help much when the weather worsens. The chief alternative seems to be to hole up and wait for the storm or the winter to pass by. The chipmunks and the groundhogs near our home follow this routine, each according to its own inherited pattern. The chipmunks store incredible amounts of grain, dry fruits, dried mushrooms, all in underground chambers. Atop one pile of food the little animal makes its bed. It sleeps long hours when sealed in its branching burrows by ice and snow, awakening at intervals to eat food from under its mattress. By spring the larders are getting bare, but the weight of the chipmunk remains unchanged.

Groundhogs take no chances on being robbed while asleep. Each one stores its food under its own skin—enough to last a winter. Sometimes we suspect that in autumn the only change the animal notices is its own girth. It gets so fat that crawling through the tunnel from the sleeping chamber toward the outdoor field must be an effort—one for which hunger no longer provides an adequate stimulus. Whatever changes the animal's behavior, it does stop eating before frost and goes into its hibernation sleep. By spring, when next it emerges from its burrow, half its weight is gone and the gaunt animal acts starved. Actually it still has enough fat to last several weeks if the weather remains bad and vegetation is slow to start growing.

Like so many true hibernators, the groundhog lets its body temperature sink 10° to 20° F. below the summer normal. This change makes use of the chemical relationship Arrhenius described, by reducing to about half the rate at which the animal uses its store of fat to keep alive. Scientists know what happens and how it benefits the groundhog.

But despite all the research work devoted to hibernators, no one yet knows how these animals reset their thermostats—downward in autumn, and back to the former level when spring approaches. They feel sure that the strange brown fat the hibernators store in special regions of the body has something to do with regaining consciousness. Somewhere in the pattern of survival for a groundhog are some important details, hidden away almost as inconspicuously as the inheritance that calls them forth at the appropriate time.

Among the hibernators we have met, the ones that live most precariously are the Columbian ground squirrels in high mountain valleys of the Northwest. For eight to ten months each year deep snow covers their rocky territory, preventing the growth of plants upon which they must feed. Two to four months seems a bare minimum in which to get ready for another hibernation. These squirrels have the most to lose— their lives—if the weather should change toward longer winters at their altitude. Yet we wonder if they would gain from a gradual warning trend that cut short their enforced period of inactivity. We suspect that they would move up the valley to the hazardous frontier once more, for it is there that frost under the rocks prevents even the powerful grizzly bears from digging them out of their burrow sanctuaries.

In a sense, the Columbian ground squirrels have come to rely upon icy weather. So have quite a number of other kinds of animals and plants. Their dormancy through a long winter has become so important for survival that no short exposure to cold is enough. Until their living chemistry has proceeded for a month or more at its lowest rate, they fail to become active when rewarmed.

Usually nothing happens when a branch of flowering quince or forsythia is brought into the house in autumn. The buds are there, but they have not yet been conditioned by prolonged cold to the state where they will open.

Moths developing inside their cocoons react in a similar way, although it is sometimes hard to convince the youngsters who find them to leave them out in the cold over winter. Last October several cecropia cocoons were brought to us, each on its separate length of twig. We had the children tie three of the cocoons outdoors to a tree and put the other two in an open box in the cool basement. At spring equinox, the youngsters took all of the cocoons to their science teacher, who had agreed to pin them up carefully to the cloth-covered notice board. The cocoons from outdoors had weathered to a nondescript gray, but within a few weeks each produced a handsome moth. The two from the basement retained their light brown color but yielded nothing. In June the youngsters cut these open and found inside only shriveled insects, dead in their mummy cases. The two moths had run out of food and water while waiting for winter to come and go. For them, it never came.

Among the hordes of insects in temperate and arctic lands, this need for winter comes at various times. A remarkable assortment lay eggs within which both cold-tolerance and cold-dependence are concealed: the masses that grasshoppers hide shallowly in sandy soil; the similar masses that praying mantises affix to exposed stems, and coat with a meringuelike froth that hardens and repels the birds; the clusters that tent-caterpillar moths produce, like varnished sheaths around twigs of cherry and other trees; and the single shining eggs that aphids (plant lice) cement singly in crevices of bark so abundantly that chickadees and nuthatches cannot find all of them before spring. Winter cold is impor- tant to the caterpillars of tiger moths, such as the wooly bears that in- spired the phrase "hurrying along like a caterpillar in the fall." They curl up under fallen leaves and spin no cocoon in which to transform until spring arrives after a long period of cold. Mourning cloak butterflies, like queen wasps and many flies, overwinter as adults, although they may interrupt their sleep to flit about on warm sunny days while the earth is still deep in snow.

Sometimes we wonder whether people too need to experience the changing seasons if they are to live fully their heritage of active days. Winter still comes to the sites of Cnossus on Crete, of Babylon and Nineveh, of ancient Athens and Carthage, Alexandria and Rome. Cold weather touched the lofty capitals of the Inca and Aztec empires, the palaces of Ghenghis Khan, and the courts of Old Cathay. We notice that the present citizens of lands with winter weather live long productive lives, and rarely regard themselves as unfortunate when frost nips the nose and cheeks. New Englanders, New Zealanders, Scandinavians and Swiss seem to thrive where cold air keeps them hurrying for many months every year.

One reason for hurrying is to get enough food and fuel set aside during the growing season to last through the cold months. And if food and fuel, why not other possessions to make the winter pass more com- fortably. The habits of hurrying and storing have less appeal to people who can reach up at any time of year to pick mangoes, bananas, coconuts and other fruits from tropical plants that grow with little cultivation.

Sometimes we debate this difference with friends who live where real winter never comes. One of them offered another explanation. "Warm, humid lands are the parts of the world that are overrun by wood-eating termites. They destroy possessions so rapidly that, until new ways to build termite-proof houses were invented, there was no use accumulating anything a termite could eat. If you lump together all stored foods, all wood products, all paper and most kinds of cloth, what do you have left to show the advance of a civilization? Or to hand on as a cultural heritage from one generation to the next?"

The destructive termites work feverishly to maintain high humidity around their bodies. (This limits their versatility, and perhaps their ability to cope with changeable weather.) They build covered runways wherever they cannot cut a gallery through one wooden object (such as the floor) into another (such as a table leg).

In honeybees the inherited pattern of behavior goes much farther than that of any other insects. These bees are able to keep their home climate uniform despite major changes in the weather outside their nest. Like people who live in high latitudes of the Temperate Zone, the honeybees industriously lay by a generous stock of pollen and honey, which appeals greatly to man's sweet tooth. The pollen provides protein and fat; the honey provides the sugars needed as a quick source of energy all winter. The bees convert the energy into movement which releases heat. Under a modest layer of insulation from a tree trunk or a covered hive, they prevent themselves from freezing. Shielding their queen next to the honey stores, the worker bees keep active in a compact cluster. Those most exposed become chilled, but burrow inward and replenish the food in their stomachs. Other workers take their places, making the cluster seethe with movement in the darkness between the tiers of honeycomb.

In summer the workers provide their own equivalent of air-conditioning whenever the hive is in danger of overheating. It must not reach the temperature at which the developing young would die. Each of the age classes of adult honeybees appears to follow its own instructions whenever this emergency develops. Most of the field bees, who are the oldest, cease their foraging and merely rest on shady leaves where their minuscule of body heat will not add to the total inside the hive. Younger field bees go for water, trip after trip. As each of them arrives at the doorway to the hive, she is met by a still younger nurse bee. Something in the eagerness with which the nurse bee accepts the water tells the field bee how urgent is the need for more. The nurse bees spread the water in minute quantities over the surfaces of waxen cells inside the hive, then cool the air there by fanning with their wings, promoting evaporation.

These instinctive actions of honeybees in protecting their vital brood and long-lived queen ensure the cooperation of separate individuals. They make possible the efficient colony the workers guard, and extend the lives of the workers too. No comparable adaptations are needed by animals that are less social, since they can go off in search of more comfortable environment when weather becomes extreme. Separately, a cold-blooded creature can do little to change the climate in its immediate vicinity. Its instinctive reactions to heat and cold serve mostly to promote its own survival.

Until recently, scientists contented themselves with experiments demonstrating how ready most animals are to move along a range of different temperatures into the zone of greatest comfort. A psychologist who had some experienced rats turned the problem around. To rats he had trained to push a lever to get food when hungry, he gave a different bar to press. The new bar switched on a heat lamp for a few minutes. Until the experimenter lowered the temperature in the laboratory, the bar went unnoticed. Then the rats learned to go to it every half hour or so to give themselves some local heat. A recording thermometer in their cage showed how well they kept the temperature in a narrow range. Rarely did they let it fall below 60° F.

At Harvard University, P. N. Rozin and Jean Mayer learned about the educated rats and decided to provide a goldfish with a comparable opportunity. They equipped an aquarium with a lever suitable for a fish to press. Each push on the lever caused a measured amount of cold water to flow into the aquarium. As soon as the fish appeared at home in these new surroundings, they turned on an electric heater below the tank. Slowly the water grew warmer. They watched the thermometer and the goldfish, for they knew that 108° would be fatal.

At 102° the fish began to swim rapidly, as though seeking a way out. By chance it bumped the lever, and was rewarded by a swirl of cooler water. Slowly, however, the heat increased again. Over and over these events were repeated, until the goldfish associated bumping the lever with quick cooling relief. Thereafter it was easy. The fish kept the temperature between 95° and 97° for day after day. All the cold-blooded creature needed was a way to control the climate in the confines of its watery world.

The goldfish and the rat alike inherit talents they have never been called upon to utilize in nature. Yet their ancestors survived some really drastic changes in climate. Geologists seek to explain these changes on the basis of natural forces they can see at work today, assuming that the present is only a continuation of the past with no change in principles —and that the future will follow the same kinds of variation.

If we look into the past as a guide to the future, it confronts us with a spectacular cool period—the great Ice Ages—all within the past 2 million years. Over vast areas of the world where the ice spread and thickened, both land and sea were effectively closed for alterations. Vegetation whose territory was taken by snowstorm moved southward as fast as new sporelings and seedlings could rise, mature and reproduce. Animals that could fly or run or swim shifted rapidly in the same direction; slugs and snails and snakes slithered along.

Four times the weather showed major signs of warming, and the ice sheet retreated northward. Where once a soil had been, peat moss and other tundra plants spread promptly over the glacial debris and bare rocks. In their wake, the evergreen forests advanced. So did the hardwoods still farther south.

Three of the warming trends were false indications of climate to come. Three times the weather chilled again, and the cold drove living things toward the equator at least as far as they had been before. Then came the slow sweep toward the present, a change all in the last fifty thousand years. In the slow commotion, as plants and animals spread north and up the mountain slopes once more, a number got lost and went extinct. Close to the ice, the wooly rhinoceros and wooly elephant vanished. Farther south in North America, the giant mastodon and all of the native horses and camels disappeared. So did the great sabre-toothed cats and the hugest armadillos. Eurasia lost the Irish elk, with the most incredible span of antlers the world has ever known. And to every continent except Antarctica came a two-legged denizen of Africa, walking with weapons in hand and a skin over his back, or paddling his own canoe, bringing his family along.

About 250 human generations ago, our ancestors learned how to use their heritage well enough to become sociable, in the first villages of which traces remain. That was around 5500 B.C., when meltwater from the Ice Ages still flowed through the soil so close to the surface that forests extended across Africa to the south of vast grasslands where deserts are today.

Two hundred and fifty times the human heritage has been reshuffled and dealt afresh in another generation since the New Stone Age—man's Neolithic period. The villages of the Lake People have been replaced by air-conditioned cities. The skin garment has its counterpart in a business suit, a bikini, and a spaceman's uniform. The canoe has become an ocean liner, a jet airplane or a rocket to the moon. By pushing the right lever, we can pick our climate or take it with us.

Sometimes the walk from the taxicab to the stateroom aboard an ocean liner, or to the seats reserved for us on an intercontinental airplane, reminds us of the long hike our remote ancestors took a million years ago, on their way from Africa to explore the unknowns beyond the horizon. We doubt that they were as burdened with belongings as we are, in trying to match whatever weather lies ahead.

Only on foot can we climb the gravel slopes of the White Mountains in California to find trees that were seedlings while the Babylonians were conquering their first empire. Some of the bristlecone pines now living have annual rings dating back more than four thousand years. Yet each summer they free into the cold winds on the high mountains a new crop of winged seeds, which ride away toward a future for the whole species. It takes no flight of imagination to think of the seedling that grew into a tree four thousand years before us. Or to think of the parent of that seedling being equally ancient while the seedling was getting its first roothold in the mountain slope. Such a parent would have been five hundred years old when mankind began experimenting with village life!

Surely the same mountain was there to support the parent of the tree we see. During the last four thousand years at least, conditions at this site have remained tolerable for bristlecone pines. Perhaps the parent of the present tree shuddered under mountain gales no fiercer than those today. Yet we cannot multiply this estimate too far back, for 250 generations of this length would reach beyond the middle of the Ice Ages. Certainly the weather has changed enormously during those million years. Where, we wonder, did the ancestors of the bristlecones live then? Where were our own progenitors?

Although no useful forecast can yet be made for the weather a thousand years from now, at least our knowledge of life's inherent versatility gives us confidence. Past changes in the physical environment have tempered the patterns by which plants and animals survive, filling their heritage with hidden details that have already matched a kaleidoscopic array of variations. All living things today have a chance tomorrow to test that special heritage against whatever the weather brings.

chapter twenty-two

Will the Daring Inherit the Universe?

WHEN Charles Darwin sought to account for the details he saw among living things, he distilled his thoughts as far as he could with the information available in his day. He pointed to familiar facts that, taken together, seemed inescapably meaningful. Regularly the number of offspring exceeded the number of parents. Almost all the offspring differed from one another and from their parents, showing variations upon the theme of their heredity. Each new generation faced a finite supply of useful resources. The natural process of selection could be expected to automatically prune away the least well adapted.

Darwin assumed that this pruning would lead to progressive changes in the inheritance carried by the survivors—to evolution. Without knowing how this change might operate, he could only point to the effects of selective breeding on the inheritance of domesticated plants and animals. He felt sure that natural selection could achieve still more since it had a longer time to operate.

No naturalist as observant as Darwin would expect offspring to stay close to their parents and starve for lack of resources, if they have any means to disperse and reach new supplies. Customarily the offspring go off on their own, and the survivors find places where they can become parents in turn. The places they find are no more equal than the hereditary features the individuals take with them. And occasionally, a happy new combination turns up: the right variation to fit a living site to which the parents would have been ill-adapted.

In this lively game of test and try, success depends upon finding conditions tolerably like those the parents had, where competition is tolerable too. Animals and plants have spread over the earth one acceptable move at a time. In each new situation they have had to wait until variation and chance made the next move possible.

All life, so far as we know, arose in the sea. A minority of kinds varied in ways that allowed them to tolerate the low salinity of river mouths, and to spread into fresh water. When new adaptations let them, some of the minority dispersed from fresh water into humid air. There they faced times of drought, rapid changes in temperature, the sudden effects of wind, and a dangerously high but exhilarating concentration of oxygen. To move where the air was dry instead of moist seems a minor change by comparison, although it too required new alterations in body and function.

Now mankind is attempting the logical successor to these daring moves, by venturing into space beyond the atmosphere of the planet Earth. For these historic flights, the 1960's can be remembered as the decade when the Soviet Union and the United States vied with each other for first place. In 1961 the two countries independently put a man into space and recovered him intact. In 1965 men from similar spacecraft in orbit from each country took a "space walk" from an opened hatch, then returned to the artificial satellite before it reentered the atmosphere. In immediate prospect is a landing on the moon more than 216,000 miles from the earth's surface, and a safe return. Every success depends upon thrusting away and guiding back a bulky vehicle carrying not only the men and instruments but enough of their earthly environment to keep them healthy.

We encounter a few of these special precautions whenever we travel by jet airplane. As the sealed metal bird taxis to the end of the runway for takeoff, the hostess demonstrates the emergency oxygen equipment we should use promptly "in the unlikely event that cabin pressure is lost" at high altitude. We remember our first jet flight, from Rome over the Alps to Paris in 1959. As we looked down on the snowcapped peaks, the captain spoke over the public address system: "Ladies and gentlemen, our altitude is now 31,500 feet, our air speed 605 miles per hour. The temperature outside the airplane is 40 below zero on both the Centigrade and Fahrenheit thermometer scales." We glanced at one another. "That's almost 2,500 feet higher than Mt. Everest. Higher than any land in the world. Yet we're as comfortable as though home in an easy chair."

Although nonstop service across oceans and continents has become commonplace, travel from point to point on earth differs completely from voyages into outer space. The jet airplanes remain in the atmosphere and can compress air into the cabins to simulate conditions atop a low mountain. They land at airports that grow increasingly similar. Conducted tours, providing most of the comforts of big cities, now reach even to the coasts of Antarctica. Nowhere on earth is more than a few days' trip from any other. Journeys are increasingly what the word signifies: the distance that can be covered in a day.

Beyond our atmosphere, the traveler must take along everything: air, water, food, fuel, spare parts and repair tools, as well as navigation equipment and means for communication. A verbal link between the daring explorers and people they know at home may be the hardest to maintain, and yet the most critical part of the arrangements. The human mind depends for normal function upon frequent stimuli from a familiar world. For the loneliness of outer space we are ill-prepared.

Few men have risked their sanity by being alone for long. All of the voyages of discovery and colonization that carried fewer than a shipload of people seem lost to history. Indeed, it was with a determination to pioneer that Admiral Richard E. Byrd established himself as a one-man weather station at 80° 08′ South for the winter of 1934-1935. But when his daily radio conversations with comrades at the main base of Little America grew less coherent, it was they who risked their lives to reach him unannounced and carry him to safety across the Antarctic ice.

We think of Captain Joshua Slocomb crossing the Pacific Ocean, and newsman Robert N. Manry traversing the Atlantic in small sailboats with only a radio, a cat or two, the whales and porpoises, sea birds and fishes for company. By their own admission, these men found loneliness their greatest danger. Without the familiar psychological cues that help an individual to function in society, their efficiency slumped and disorientation threatened their survival.

Something similar may explain the unplanned features of man's first walk in space—events that replaced for a while the initial delight at the Gemini Control Center over a mission progressing on schedule. At the end of his twelve minutes maneuvering outside the space craft, co-pilot Edward H. White showed a strange reluctance to return. That his earphones brought him the voice of his pilot only a few feet away, and the commands from anxious officers on earth to go back inside, seemed not to register fully while the world was 135 miles distant. After twenty minutes he reentered but had difficulty in refastening the hatch cover, without which the cabin could not be repressurized. Yet all of these moves had been practiced repeatedly before the flight began, in the familiar surroundings of the space center. His orders were clear. His own life and that of his pilot depended upon his compliance with them. What stimuli are needed to make a man care? These stimuli must be sent along to ensure the success of an astronaut.

In a very real sense the space travelers are jetting off into a future that has been but vaguely charted. Alone or in groups of two to three, they seek to leave civilization behind and to discover what lies ahead. This is a far more perilous venture than for a remote tribe of mountain people in New Guinea to step from the Stone Age primitivism they inherited from their ancestors into the twentieth-century way of life they can see in the coastal communities. The New Guineans have time to smell and taste and feel and listen to the new ways before they discard the old. Their pace is their own, and they can reach agreement among themselves before proceeding. But the course of the astronauts has been chosen before they start out, and their decisions to modify it must be made at better than seven thousand miles an hour. Once well on their way to the moon or Mars, they cannot change their minds and return without first using the distant target as a force to reroute their flight. For them it is "No go" or "Go"—all the way.

Earthlings are fortunate in having a moon so close to practice on before trying longer flights through space. The supply problem is only a few times greater than to mount a major expedition for a stay in Antarctica. Few can go where every ounce of air, water, food and fuel must be shipped by rocket. But if astronauts are to leap farther into the future, they must learn on the moon how to cope with more distant goals.

After the moon, the next real hurdles are time: time to get there, to explore, and to return. For many a man dreaming toward outer space, this fact was borne home by 21 photographs of the planet Mars, taken on July 15, 1965 at a distance of less than ten thousand miles. They were radioed back by the space probe known as Mariner IV, which is still racing away from us at almost 7,300 miles per hour. By terrestrial standards this is a tremendous pace. Yet it took 229 days after launching for the probe to fly by the red planet and get those photographs. They showed a surface as pock-marked as the moon, and gave strong indications that

Mars offers useful amounts of neither oxygen nor water in any form. What is it worth to send men on a two-year trip so that they may spend a few months exploring the planet Mars?

Venus is closer, but the flyby measurements sent back to earth by the space probe known as Mariner II indicate a surface temperature of about 800° Fahrenheit day and night, with no relief under the dense cloud cover from this ovenlike heat. Mercury has a cool side, but is so close to the sun that only a rocket ship with enormous reserves of power and spectacular shielding from destructive radiations could be maneuvered for a landing and later return to Earth.

Probably the outer planets which are so big—Saturn, Jupiter and Uranus—will never become places for men to visit. Not only are their temperatures low and atmospheres corrosive, but the pull of gravity on each of them would keep a person flattened against the ground. The same gravitational force would have to be overcome to depart for more hospitable sites in space. But each of these planets has moons and asteroids at a safe distance, on which interplanetary ships might settle for observations and while planning the next move across the vast distances in these parts of the solar system.

Because of its small size, the most distant of all—Pluto—may be easier. Yet at 2,669,000,000 miles away, only a fast rocket ship could make a round trip in a human lifetime. At the speed of Mariner IV, a space probe would take 570 years to pass Pluto.

With ion engines and perhaps nuclear power, it may be possible to increase velocity to 730,000 miles an hour, one hundred times the speed of Mariner IV. This is more than enough to free the space travelers from the pull of our sun's gravitational field, and to let them aim for the nearest star beyond. It is Alpha Centauri, visible only from the Southern Hemisphere and the third brightest star in the sky. In astronomical terms, it is 4.3 light-years distant. Since light travels 186,324 miles per second and there are 31,536,000 seconds in a year, the mileage to Alpha Centauri is 25,266,428,755,200. The rocket ship with human passengers traveling at 730,000 miles an hour would reach the vicinity of Alpha Centauri 34,552,642 years after launching. To make the trip one way in ten years would require the vehicle to go at a pace approaching the speed of light for most of the way. The rest of the time would be needed to accelerate and decelerate, and to explore for a landing place at the distant destination. Maneuvering at such high speeds would present tremendous problems. Yet any slower travel than this seems out of the question.

From the Age of Reptiles, when dinosaurs were dominant, one ancient type (*Sphenodon*) survived—known by the Maoris of New Zealand as the tuatara. Now this living fossil survives only on small islands where the government is trying to save it from becoming extinct. Of all reptiles known, this one takes longest to become an adult, about 20 years. It may live as long as a person, emerging chiefly at night to feed on crickets and snails.

New Zealand Information Service

The velvet worm or peripatus (*Macroperipatus geayi*) of Panama has an ancestry that can be traced back almost without change for 600 million years.

We regard the people who ride along on such a mission as extremely daring explorers, going to bring back exciting information. Their feat will test far more, however, than the habitability of remote parts of the universe. Upon their return to our earth they will have to interpret their observations in a culture they will scarcely understand. Suppose each astronaut can be judged suitable for the costly trip by age thirty, trained by then in all the imaginable techniques for survival and investigation. At age fifty the space traveler is back, older and more experienced, but now faced with adapting to a culture that has surged ahead, with new words, new technologies, new attitudes and interests. Peace Corpsmen have to cope with a problem of reentry into society after an absence of only two years, with ample communication by mail and perhaps an occasional telephone call around the world. Twenty years would match the sleep of Rip van Winkle.

In Washington Irving's delightful story, no one recognized Rip at first or credited him with much sense when they found out who he was. We wonder how an astronaut will fare after an absence of comparable length, during which no communications from home could be received. "We all need," says psychiatrist John R. Rees, honorary president of the World Federation of Mental Health, "a sense of our own identity, that we have a certain place in the structure of our society, and that we fit into that. We have constantly to change our identity when we move into a different sort of world . . ." And we think how different our own world was twenty years ago, as we try to imagine it that far into the future.

Sooner than we realize, travel agents will be selling excursions to the moon. Committees will be seeking international laws to forbid desecrating the lunar landscape with the junk of abandoned rocket ships, and to protect outer space from pollution with the garbage of commuters. Our mailman will bring advertising folders telling destinations and departure dates for conducted tours on the continents of Mars. The Department of Commerce will consider legal proceedings to curb the monopoly of any Trans-Universe Rocketline that succeeds in getting regular service started.

After "one world," the next step is "one universe." Certainly the space ships and the advanced space stations will constitute a new environment, an evolutionary opportunity for life on earth. Already the planners are searching for the best living companions to go along with people on the longer flights. Green algae will be needed to absorb the carbon dioxide from human respiration, and to replace it with oxygen while synthesizing materials an astronaut can eat. Certain molds and bacteria must be taken to complete the digestion of human wastes and convert them into nutrients the algae can use. Other creatures have a place in the same cycles, to crop the molds and bacteria while producing still other usable materials. The larger the variety among these chosen companions, the less attention they will need to keep the human travelers supplied with a liveable environment.

An equal challenge is to select the people who can adjust most completely to life in such isolation. Some among the young men and women who are really interested have inherited hidden features that already preadapt them for the new environment to be carried far from the Earth. It is too early to think of them as a race apart. Yet they could become the ancestors of a distinctive branch of the human species. That they would consciously accept this responsibility is something new, a feature of the future that is now at hand.

With conditions beyond our atmosphere so different and travel time to remote planets so long by comparison with a human lifetime, it may be better to think of one-way trips. Mature men and women born on Earth might not choose so permanent a change. But their children, born in an air-conditioned space station on Mars, need feel no sentimental attachment to our planet. On holidays they might go off to one or the other of the two Martian moons, Deimos and Phobos, which have no atmosphere and virtually no gravity. Space children might enjoy the sensation of weightlessness, even take pleasure in being alone with only a few companions. As young adults, they would hardly hesitate to start out on a well-planned venture into unexplored parts of the universe.

One-way travelers who speed along at close to the velocity of light have on their side a phenomenon suggesting the make-believe of Alice in Wonderland. Called time-dilation, it would make their trip seem far shorter. During it they would age less because the rate of living of each person would slow down, as would every clock aboard. According to the Special Theory of relativity, which applies to objects in such rapid motion, time in the hurtling space craft would pass only a third as fast as at the launch site once its velocity reached 175,000 miles per second. A distance of thirty light-years could be traversed while growing only ten years older. This too would have to be allowed for in setting the automatic pilot to slow down the craft after the correct interval, to avoid overshooting the destination.

While a few people and their chosen companions go shooting off into the future, often with no plan to return to the Earth, the vast majority of living things will go on without missing such adventures. Yet at home on our planet, fresh adaptations are needed as the price of survival. They must match the crowding of the land with human kind and the creatures man has introduced from place to place. Countries, even continents, grow more homogenized every year. Privacy becomes virtually unattainable. These changes are rapid and challenging enough to direct the course of inheritable adjustments.

Does it really matter which star in the universe gives life its guiding energy? The capacity for adaptation in living things may have limits, but they have yet to be discovered. Each successful pattern of survival seems to gather potential immortality around itself, and be ready for new directions.

As we contemplate the future and look for the plants and animals that will increasingly have major roles to play, we have the credo of the geologists to guide us. Their principle is convincing: the present is like the past and follows the same physico-chemical laws. The future will continue in the same way, subject to unpredictable crises. The fossil record shows what happened, but gives no hint as to when another devastating disaster can be expected or what it will be; perhaps a series of volcanic outbursts, a great epoch of mountain building, or another glacial period. Yet one conclusion seems inescapable: the forms of life that rise to dominance never belong to some ancient group that has clung to survival for millions of years. The dominant position goes instead to inconspicuous, less specialized plants and animals in which a new adaptive pattern arises, appropriate to the moment in time.

Trying to forecast the winners is like predicting the outcome of a giant lottery. We could even believe that, given all the facts, an electronic computer might reconstruct the steps that lead to a particular lottery ticket coming into the winning place, as though this were inevitable. But until the drum stops turning and the number comes into sight, all the facts have not come forth. Until that moment every holder of a ticket is as meek as any other, as uncertain of what the future will soon bring. We feel certain that the living things that will inherit the earth are all around us. They will remain equally anonymous until the planet makes the critical turn, until the next crisis comes and can be identified, until the very hour when the new winners get their season in the sun.

We need not wonder: Will mankind hold the top position? Already the human species teeters precariously in this role, using more of the world's resources than any other single kind of creature ever has. The favored

plants and animals upon which human life depends receive a dispropor-
tionate share of the sun, the water, the mineral nutrients and protection
from competitors for space. Our question, instead, is how long this can
last before a new crisis comes—one that makes man and his cultigens
less suited to the dominant role than some others that still roam wild.
To survive we must identify each imminent disaster in time to dull its
impact, as though it were a storm wave that would swamp our boat if
not met at the correct angle.

One detail in the human pattern distinguishes us from the dinosaurs
in their heyday. Unlike them or any of the other dominant species that
have dwindled toward extinction, we have the mind to recognize our
place on the pinnacle and to sense our vulnerability. By improving our
relationships with nonhuman kinds of life, we could turn the peak into
a plateau. We need to prolong our present status, to perpetuate it by admitting that our aggressive drive for power has already reached its goal.
We can become gentle—a word whose modern meaning matches closely
what "meek" signified to the translators of the Bible in King James' day.
If we stumble and fall, we miss our chance forever.

The meek among the inconspicuous living things around us are waiting
to take over.

Index